Framework for the World

Edited by David Rhind

GeoInformation
International

GeoInformation International
A division of Pearson Professional Ltd
307 Cambridge Science Park
Milton Road
Cambridge
CB4 4ZD
and associated Companies throughout the world.

Copublished in the Americas with John Wiley & Sons Inc,
605 Third Avenue, New York, NY 10158

First published 1997

British Library Cataloguing in Publication data
A catalogue entry from this title is available from the British Library.

ISBN 1-8624-2021-1

Library of Congress Cataloguing in Publication data
A catalogue entry for this title is available from the Library of Congress.

ISBN 0-470-24440-2

Printed in the United Kingdom
by Biddles, Ltd.

The opinions expressed herein by the authors are
theirs and not necessarily those of their employers.

Trademarks
Throughout this product trademarked names are used. Rather
than put a trademark symbol in every occurance of a
trademarked name, we state that we are using the names
only in editorial fashion and to the benefit of the
trademark owner with no intention of infringement of the
trademark.

CONTENTS

Contents

LIST OF PLATES

1 Maps produced in the range of 1:200,000 to 1:250,000 scale by different
  National Mapping Organizations
   (a) Part of Langadalsströnd at 1:250,000 scale, produced by and
       copyright of Icelandic Geodetic Survey
   (b) Part of Marrakech at 1:250,000 scale, produced by and copyright of
       Division de la Cartographie, DCFTT
   (c) Part of Rajasthan at 1:250,000 scale, produced by Surveyor General
       of India and copyright of the Government of India, 1974
   (d) Part of Jordan at 1:250,000 scale, produced by the Royal Jordanian
       Geographic Centre and copyright of the Royal Jordanian
       Government
   (e) Becher in Algeria at 1:200,000 scale, produced by Soviet
       cartographers in 1987
   (f) Pinnaroo area of South East Australia at 1:250,000 scale, produced
       by Australian Survey and Land Information Group (AUSLIG) and
       copyright of the Commonwealth of Australia 1983

2 Different map representations centred on the same area in Britain,
  showing different levels of generalization in Ordnance Survey maps at
  different scales. Crown Copyright reserved
   (a) Landline data plotted at 1:1250 scale, showing house names,
       property seeds, pavements, road centre lines, etc.
   (b) Landplan map plotted on customer request from generalized
       Landline data at 1:10,000 scale
   (c) Meridian data assembled from different sources and plotted
       at 1:25,000 scale, showing selected features only in a highly
       generalized fashion
   (d) Pathfinder mapping produced to a traditional specification and
       plotted at 1:25,000 scale
   (e) Landranger data plotted and published at 1:50,000 scale
   (f) Travelmaster data plotted and published at 1:250,000 scale

3 Geodetic-quality Global Positioning System receiver as of 1996

4 Typical monumented survey control point in Malawi before the advent
  of the Global Positioning System (courtesy Ordnance Survey)

5 A typical Global Positioning System permanent receiving station
  (courtesy Japanese Geographical Survey Institute)

6 The horizontal components of the displacement vectors after the 1994
  Hokkaido-Toho-Oki earthquake, as monitored by the GRAPES system
  of the Japanese Geographical Survey Institute (courtesy Japanese
  Geographical Survey Institute)

7 Crustal deformation following the 1995 Hyogo-ken Nanbu earthquake in the densely-populated Kobe area, as immediately detected by GRAPES (courtesy Japanese Geographical Survey Institute)

8 The result of Synthetic Aperture Radar (SAR) interferometry which reveals the crustal deformation associated with the 1995 Hyogo-ken Nanbu earthquake. The SAR data used were acquired on 9 September 1992 and 6 February 1995. The fringes in the figure indicate the amount of displacement of each spot in the direction towards the satellite. A full cycle of colour change (blue-purple-yellow-green-blue) corresponds to a displacement of 11.8 cm (courtesy Japanese Geographical Survey Institute)

9 1 km square extract of a USGS Digital Orthophoto Quadrangle image made up of 1 m pixel resolution data for DeKalb County, Georgia (courtesy US Geological Survey 1995)

10 Simulations of high (1 metre) resolution imagery (*a*) with others of the same area shown at 3 metres (*b*) and 10 metres (*c*) resolution. The views are all shown at a large scale to demonstrate the differences

11 Sample Census collector map produced under the Australian PSMA/ICSM initiative to create a 'first pass framework' showing combination of cadastral and topographic data

12 New South Wales Natural Resources Inventory and the Primary Spatial Database

LIST OF FIGURES

LIST OF TABLES

ACKNOWLEDGEMENTS

The creation of this book owes a great deal, both directly and indirectly, to many people. It arose from the 1995 Cambridge Conference for National Mapping Organizations (NMOs). Some of the papers given at that conference have been modified and updated to fit with the theme of the book and others have been specially commissioned. In all cases the views expressed herein are personal to the authors, and do not necessarily represent those of the organizations in which they are presently or were previously employed. To all the authors of papers in the conference and the new ones in the book, I offer my heartfelt thanks for their dedication and the quality of their work. In particular, the authors of the chapters in this book have endured my determination to impose some coherence of style and form (and English English) on all the individual chapters! This has sometimes led to apparent anomalies, the most obvious of which is the use of American spellings (such as in Department of Defense) in proper nouns as used in the USA but English versions everywhere else (for example, defence).

The Cambridge Conference is a very unusual one. It is the lineal descendant of a conference held every four years since 1928 for land surveyors. Attendance has always been by invitation and, until 1995, this was largely restricted to the most senior staff in NMOs in the Commonwealth. In 1995, we changed this and issued invitations to all the known NMOs of the world: representatives of 78 countries attended and contributed. The objective is not simply to present many papers but rather to listen to a relatively small number of talks by senior managers and to discuss at length, both publicly and privately, the roles, responsibilities, challenges, and opportunities which NMOs enjoy. As will be clear from the Introduction which follows, there is a revolution in progress in all these matters. That the conference was a rousing success and all participants demanded another in 1999 is testimony to the existence of a real need for such a meeting. But it is even more a reflection of the dedication of the Ordnance Survey staff who organized the meeting, of the help given to us by an international advisory committee and of the support given by other organizations who supplied staff as rapporteurs. Amongst OS staff, particular mention must be made of Eric Gilbert (Conference Director), Paul and Susan Newby (the former being Conference Secretary), Margaret Barrett, Fred Brazier, Paul Elswood, John Leonard, Marion Luthwaite, Carol Nicholls, Nick Papps, and Mike Taylor. One other individual must be singled out for his contribution – David Wallis. He organized and ran the exhibition; his expertise and his commitment to the cause, whilst simultaneously running his own business, were immensely important. All the participants were extremely grateful to the commercial exhibitors for displaying their latest wares at Cambridge, not least in the midst of a 35-degrees-Celsius heat-wave which prompted one Middle East delegate to return home early for respite!

Since the conference, the work of administering the book project within Ordnance Survey has fallen largely on my highly competent Personal Assistant, Helen Stirrat. She has become known to many authors as the human face of the book and of Ordnance Survey. Thanks are due to Brigadier Philip Wildman and his colleagues in UK Military Survey for various types of help. I am also grateful to the many colleagues, friends, and family members who have made helpful comments on sections of the book or aided this computer simpleton with the intracacies of Word or other software. The publishers have acted efficiently and effectively; particular thanks are due to Heather Burkinshaw and Sarah Langman Scott. Vanessa Lawrence accepted the original proposal on behalf of the publishers and did much to make it a practical proposition.

Beyond all these people who have been directly involved, I personally have gained much from talking to my peers in NMOs around the world. Though it seems trite to say so, we all have much to learn from one another – particularly as globalization of our activities proceeds. I look forward to seeing them all again at the 1999 Cambridge Conference.

David Rhind
14 February 1997

Copyright acknowledgement

Thanks are due to those who granted permission to reproduce their copyrighted material. In the case of the maps in Plates 1 and 2, these are specifically referenced in the captions to each map. In addition, however, Chapter 14 is a provisional Working Document and is reproduced by permission of the European Commission's Directorate General for Telecommunications, Information Market and Exploitation of Research (DGXIII/E/3, Information industries, awareness heightening and training).

Any inadvertent omission of copyright acknowledgement or of thanks for help given is deeply regretted and will be corrected in any future edition of this book.

CHAPTER 1

Introduction

David Rhind

This book is about something so fundamental that it affects the lives of everyone on earth. Despite this, the subject matter is usually seen in a much more limited way. Typically, maps are regarded as no more than a collection of pieces of paper covered by coloured lines and symbols meaningless to most people. The ultimate aims of the book are to dispel this myth and to ensure that the geographical framework for the world provided by mapping is more widely understood and exploited.

THE GEOGRAPHICAL FRAMEWORK FOR NATIONS AND THE WORLD

'Knowledge about the world and its occupants is readily, even instantly, available.' Many people in Western nations regard this as a truism: it is part of our 'taken-for-granted' experience. Our world has become shrunk and more familiar. To travel to the other side of the world now routinely takes less time than did travelling from London to Paris in Napoleon's time – a speeding-up factor of no less than 60 times. Moreover, this speed of travel is available to millions, not simply to a rich elite. Armchair access to geography is even more impressive: television brings to its passive watchers massive amounts of information on places once far away. Queries on other parts of the world are answered by a visit to the local bookshop or library, by a search of a CD-ROM, or by surfing on the Internet. We talk by telephone to colleagues thousands of kilometres away, sometimes linked to them via satellites on expeditions in the depths of a rainforest or in a remote desert – and we think little of it. Of course all such facilities are not yet available to all of the earth's inhabitants: television has penetrated far more widely than has the ability to travel or to exploit the Internet. But for the fortunate ones, the world is dramatically smaller and more familiar than it was for our parents, let alone for their parents.

Almost all of this is based on a knowledge of where things, places, and people are in relation to one another. Satellite launch sites are carefully chosen to minimize the effort required to launch the rockets which carry them; at the local scale, the location of cellular telephone antennae is based on maximizing the area which can be 'seen' from each antenna. Navigation of ships, aircraft, cars, and even walking require geographical guidance.

Statistics used to underpin momentous decisions by governments and multi-national organizations alike are made available for defined geographical areas (and these statistics are increasingly needed for smaller and smaller areas). Distributing goods (which underpins much of commerce) and supplying emergency aid are two manifestations of the same actions: both need geographical information in order to be successful. It is the geographical framework which provides this detailed geographical knowledge. And the organizations which provide the basic framework – on which most other information is 'draped' – are the National Mapping Organizations (NMOs) of the nations of the world.

In a world where competitive advantage and knowledge of niche markets is ever more important, personal knowledge and perceptions of geography are an inadequate basis on which, say, to build a marketing campaign or fight a battle. As a result, the whole of the Geographical Information 'industry' is coming to rely on computers and databases. Curiously, the advent of computerized tools makes the availability and nature of this framework even more important: computers are much less able than trained humans to cope with uncertainty, inconsistency, and missing information. To be effective, the framework must now be in a standardized, easily understood, frequently updated, and well-documented form. *Everything* must now be explicit.

WHAT IS A MAP?

Standard dictionary definitions are wholly inadequate to cover what this book embraces. Consider, for instance, the following two definitions of a map:

> a representation on a flat surface of all or a part of the earth's surface ...
> *(Oxford Dictionary of Geography)*

> a flat drawing of part of the earth's surface, showing various details (e.g. rivers) ...
> *(Chambers Mini Dictionary)*

Such definitions strongly associate the concept of maps with the features of the earth's terrain and, by implication, with flat sheets of paper or other similar material. The latter definition specifically includes 'drawing' even though photographic images now form the basis for some types of maps in many countries. The concept of change is also missing: stasis is the norm. Such a concept of maps is at least 20 years out of date, as Morrison shows in his chapter in this book. Today, there is a proliferation of mutant forms, some wholly virtual – existing only as an ephemeral manifestation of a bombardment by electrons of phosphor coatings on a glass screen. The reality is that it seems impossible to agree a simple-to-understand

and comprehensive definition of a map at the present time. For those of a philosophical or academic bent, there are many good books on this subject: Robinson and Petchennik (1976) and Monmonier (1996) both form a good starting point. But for those with less time, it is best to start by recognizing that maps both form and describe the framework for the world. The most complete and consistent descriptions of the geography of the world have long been given in this form, rather than lists of routes, tables of distances, and other statistical abstractions.

There are many kinds of maps. For our current purposes, however, only topographic maps – those showing the shape, form, or nature of the natural and the built environment plus selected cultural features (such as boundaries of states and administrative areas) – will be considered. Most other maps, of population, geology, land use, shopping, or travel-to-work patterns, are assembled on top of these topographic maps and draped on the topographic information when displayed. Although 'maps' may now be made by removing distortions from photographs taken from aircraft or satellite, these are rarely satisfactory as maps on their own: only when some of the features in the photographs (such as rivers or streets) have been stylized and named can they be readily be used by many people as a suitable framework.

The reader should be aware of two fundamental and related 'truths' in portraying the landscape in maps. The first is that hugely different 'levels of abstraction' can be employed. Maps at large scales (for example, 1 cm on the map represents 1000 cm on the ground) can portray great detail, whilst those at much smaller scales (for instance, 1 cm on the map represents 10 kilometres or a million centimetres on the ground) can show much less. Not all maps at the same scale show the same amount of detail, but 'scale' is normally used as a rough and ready approximation to the 'level of abstraction' embedded in the map model of the world. NMOs have traditionally produced map series at different scales. The US Geological Survey's National Mapping Division, for instance, produces and prints maps from 1:24,000 scale down to others at 1:2 million scale or smaller and disseminates data derived from these sources. Different nations have created maps at the same scales which contain different features and look very different (Plates 1a to 1f). The second and related 'truth' is that individual carto-graphers simplify reality to make it understandable and possible to fit into their maps in a number of different ways: they *generalize* more detailed information to make less detailed versions. All this is illustrated in Plates 2a to 2f, showing the same area at different map scales made by the same organization. There is then no unique 'right' map of the world – different maps may contain different information and even the common information may have been adjusted in shape and position by different map makers. The effects of generalization are normally less severe as the map scale increases: generalization in maps at 1:1000 scale causes few practical problems for current applications.

There is an important further point here, especially when dealing with maps in computer form which are used as the national geographical framework. Although there are many possible different representations of the world, having and using only one framework or national map seems to have huge benefits, even if these cannot be measured very precisely in money terms (Coopers and Lybrand 1996). This ensures that data collected or maps made by other organizations and people can themselves fit together since all have used a single, high-quality framework. This aspect of mapping is examined in more detail later in this introduction.

WHY ARE MAPS IMPORTANT?

Maps form and describe the framework of our known world. Their use is long established. Some maps survive from over 3000 years ago and must inevitably have been in use long before that time. The leading article of *The Times* of London on 14 October 1992 summarized this when it said: 'Mankind has invented three great forms of communication: language, music and mapping. But by far the oldest of the three is mapping.'

Contemporary types of maps help us to answer questions such as:

- what is at position X on the earth's surface?
- where can we find features of type Y?
- how do I get from point A to point B? (or what is the most efficient way to travel to a number of different places? or where should I locate my shop in relation to my customers?)
- what geographical pattern (if any) is formed by features of type–?
- how has the geography changed between Z years ago and now?
- how can I hide my forces and their movements from my enemies?
- what will happen if I change the geography (e.g. by building a new road)?

In many cases maps alone cannot answer the questions. But they are the starting point to answer most questions involving geography (and most questions do involve it). They structure the world in that other information is draped upon them. And they provide the basic *lingua franca* – the common language – by which we discuss events and activities outside our immediate personal experience. The map provides a way of asking questions about the world and understanding the answers.

Beyond these high-level generalizations, the uses of maps vary greatly in many countries, according to the local laws and practices. In all countries, however, the military role of mapping has long been highly significant. In Britain, for instance, the threat of French invasion in the late eighteenth century and the consequent need for maps to permit military planning was the rationale for consistent and detailed mapping being completed over the whole country. Another early 'driver' of the need for mapping was property registration or taxation: Sweden had highly detailed mapping for these purposes in the early seventeenth century.

A recent study has investigated the use of very detailed mapping in Britain. Whilst the situation is certainly different in other countries, the results show how mapping underpins the activities of the state and, increasingly, of business. Moreover, they demonstrate that mapping has a national interest role. There are socially beneficial uses of it which cannot easily be charged for, especially in low population areas, and some needs (such as in emergencies) which must be met immediately and without negotiation. In the latter case, the mapping forms part of a national insurance policy. Figure 1.1 is based upon results from a questionnaire answered by representatives of 168 different organizations in Britain in 1995 (OS 1996). Many of these organizations had national responsibilities – for instance, the entire utilities industry and some 48 central government departments and agencies contributed to the study. The results show that this mapping plays a key role in a huge range of applications. On average, each organization was able to identify about 15 applications of the mapping, usually spread across many different departments or units within the organization as a whole. The survey largely dealt with detailed mapping and thus excluded most of the applications of smaller-scale mapping (such as leisure, motoring, and strategic planning). Equivalent studies elsewhere show that, whilst the importance of different products varies in different countries, the same overall conclusions are replicated time and again. It is no exaggeration therefore to claim that the entirety of national mapping underpins the business of the state, whether this is carried out by commerce or by government in all forms.

MAPS AND NATION STATES

One of the most important characteristics of mapping is that it has always been very much a matter for individual states. For understandable reasons, the quantity and quality of mapping have therefore varied a great deal. A series of studies in the 1980s (see Morrison's chapter in this book) showed that only about half of the world had ever been mapped at 1:50,000 scale or larger. Even in this area, much mapping is now hopelessly out of date. In some parts of the world the framework provided by topographic maps is also a matter of state secrecy.

Beyond the lack of availability of mapping and apart from small-scale maps of the world or of large regions – like the ill-fated International Map of the World launched at the 1880 International Geographical Congress and 'killed off' whilst incomplete a century later – the design of map series has been driven by national, often pragmatic, factors. These factors have obviously included the needs of local users: as one example, since there are

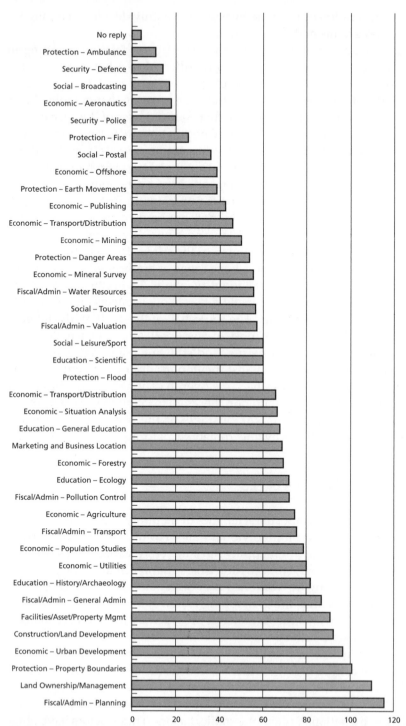

Fig. 1.1 Application of detailed Ordnance Survey map information amongst 168 major organizations

many different ways of registering land across the world and many different organizational structures in government, mapping has typically responded to these local realities. Map scales, the data and map projection used, the features shown and their symbolism have been chosen to meet national considerations. Once it is established, change to a basic specification is time-consuming and expensive. In particular, the extra investment involved in re-creating these map series to produce international harmonization has proved prohibitive thus far. This is not unique to topographic maps and the framework: experience in assembling environmental data for the then 12 countries of the European Community in the 1980s showed that, for many environmental variables, the greatest rate of change occurred at national boundaries! In other words, the methods by which the data are collected and processed may render them strictly incompatible, with the magnitude of the problem depending on local circumstances.

We are now increasingly operating in a whole-world economy. What happens in one area (like emission of pollution, such as that from the Chernobyl nuclear power station) may well affect many other places outside the national domain of the source. As indicated above, we are far from having good environmental data for the terrestrial environment or a consistent global framework at any reasonable and ungeneralized level of detail. Htun makes a powerful plea in his chapter for a global effort to produce harmonized and up-to-date Geographical Information, especially a framework. Without it, this senior figure in the United Nations argues, the cause of sustainable development will be seriously retarded. In principle, governments of the world have already accepted the need to have consistent environmental data and to share it: a section of the Agenda 21 agreement signed in Rio in 1992 covers these points. Writing from the perspective of environmental scientists, Collins and Rhind support Htun's views in showing how a lack of consistent framework data and different national policies inhibit the ability to monitor threats to biological diversity and model environmental disasters. In a third complementary view, Lenczowski shows how the defence forces of the USA and its partners also require consistent, current framework data: she describes the considerable efforts which the US National Image and Mapping Agency (formerly the Defense Mapping Agency) is devoting to building global frameworks and the computer infrastructure to handle such Geographic Information.

The situation so far as the framework is concerned has improved somewhat, with the increasingly widespread availability of the information in computer form. Some algebraic transformations can be applied to change the geometry of national maps into a consistent form; the advent of the Global Positioning System (see Calvert et al in this book) has been a massive factor in harmonizing the basis on which an increasing number of national frameworks are held. Nevertheless, there are still substantial differences in the features shown, the accuracy with which their position is measured, and the classification of their characteristics between maps produced by different agencies. The advent of much higher-quality 'pictures' from a new generation of satellites (see Calvert et al again) may also reduce the magnitude of these incompatibilities but international harmonization is still a very long way in the future. Even if harmonized data were available, however, that does not guarantee they would be useful. To be of value, they must be 'fit for purpose' and must be inter-operable – that is, they can be used easily by different computer systems. For this to be achieved in the future – for it is not now possible except in limited ways – data emanating from NMOs and others must conform to regional and global standards. Salgé describes in his chapter what progress has been made in this respect and what is likely to happen in the future, whilst Lenczowski emphasizes the practical importance of these developments.

THE INFORMATION REVOLUTION AND MAPPING

In the 1970s, some cartographers still saw the computer as simply another tool for map production and reproduction. To them, it was one more in the sequence of transitions from lithography based on stone through copperplate engraving to pen and ink and scribing of lines and symbols on plastic film. They saw the computer as simply another tool to make the same maps, perhaps more efficiently but probably less attractively. As Morrison demonstrates, that view – short-sighted as it was at the time – is now completely untenable. The advent of the computer has changed the creation of mapping and, in particular, the nature and use of the framework to a greater extent than anything else in the last 3000 years.

The reason for this is that mapping has generally become associated with databases rather than with printed paper documents. The creation of these databases is facilitated by new surveying tools such as the American Global Positioning System and the Russian GLONASS equivalent and by ever-improving photograph-like imagery from satellites and aircraft. From such databases, maps can be created or 'spun off'. If the computer systems – generally termed 'Geographical Information Systems' or 'GIS' (Longley et al 1997) – are well designed, they can be produced much more speedily, usually more cheaply, are normally more up-to-date and certainly better tailored to meet individual needs. The map may be transmitted to distant users at minimal cost over computer networks in a few brief moments. And copies of the same, most recent version can be held by many different people simultaneously in order to minimize incompatibilities and duplication of effort. Calvert et al describe the most important technological developments affecting the creation and maintenance of the framework later in this book.

Maps, then, are one type of Geographical Information (or GI). The extent of GI is, however, much wider than traditional maps, as shown by the following, widely accepted definition:

Geographic information is 'information which can be related to a location on the Earth, particularly information on natural phenomena, cultural and human resources'. (AGI 1991)

The GI industry is growing rapidly world-wide. Estimates made by international consultancies suggest that the total market for GI (including software, data, and services) amounts to around US$2000 million in 1996 and is growing at around 10 to 20 percent per annum. Other evidence shows that the multiplier effect through hardware purchases, labour hiring, etc. may well be in excess of this by a factor of four. Even this estimate may be a serious under-statement since it does not include labour costs expended by NMOs, cadastral bodies, National Statistical Institutes and others involved in collecting and disseminating GI; globally they expend billions of dollars annually, though little of this is manifested directly at present in the commercial market. Beyond its commercial appeal, GI also plays a key role in the efficiency and effectiveness of governments at all levels, as Onsrud and Rushton (1995) have shown in an American context.

The computer version of the framework is not simply of value as a passive 'back-cloth' to other Geographical Information. Its newest and most fundamental significance comes from the added value which can be created by use of maps in this form. This arises for at least four reasons:

- the framework itself can often be summarized with minimum effort in statistical form (e.g. area of woodlands) or some other abstract way (e.g. as the centre lines of roads) which is valuable for other purposes;
- by linking different data sets together, it may be possible to infill 'holes' in one data set by information from the other data set, thereby reducing the cost and need for new surveys;
- through such linkage, it is possible to check the consistency of the two data sets. Accuracy checking then concentrates on where differences have been found; and
- data linkage vastly expands the range of applications which can potentially be tackled as compared to data sets held separately. Thus with two data sets, there is only one combination (e.g. soil type and crop productivity); with 20 different data sets for the same area, there are 190 pairs of data sets and over a million combinations overall.

It is also worth pointing out that there are, in many countries, hundreds or even thousands of data sets already in existence which – subject to finding where they are and whether they meet specific needs plus not breaching any laws – can be linked together. This state of affairs and the newly found capacity to carry out such linkage readily by computer (rather than hugely laboriously by hand) is encouraging the creation of National Spatial Data Infrastructures (NSDI) in many countries. Tosta, Mooney and Grant, Dató A Majid Mohamed and the European Commission (EC) all describe important NSDI developments later in this book. Such is the importance of these developments – as Tosta points out – that the creation of the US NSDI was mandated by an Executive Order of President Clinton. Most fundamental of all, however, data linkage (and hence obtaining the added value described above) can usually only be carried out using the geographical framework: the description of geography – whether in latitude and longitude, street addresses, post/zip codes, national co-ordinate systems, area names or whatever – is the only common key between most data sets. The authors of different chapters in this book have many different perspectives on the relationships between NMOs and the supply and use of geographical data in future – Morrison, for example (perhaps influenced by the size of the USA and the structure of government), sees a major part of their role in future as co-ordinating local data collectors who will all work to common standards. All of the authors, however, see it as essential that the creators of the framework – the National Mapping Organizations – are centrally involved in the development of NSDI or equivalents world-wide. Only the nature of that involvement is in question.

WHO MAKES THE FRAMEWORK AND KEEPS IT UP TO DATE?

In so far as the global framework exists at present as the sum of the national ones, it is almost entirely a product of the efforts of NMOs working over an extended period. Every nation known to the editor has some kind of NMO, though their form and responsibilities differ greatly. In countries organized on a federal basis – notably Australia, Canada, Germany, and the USA – the states or provinces may actually do more than the central mapping organization. But in countries such as France, Russia, India, Sweden, and the UK, central government has the primary responsibility for national mapping. Even within each of these groups, however, considerable variety exists: the power and responsibilities of the Australian states is much greater than their US counterparts. The situation in Sweden, where the land registration function has recently been merged into the National Land Survey (the NMO, as described by Sandgren in this volume), is very different from that in Britain. An additional complication is that many NMOs remain military organizations: in Europe, those of Greece and Italy are parts of the military and the Dutch NMO is a civilian organization operating under a board dominated by military representatives. This international diversity is demonstrated by chapters written by Warita and Nonomura, Clarke, Jarque and Zhdanov. These describe the role, aims, and achievements of their own NMOs; the last three in particular have undergone dramatic change either because of national development programmes or because of political change of huge proportions in South Africa, Mexico, and Russia.

Some NMOs (like those of Russia and the USA) see themselves primarily as scientific and technical bodies. Others, however, have a different perspective. Like many other public sector organizations in many countries, NMOs generally have been subject to review and 're-engineering' in recent years. Osborne and Gaebler (1992) made a number of proposals for reforming government which were already being applied in countries like New Zealand and the UK. More recently, Foster and Plowden (1996) have summarized the successes and failures of these policies, driven as they see it by widespread fiscal crises in government. The reform of government which began almost simultaneously in Britain, Canada, New Zealand, and the United States has led to the expectation that government should be smaller, more efficient and effective. A common out-turn has been a greater role for the private sector. Indeed, it seems clear that NMOs in many countries have evolved as 'type examples' of what governments have set out to achieve. Issues such as contracting out of work (as opposed to in-house production), the assessment of and responsiveness to user needs, how to value the work of the NMOs (including externalities), the appropriate level of freedom from central control and the nature of accountability to the taxpayer, equity of treatment in mapping rural and urban areas and relevant measures of success have all been addressed in different ways. To that extent, the story of what has happened to NMOs has relevance far beyond mapping. Chapters by O'Donnell and Penton, Grelot, Sandgren, Robertson and Gartner, Jakobsen and Rhind all describe the challenges and opportunities faced by their organizations. They show how determined management actions, allied to a clear vision of the future, have led to major improvements in the performance of these NMOs. And some of them are bold enough to extrapolate their experience to other countries!

THE PURPOSE OF THIS BOOK

As will be obvious from all of the above, several inter-twined threads run through the chapters of this book. These are:

- the impact of new technologies on NMOs, changing what they do, how they do it, and the consequences for their customers;
- rapid change in the expectations of users of the framework. Few are now content to be told what they can have and, as a result of this and financial changes, the power of the customer or user is now much greater. Fewer and fewer NMOs are now production-led;

- changes in society values, such as the greater concern for privacy and a diminution of trust in government;
- the effects of reform in government, such as massive reductions in staffing, new management approaches, new approaches to financing the framework, and public exposure of successes and failure. Some are manifested in new roles for NMOs, as seems to be arising from the 1994 Executive Order of the President of the USA;
- the effects of regionalization and globalization of business and even government. In Europe, Directives made centrally within the Union force change in national laws on intellectual property, trading practices, and much else. At the global scale, the work of the World Trade Organization may well impact on information trading. The advent of commercial organizations selling satellite imagery on a global basis in 1997 may well be very significant for NMOs and their customers. All this should be contrasted with the need for global data for scientific purposes, where little funding is usually available to pay for the data.

Almost all of the chapters which follow contain something on every one of these threads. Thus the book could have been structured in many different ways. In practice, a compromise has been adopted: the chapters are arranged on the basis of their primary subject, and links to other chapters are made by cross-referencing in the body of the text and in the short introduction to each section.

A curse of this field is that different people use different terms for the same thing and the same terms for different things. Thus 'spatial data', 'geographical information', and 'geospatial data' mean essentially the same thing in practice. It is impossible to harmonize this use of terminology completely and, indeed, unwise: the way in which Tosta and Mooney and Grant use the term 'National Spatial Data Infrastructure' reflects different ways in which it is actually used in their own countries. Fortunately, the context in which these terms are used is clear in the chapters which follow, so ambiguity should be minimized.

Irrespective of these terminological and structural matters, this book demonstrates conclusively that NMOs currently play a key role in the operation of the nation states, that they increasingly support business effectively, that a growing number of them are important players in the 'information market', and that they face continuing technological and other challenges in the years ahead. Most important of all, however, is that, because of the investments of governments to date, there is an imperfect but improving geographical framework to support human life on this planet.

REFERENCES

AGI 1991 *GIS dictionary – a Standards Committee publication of the Association for Geographic Information (AGI)*. UK, Version no. 1.1, STA/06/91, January

Coopers and Lybrand 1996 *Economic aspects of the collection, dissemination and integration of government's geospatial information.* Southampton, Ordnance Survey

Foster CD, Plowden FJ 1996 *The state under stress.* Buckingham, Open University Press

Longley P, Goodchild MF, Maguire DJ, Rhind DW (eds) 1997 *Geographical Information Systems: principles, techniques, management and applications.* London, Longman

Monmonier M 1996 *How to lie with maps.* 2nd edn. Chicago, IL, University of Chicago Press

Onsrud HJ, Rushton G 1995 *Sharing geographic information.* New Brunswick, NJ, Center for Urban Policy Research

OS 1996 *Results of the consultation exercise on the 'National Interest in Mapping'.* Southampton, Ordnance Survey

Osborne D, Gaebler T 1992 *Re-inventing government.* Reading, Mass., Addison-Wesley

Robinson AH, Petchennik BB 1976 *The nature of maps. Essays towards understanding maps and mapping.* Chicago and London, University of Chicago Press

CHAPTER 2

Topographic mapping in the twenty-first century

Joel L Morrison

SUMMARY

National mapping organizations (NMOs) have existed for up to 300 years. Many of them were created at the outset of the scientific and industrial age, especially to support national defence purposes. They were creatures of the prevailing paradigm and, to some extent, the technologies of that day. These factors facilitated the creation of substantial centralized organizations responsible for the official mapping of the entirety of a nation – and, in many cases, actually carrying out that mapping from within the same organization and controlling the distribution of the results.

A new paradigm is now in place – of public access to information and of individuals making products tailored to their own needs rather than living with mass production products. It has been fostered by the dramatic changes in technology and, in particular, the sharply decreased cost of computing and access to remote data sets. This chapter explores the changes in paradigms which affect cartography. Paradigm changes coupled with current technology have interacted with society to produce organizational changes in many nations. The implications of these changes for NMOs are discussed and examples are drawn from five leading mapping organizations. It is concluded that the NMOs of the future will still vary somewhat in their characteristics in response to national needs. But many of them will be smaller, more flexible, and concerned more with enabling mapping of a defined quality and standard to be available than producing it.

BACKGROUND

Two paradigms – or approximately 350 years – ago in cartographic history, the sophisticated public of Europe was enjoying the beautifully engraved and elegantly coloured atlases produced by Dutch and Flemish cartographers. These products drew heavily on commerce and travel and were in the tradition of the Greek cartographer Ptolemy and classical geography. The atlases served a purpose, being studied as syntheses of the current knowledge of geography and of the geography of the ancients, and they were consistent with the prevailing paradigm for the cartography of that age (Brown 1949: 241). That paradigm might be termed 'armchair' geography. In a real sense it was theoretical or hypothetical. Scholars studied maps and speculated on the characteristics of places without first-hand knowledge. The maps were not intended to be used by geographers for practical purposes. We may think of this period of artistic cartography as fundamental support for a formative or theoretical period in geographic thought.

In 1666 the Académie Royale des Sciences was founded in France with the express purpose of improving and correcting maps and sailing charts. The activities of the members of the Académie focused on a paradigm shift for the cartographers of that time and led directly, over the next decades, to the scientific use of surveying tools and more precise methods for correctly mapping the land surface and its forms. The Académie for its first 100 years worked feverishly to devise a satisfactory method for the determination of longitude, while simultaneously perfecting other methods of measurement of position on the land surface of the earth. Cartographers began to produce accurate maps that contained information based on these scientific measurements (Brown 1994: 213ff). This paradigm, which we might term 'scientific measurement' paradigm, was based on the use of maps for practical purposes, such as ocean navigation, land travel, and war. In one sense the speculations of the earlier period of armchair geography were tested under this new paradigm by obtaining first-hand, accurate information about places.

During this seventeenth century paradigm shift from artistry to use of scientific measurement, the technology used by cartographers, evolved but did not drastically change. The ultimate products of cartographers, both in the Dutch and Flemish atlas period of geography and under the more scientific paradigm of the French Académie, remained multi-purpose printed maps.

Throughout the eighteenth and nineteenth centuries, and into the twentieth century, the need for precise positioning and accurate maps of national territories fostered the continuation of the scientific measurement paradigm in carto-graphy. Warfare became more precise and weaponry allowed greater distances to separate armies, thus creating a critical need for accurate maps of a nation's territory for defensive purposes and equally critical needs for accurate maps of the enemy's territory for offensive purposes. Improvements in the printing technology continued as well, allowing cartographers greater flexibility in producing multi-purpose printed maps.

It should not be surprising, therefore, that today there exists in almost every nation of the world an NMO devoted to producing complete, consistent, large-scale, topographic coverage of the nation. This is the obvious organizational form needed to utilize the cartographer's skills, meet the then-perceived national needs, and exploit the prevailing technology under the scientific measurement paradigm. Clearly, a nation needs standardized topographic information about itself. This information needs to be controlled. The nature of the analogue technology of printed maps allows its control by a single organization because it requires a large capital investment in equipment, highly skilled cartographers, tightly controlled sources of information in order to produce accurate maps, and in some cases tight control of a single channel of map dissemination.

Using analogue technology, the ultimate product of NMOs has evolved to become printed, large-scale topographic maps. These maps are produced usually in one or more series of consistent scale, of consistent accuracy, and which cover the entire territory of the nation state and, to a very large extent, contain similar information from nation to nation. Periodically the United Nations has asked Dr Brandenberger of Laval University in Canada to compile a status of topographic mapping coverage of the world (Brandenberger and Ghosh 1990: 1ff). These status reports have documented, to the extent that such information is publicly available, the output of our national mapping agencies. More recently Bohme has produced three detailed volumes on the topographic mapping of the nations of the world (Bohme 1993).

CHANGE IN TECHNOLOGY: ELECTRONIC MAPS

During this last half century a new electronic technology has been developed. The application to cartography of this digital electronic technology has proved to be very useful. This major change in the technology enables cartographers to accomplish topographic mapping under the existing scientific measurement paradigm more efficiently. Not surprisingly, cartographers have tried and have successfully replicated the production of printed, large-scale topographic maps using electronic technology (US Geological Survey 1993).

The use of digital technology for cartographic purposes, however, is proving not to be merely a further evolution of the older analogue technology, as Calvert et al show later in this book. Some methods which were hard to accomplish using the analogue technology are now much easier using digital technology (for example, hill shading and the production of classless choropleth maps). But entirely new methods have also been created (for example, generalizing of a line using the Douglas-Poiker algorithm or performing interpolation using kriging) and entirely new capabilities are presented to cartographers by the electronic technology (for example, zooming or panning a display, or the use of sound or other multimedia techniques in conjunction with a spatial display). As a result, electronic technology is now viewed as rather more than a replacement technology to analogue technology.

Given digital technology as a replacement technology, however, cartographers can now pose questions about the efficient use of this new technology. These questions, and particularly their answers, serve as a catalyst to creative cartographic thinking. In combination with other forces, they are leading to another major paradigm shift in cartography. The technology itself adds pressure for yet another paradigm shift: the low cost and widespread availability of the capital equipment needed for electronic mapping and the ease with which topographic data can be collected for mapping purposes using electronic instrumentation (such as airborne scanners, digitizers, and GPS receivers) are radically changing the previous technology's cost considerations.

Additional non-cartographic and non-technological forces are supporting a shift in the prevailing cartographic paradigm. These forces include society's desire to have immediate or real time, unlimited access to spatial information, and a complementary renaissance in geographical thinking by society. Particularly in the United States, the field of geography is undergoing a tremendous renaissance that is resulting in the development of entirely new curricula for geography at every level of education. Business is awakening to the fact that the spatial dimension is a necessary consideration for many of its late-twentieth-century opportunities. These opportunities range from the use of knowledge about point sources of pollution relative to the geological structure of the area in which property is owned, to the efficient routing of overnight delivery trucks in a large metropolitan area. The public wants unlimited immediate access to this information and the new technology will allow it. This pressure, external to cartography, speeds the shift in the change of cartography's prevailing paradigms.

THE PARADIGM SHIFT: THE DEMOCRATIZATION OF CARTOGRAPHY

Using electronic technology, no longer does the map user depend upon what the cartographer decides to put on a map. Today, the user is a cartographer. This represents a 'democratization' of cartography in which all individuals are potentially empowered with the available electronic tools to think geographically and to make visualizations of their thinking.

The manifestation of all this is seen in a transition away from the cartographer's definition, development, and evolution of one controlled set of highly accurate, hard-copy products intended for multiple uses. There is a trend towards multiple single-use sets of products of varying accuracies, reproduced in hard or soft copy which are derived from an electronic database that can serve multiple specific stated purposes (such as answers to geographically based questions about features and their relationships, and visualizations of these answers and relationships). These multiple single-use products are produced by the general public user. Thus we, as cartographers, find ourselves in the midst of two fundamental changes occurring simultaneously, not sequentially. This coincidence of a technological change and a paradigm shift is perhaps unique in cartographic history.

These changes enable any user of electronic technology to produce a map or visualization as easily as can a cartographer. Such a user is freed from the traditional cartographic necessity of accurately rendering the data; that is, the scientific measurement paradigm. ISO-9000, an international standard, is illustrative of the change in paradigm which we are experiencing. The two underpinning tenets of ISO-9000 are (1) do it right the first time, and (2) give the customer no more, and no less, quality than the customer wants or is willing to pay for. The paradigm shift has removed the 'accuracy' constraint and substituted an 'ultimate use' or 'fitness for user' constraint. In a cartographic context, this means that users are now able to produce analyses and visualizations at will to any accuracy standard that satisfies them – provided that the information available to them is of sufficiently high quality at the outset.

The democratization of use of spatial data and a renaissance in geographic thinking by the general public means that the user has become empowered to use algorithms which cartographers provide, on spatial data which cartographers collect. As a result, our future as map makers – even ten years from now – is uncertain.

DERIVATIVES FROM THE PARADIGM SHIFT

There are several derivatives from this paradigm shift which are worth exploring. First, the long-term conflict in traditional analogue map making between accuracy and visual display is no longer relevant. The history of terrain representation over the past three centuries is one of competition between the display of accurate data about elevations, slopes, and aspects of the ground surface, and the visual impression reproduced on a flat sheet of the surface of the ground in a given area of interest. The substitution of electronic technology brings that competition to an end. Cartographers, or the users themselves, can produce data, to any precision desired, about the ground surface and realistic visualizations of the surface of the ground then present both to the user at the same time, using different but complementary media.

Visualizations are relieved of the exacting necessity for placing data so that precise information can be manually extracted from the display. Information to any desired level of precision can be directly queried from the database. A visually realistic rendering of the surface of the ground can be roamed by a user asking at specific points for exact information about elevation, slope, soil type, vegetation cover, climatic statistics, and so on, without these latter attributes interfering with the visualization. Not all data need to be displayed at the same instance.

These changes require increased experimentation and algorithmic design by cartographers into both the expression of data precision and more realistic visual display. Rather than competing, each can be enhanced. With the potential for multiple products and using multimedia, cartographers can concentrate quite separately on the accuracy and precision of the attribution of the data in the database and also on the realistic nature of the visual display.

A second derivative concerns the importance of scale. In analogue mapping, scale was of critical importance. It was one of the first decisions that a cartographer had to make. The choice of scale controlled the size of the printed map and the area of coverage. It controlled the symbolization of the data layers portrayed on the map. And ultimately scale controlled the usefulness of the map, allowing detailed data to be extracted or more generalized spatial relationships to be visualized. Using electronic technology, scale of the visualization does not have to be static. Users can 'zoom in' or 'zoom out' on a geographical area of interest. The amount of generalizing, if any, becomes situation- or query-specific. The controlling factor becomes the resolution of the digitized feature and its attributes contained in the database. Thus resolution of data becomes of major concern to the professional cartographer, and information about the resolution of the data must be contained in the metadata accompanying each feature so that users can determine its 'fitness' for different uses. Scale of any output maps becomes a variable over which the user assumes control, and can vary at will.

Another important derivative resulting from the paradigm shift is the emergence of the user as a cartographer. In analogue technology, cartographers produced products for users. As indicated already, electronic technology empowers *all* persons to become cartographers and to create their own products which they will use to the extent of their abilities.

A final derivative is the shift of the focus of attention from a geographic area to an individual feature. Data layers composed of similar features are the basic building blocks for the data which will flow over a nation-wide spatial data infrastructure in an electronic world. With the possibility of distributed databases and the availability of an information highway, centralized production of data becomes unnecessary, if not unwieldy and inefficient. The world of cartography will rapidly adapt the capability to extract data from sensors automatically and enter those data into one or more databases. Data which cannot be extracted from sensors will best be collected and entered into a database from the local geographic area, not by a national cartographic agency. Thus sensors controlled by national agencies will collect consistent national data of features that can be remotely sensed, and local offices will collect data about features that cannot be remotely sensed. The co-ordination of these efforts and the standards necessary to allow the simultaneous use of nationally or internationally remotely sensed data with non-sensed, locally collected data are not yet in place. It remains for reorganized NMOs to ensure that such co-ordination and standards are available for a nation.

These four derivatives are rather obvious. More important derivatives, resulting in greater change, will undoubtedly become evident over the next few decades. Naisbitt has suggested that our stage of development in using electronic technology is analogous to the period in world history when only a few people, scribes, knew how to write. Scribes had to know as much about making ink or baking clay tablets as they did about writing (Naisbitt 1994: 128). Today cartographers talk primarily about the technology changes (or, in a scribe's terms, how to make ink or bake clay tablets). Think about the future time when the electronic technology is so embedded in our civilization that we need not talk about the technology. Civilization only needs to utilize the technology to communicate as we presently do with writing. What then will an NMO be?

IMPLICATIONS FOR NATIONAL MAPPING ORGANIZATIONS

The world is rapidly moving from static, multi-purpose, two-dimensional hard-copy displays to the use of electronic multimedia. Text, graphics, animation, videos, speech, and mood-inducing colours and sounds are all being used to accompany individualized products. There are three developments in particular that have major implications for NMOs.

First, the creation of a national spatial data infrastructure (NSDI) will serve as an enabling agent to bring the vast investment in observed monitoring data which NMOs currently possess, into an integrated network for scientific, policy, and operational uses. The same spatial infrastructure will also serve for disseminating spatial data among the general public, agencies, landowners, educators, students, and the press. Other chapters in this book, notably those by Tosta, by Majid Mohamed and by Mooney and Grant, expand on the nature and likely future of NSDIs.

A key strategy for enhancing the quality of life of a nation and for sustaining that quality through greater public education is the broad and minimal cost dissemination of spatial data. This will allow the public to have a greater stake in preserving, enhancing, and sustaining its standard of living. On this basis, adopting such a key strategy becomes paramount for the survival of an NMO (Morrison 1996). Every day people make decisions in the market place and in their ordinary activities which utilize spatial data. By allowing access by all people to the data necessary to evaluate the consequences of their decisions, sustainable lifestyles and further economic development will emerge. Both the market place and community awareness will combine to help to produce beneficial results, complementing government action.

Second, and at the risk of repetition, the cartographer working in the analogue world produced an accurate printed map (hard copy) that was then passed on to others for use. The cartographer controlled the content and accuracy of that map and the methods of analysis and visualization of the spatial data content or information. In the digital world, the professional cartographer at best controls the contents of a spatial database (disregarding additions by users) and may be responsible for its maintenance. The cartographer may also provide a tool kit of analytical and visualization algorithms for the user, and perhaps the potential for the production of a series of standardized products; these may or may not resemble former products produced by a NMO. But the professional cartographer no longer controls the ultimate product's use or its organization's spatial data, as was the case with analogue technology.

Third, in digital technology, the basic building blocks of the database are the digital representations of real world features. What is a feature? In order for millions of people to use its representation and avoid misinterpretation, someone still must define it. Moreover, if data from different sources are to be used, agreements among cartographers in a given nation – or among those organizations sharing a database – on a feature definition must now be standardized. Methods to transmit to potential users the precise definitions of features that reside in a digital database must also be standardized. In contrast, because the cartographer using analogue cartography 'knew' a feature, there was no need for an exactly agreed-upon definition of a stream or a road; rather, the cartographer interpreted from the source material and declared a feature to be a stream or road by its printed symbolization. It was possible for a cartographer to vary the criteria for interpretation and, thus, the definition from feature to feature depending upon context. In the networked digital world of the future, features will have to be semantically standardized. The use of attributes tied through well-defined relationships to features will create the equivalent of context.

Some of these changes are readily predictable. NMOs, created for the production of a standardized systematic coverage of the area of a nation, are well positioned to set standards for definitions of real world features whose digital representations are contained in a NSDI.

Non-sensed data collection will be accomplished by many local and regional offices and ideally should be done to consistent national standards. Unfortunately, it would appear at this time that this will only be accomplished in a negative way; organizations appear to have to experience the costly waste of failing to adhere to a consistent set of standards before agreeing to embrace a common national standard. Similarly, rules contained in the tool kits that can be used to aggregate features, manipulate, analyse, attribute, or otherwise exaggerate, simplify, and classify – that is, generalize the digital features – must be defined. A NMO can derive and/or certify standard tools for the use of spatial data from an NSDI. It can also serve as a certifying agent for non-sensed data collection by locals. A NMO must also be able to create the database containing the features of a nation which are, for a variety of reasons, not collected by locals.

Finally, cartographers can expect the combination of electronic technology and the shift to the democratization paradigm to be reflected in institutional arrangements, if not in the structure, of the institutions themselves. To enforce the *status quo* of the institutional arrangements while introducing a new and enabling technology will eventually force major changes on the institution or else require legal rules that will allow the perpetuation of the inefficient use of the enabling technology. In the long run, institutions will have to change because inefficient and ineffective use of technology will not be tolerated by a spatially aware, democratized society.

REALIZATIONS BY NATIONAL MAPPING ORGANIZATIONS

Changes in NMOs are already taking place. Whether these are in response to fiscal realities, as is often stated, or in response to the changing capabilities resulting from technology change and paradigm shifts in cartography is uncertain. Who is to determine that the technological and paradigmatic shifts in cartography are not just microcosms of similar shifts in society at large, and that the fiscal realities are only a manifestation of these more fundamental changes? A survey of some NMOs in nations pre-eminent in cartographic tradition bears out the already changing natures of NMOs. The following brief list of examples is neither exhaustive nor without bias – it covers only major English-speaking nations of the world. In no sense does it pretend to match the level of detail given in the other chapters in this book. Rather, it simply draws together in close juxtaposition what has happened in some NMOs already experiencing a revolution.

Australia

Historically, the states in Australia have played a more major role in mapping than has the federal government. They have had a degree of autonomy unprecedented in countries such as the United States. Nevertheless, the changes in the Australian NMO resulting from technology change and paradigm shift have been drastic, and were made in a relatively short period of time. The current Commonwealth agency, the Australian Surveying and Land Information Group (AUSLIG), refers to itself as a 'business unit of the Commonwealth Department of Administrative Services'. AUSLIG is the lead agency for surveying and mapping at the national level. Its job is national co-ordination. A brief quotation from a publication in 1995 will illustrate the changes that have taken place:

> they are principally concerned with developing standards of data interchange, data infrastructure and data distribution. This is stated not to imply criticism, but to demonstrate that the era of highly co-ordinated

mapping activities in the form of a national program is well and truly over. In the vernacular, topographic mapping as we have known it is 'dead in the water'. *(Skitch 1995: 13)*

Canada

The changes in Canada have been equally drastic but the process has been taken step by step, which, over a period of a few years, has been more painful for the employees involved. O'Donnell states:

[in] attempts to look 5 to 10 years down the road to see what national mapping agencies might look like, in terms of their roles and responsibilities . . . it is certain that the traditional surveying and mapping organizations are becoming dinosaurs, threatened with extinction. . . . But we can create our own, preferred future. That lies in leading the creation, maintenance and adherence to national standards of a national spatial data infrastructure, linked to other NSDI's of the world via the Information Highway. We will no longer accumulate data, but will be involved in transforming that data into information, and, ultimately, into knowledge. *(O'Donnell 1995: 1/16)*

In both cases the size of the Australian and the Canadian NMOs have been drastically reduced in terms of numbers of personnel and budgetary dollars.

Great Britain

The venerable Ordnance Survey has also experienced major change, but the outcome has been somewhat different. To quote the current Director General:

Five years ago, OS was still an organisation whose primary role was making standard series of paper maps. The changes since then have been substantial . . . from maps in computer form 81,248 [1990] to 230,000 [1995]; from largely paper maps, all in standard map sheet format revised to a timetable set by OS, typically extending between 10 and 40 years [1990] to many maps sold as computer data; to many paper maps tailored to the needs of specific individuals; national road centreline data; a national address database; all data and paper maps being updated more frequently [1995]; from 2525 employees [1990] to 2006 employees [1995]; and from revenues of £44.9 million [1990] to £66.7 million [1995]. . . . Our maps remain vitally important in their own right. But OS data also serves as the 'template' or national topographical framework. On this template is collected virtually all other geographical or geospatial data, ranging from population information to the geology of Britain. What OS does therefore affects thousands of organizations directly and all of the population of Britain indirectly. Under our remit to advise all of the British Government, we have set out to facilitate and extend the use

23

of geospatial data held by many government departments and others. . . . The vision we have of OS in the future is one in which all colleagues – not just senior management – are involved continuously in improving the organisation. Innovation is a matter for everyone. This requires a substantial shift from a mass-production factory with hierarchical controls to one of 'knowledge workers'. *(Rhind 1996: 4-5)*

Whereas the NMOs of Australia and Canada have been substantially downsized in all respects, the OS downsized in staff numbers but increased its range of activities, many of them in conjunction with the private sector. It is largely but not totally (see the chapter by Rhind in this book) operating on business-like lines today: OS operated in 1995/96 at a 78.2 percent cost recovery level. The OS has a business plan with published annual targets. Its progress is measured against these targets. The ability to hold copyright on digital data has been fundamental to these changes.

New Zealand

Similar in some respects to the United Kingdom, the Department of Survey and Land Information in New Zealand has been mandated to act more as a private business and has been given targets for cost recovery. The NMO has identified a long-term vision and began taking both strategic and short-term steps towards a long-term goal. To quote WA Robertson:

In New Zealand we have now experienced over a decade of major change. For my Department of Survey and Land Information this has presented a great opportunity to manage this change such that it enables a transition of a traditional manual survey and mapping organization into an automated spatial infrastructure organization geared to providing for New Zealand's needs in the 21st century. *(Robertson 1995: 1/10)*

The early emphasis was on achieving cost recovery targets while investing in systemic conversion of traditional manual systems to digital automated systems. In 1993 we reorganised to reform other areas that needed change and development to expedite a full transition. This included full client orientation, re-engineering of systems and procedures to take fullest advantage of the efficiencies of new technology and a complete transformation of human resource management approaches. This has involved a complete disbanding of traditional structures. Our organisational development has involved identifying core business systems enabling strong business thrusts balanced by overarching single department business planning and reporting and business development and customer co-ordination. The flattened organisational structure has emphasised the role of management jobs as 'enablers', team builders and performance coaches. A serious attempt has been made to facilitate vastly increased self management and individual motivation and ownership by all staff. *(Robertson 1995: 5/10)*

As Robertson and Gartner point out in another chapter in this book, how-ever, the situation has continued to evolve and DOSLI is now split into two parts: one a small government department charged with regulatory and purchasing activities, and the other a State Owned Enterprise. It is obvious that change, once begun, is a continuing process affecting NMOs at least as much as any other organization.

United States

In many respects the changes to date in the US Geological Survey (USGS) National Mapping Division (NMD), the governmental NMO in the United States, have been far less drastic than those experienced in the four nations detailed above. Indeed, many of the greatest changes seem to have occurred within the US military mapping organization, now known as the National Imagery and Mapping Organization (see the chapter by Lenczowski in this book).

Whereas we see the former NMOs of Australia and Canada were reduced increasingly to governmental co-ordination agencies, and those of Great Britain and New Zealand completely reorganized along lines with some resemblance to a private business, the situation in the United States is evolving differently. One could debate many possible reasons for this. Clearly, one important difference is the lack of the ability to copyright data by the USGS. The government's philosophy of basic spatial data as a 'public good' paid for by the taxpayers and available for the cost of reproduction and distribution to any potential user contrasts starkly with the prevailing business-orientated, cost-recovery philosophies in the other nations.

The development of the concept of a NSDI and the necessary standards that an NSDI depends upon, has proceeded more quickly in the United States but the initial implementation may not be as quickly realized. Once again varied reasons can be cited to explain this. The forces that prevailed in Australia and Canada are present in the United States, with the exception of strong state mapping organizations, and continued attempts to get the government out of the business of topographic mapping can be recognized. Likewise, the forces that prevailed in the United Kingdom can be heard in the United States but, without the ability to copyright digital spatial data, almost everyone concedes that turning the American NMO into a cost-recovery executive agency cannot be accomplished. The form of an NMO in the United States devoted to spatial data during the early part of the twenty-first century remains unclear today.

CONCLUSIONS

Some of these changes were readily predictable. For example, NMOs no longer need to produce standard multi-use products. This alleviates the large warehousing and cumbersome shipping of hard-copy products, functions in current NMOs.

NMOs no longer need to 'do' cartography but rather need to enable all citizens to do cartography. Special teams involving national, local, private, and academic interests are needed from time to time to insert innovative changes and additional capabilities into the developing NSDIs. The current legal barriers to efficient teaming by NMOs and others, including the private sector, will need to be modified in almost all nations.

Viewing the experiences to date, NMOs of the future will probably be smaller in numbers of employees, more flexible, richer in technology and capability, and serve as a steering and certifying body and as a standards-setting agency. Such an organization will need to ensure that digital base data and software to enable the analysis of spatial data and the production of visual displays by consumers are available on a national basis. It can be assumed that consumer needs will continue to vary from nation to nation as they do today, and as they can be expected to do to reflect differences in the legal bases of each nation. But the need for a national mapping agency is to ensure that the capability is available, not necessarily to create or operate that capability. Production and utilization of spatial data will be accomplished by many more diverse actors, which again will vary between nations. Just as the NMOs of 1950 represented organizations perfected over 300 years of technological change and paradigmatic shifts, the NMOs of 2050 will result from today's rapid technological changes and paradigmatic shifts. A better question for the twenty-first century NMO might be, 'What is the status of your area of responsibility for the Global Spatial Data Infrastructure (GSDI)?'

REFERENCES

Bohme R *Inventory of world topographic mapping.* London, Elsevier Applied Science, vol. I (1989), vol. II (1991), vol. III (1993)

Brandenberger AJ, Ghosh SK 1990 Status of world topographic and cadastral mapping. *World cartography,* vol. XX. New York, NY, United Nations: 1–102

Brown LA, 1949 *The story of maps.* New York, Bonanza Books

Morrison JL 1994 The paradigm shift in cartography: the use of electronic technology, digital spatial data, and future needs. Advances in GIS Research. *Proceedings SDH 94, Sixth International Symposium on Spatial Data Handling.* Edinburgh, vol. 1: 1–15

Morrison JL 1994 The changing roles of academia, government, and private industry resulting from the diffusion of GIS in education and the workplace in the 21st century. *Europe in transition: the context of Geographic Information Systems, Proceedings.* Brno, Czech Republic: II-2-II-10

Morrison JL 1996 *Data, information, business, and pricing.* Paper presented at the Geographic Information System/Land Information Systems 96 Conference. Budapest, Hungary

Naisbitt J 1994 *Global paradox.* New York, NY, Avon Books

O'Donnell JH 1995 National mapping agencies: looking to the 21st century.

Conference Papers, Cambridge Conference for National Mapping Organizations 1995. Cambridge

Rhind DW 1996 *Annual Report and Accounts 1995/96, Ordnance Survey: Chief Executive's Statement.* Southampton, Ordnance Survey

Robertson WA 1995 A strategic response to turbulent times. *Conference Papers, Cambridge Conference for National Mapping Organizations 1995.* Cambridge

Skitch R 1995 Mapping Australia – national overview, National Report to ICA, 1995, Australia. *Cartography* – Supplement: 13–15

US Geological Survey 1993 *Des Plaines, IL, 1:24,000-scale quadrangle.* Reston, VA, USGS National Mapping Division

SECTION 1

Building the national frameworks

Perceptions of what *is* the framework are strongly influenced by local experience. Thus in the USA, residents might see the road network as perhaps the fundamental part of that framework. In Britain, a wider range of features would be regarded as the framework. To that extent, it is essential to demonstrate that the geographical framework for the world is primarily the aggregate of national frameworks and that these differ considerably in content, up-to-dateness (currency), form (many are not yet in computer form), and availability. In addition, the political changes of recent years in certain countries have had profound effects upon the organizations creating the framework and, in some cases, on the nature of the description of the landscape itself.

The four chapters in this section demonstrate some of these differences and the commonalities. The first chapter, by Warita and Nonomura, describes the activities of the Japanese national mapping organization (NMO) and the influence which the Japanese terrain has upon this work: their continuous monitoring for earthquakes and the high-technology tools employed form one manifestation of this influence. Another, but less easily predictable, role of their organization is its leadership of the project to create a Global Map. Clarke's chapter, like that of Zhdanov, reflects the dramatic political changes which have occurred in the last few years. In South Africa, the new government has as its priority the reconstruction and development of all communities. The South African NMO has had to adapt to these new priorities and new demands for spatial information. Clarke cites some examples of these new demands and demonstrates the growing acceptance of the NMO as *the* authority on spatial information contained on maps and aerial photography. He also summarizes experiences gained from working on projects of the government's Reconstruction and Development Programme which have provided some major challenges for the NMO.

Jarque's chapter on the situation in Mexico stresses again the changing needs for information, but places great importance on the revolutionary changes in technology which have enabled his organization to meet these needs. In effect, these changes have enabled INEGI – the national mapping and statistical organization – to 'leap-frog' technological generations from a position where relatively traditional techniques were used to make maps to one at the front edge of framework databases on a world-wide basis. The lessons of this for other organizations are obvious.

Finally in this section, Zhadanov describes how surveying and cartography are organized under the new Russian state and the legal and statutory instruments which set the role for the NMO. Again the role of new technology is vital but Roskartografia's key responsibilities include definition of national boundaries and support of the land reform process. Heavy stress is laid on the need for high levels of research and development to achieve the ambitious plans for a new digital framework and emphasize the importance of international contacts to our Russian colleagues.

CHAPTER 3

The national and global activities of the Japanese national mapping organization

Yoshio Warita and Kunio Nonomura

SUMMARY

Japan is a land with a great variation in landscapes, many of them liable to change suddenly through the effects of volcanoes, earthquakes, tsunamis, man, and other agents. This, together with Japanese history and culture, has led to the emergence of a national mapping agency with unusual roles. The work of the Geographical Survey Institute (GSI) spans monitoring the landscape and crust of the earth, mapping Japan at various scales, and creating multiple databases and much research and development. The relationships between GSI and other parts of government in Japan and its funding mechanism are described. The Institute is substantially involved in many new developments which are described in the chapter, together with GSI's involvement in international mapping to facilitate global change studies; the results of meetings to advance the Global Map proposal and develop a Global Spatial Data Infrastructure are described.

INTRODUCTION

The Geographical Survey Institute (GSI) is the major governmental organization for surveying and mapping in Japan. It carries out the basic surveying and mapping of Japan and associated research.

One of the most remarkable characteristics of GSI – which seems to differentiate it from other mapping agencies – must be the variety of its activities. These derive from various factors such as the national legal, financial, and historical conditions. But one of the most influential factors is the unique character of the surveying and mapping target – the land of Japan. It is essential therefore to summarize this before explaining GSI and its activities in detail.

THE LAND OF JAPAN

Japan is an arc of islands, consisting of four major ones and thousands of smaller ones, lying in middle latitudes between 25 degrees and 45 degrees north. The archipelago is situated off the eastern margin of the Asian continent, stretching 3000 km from north-east to south-west. Its total area is approximately 378,000 km^2, and three-quarters of this is mountainous. Generally, the mountains are steep and rivers flow rapidly. Flatter areas suitable for habitation and cultivation are located for the most part along the coast. Most of the Japanese population of 124 million people are concentrated in these narrow areas; consequently each land-use unit is small and their patterns are complex.

Climate is generally temperate, showing both maritime and continental influences. Annual precipitation varies from 1000 mm to 3000 mm, but almost all places in the country are liable to heavy rain from typhoons and extra-tropical cyclones. This, coupled with the steepness of the mountains, results in relatively rapid erosion of the earth. As a result there are frequent occurrences of mass-movement – namely, landslides, debris flow, and so on. In addition, the north-western area of the main island suffers from heavy snowfall in winter. This results in more than 10 m of accumulated depth in one season in some parts of the area.

Japan is also situated in the most active zone in terms of crustal activities. Some 200 Quaternary volcanoes are recognized, of which 83 are designated active. There are hundreds of records of eruptions in historical times. Japan has also frequently been affected by large-scale earthquakes and tsunamis, resulting in severe damage. It is said that about 10 percent of all the earthquakes on earth occur in and around Japan.

In summary, the characteristics of the land of Japan are summarized as follows from the viewpoint of survey and mapping:

- the land is physically rather active. From the results of geodetic control survey, coseismic and non-coseismic displacement has been observed. For example, at the time of the 1923 Kanto earthquake, more than 5 m of displacements were observed;
- the social-related fabric of the landscape is also rather changeable. The total area of land-use change in one year amounts to some 0.5 percent of the national territory. The rate of change from agricultural land to residential usage is remarkably high in the vicinity of larger cities;
- the land is at relatively high risk of suffering natural disaster caused by flood, landslide, debris flow, heavy snow, avalanche, volcanic eruption, earthquake, etc.

THE ROLE OF THE GEOGRAPHICAL SURVEY INSTITUTE

The origins of organized modern survey and mapping in Japan lie in the creation of the Survey Division of the Ministry of Civil Services in 1869, which can be regarded as the original organization of the present GSI. In 1888, the Army Land Survey was established in the General Staff Office, taking over the Survey Division. It carried out the entire fundamental surveying and mapping of Japan, including publishing of base maps for the general public. After World War II, as part of the dismantling of the military, the organization was 'civilianized' and established as GSI in the Ministry of Home Affairs. In 1948, GSI was transferred to the Ministry of Construction.

The headquarters of GSI is located in Tsukuba Science City, about 60 km north-east from Tokyo. It also has 10 Regional Survey Departments all over the country and two Geodetic Observatories. The total number of its staff as of 1996 was 844. It is a 100 percent national government organization; that is, all of the staff are national government employees and all of its budget comes from the Exchequer. The total budget of GSI in the 1996 financial year was ¥10,815 million – approximately US$94 million (as of January 1997). Distribution of its products (paper maps and digital data) is entrusted to the Japan Map Centre, a semi-governmental foundation. Prices of the products are officially set and publicized by the Minister of Construction. Revenues from the sales are immediately paid to the Exchequer and do not accrue to GSI.

The major tasks of GSI are as follows.

Administration concerning survey and mapping

Basically, surveying and mapping in Japan by all public agencies are controlled under the provisions of a Survey Act. When a body in the public sector intends to conduct a surveying project for its own purposes, the survey plan must be submitted to GSI. GSI must then check it and provide technical advice in an effort to avoid unnecessary expenditure and to maintain the required accuracy of public surveys. GSI also conducts national examinations and registration of surveyors to elevate their skills and promote their social status.

Establishment and maintenance of geodetic control points

GSI maintains all national control points in order to provide a reliable and accurate reference for the horizontal and vertical positions. These control points are subjected to resurvey at regular intervals. The data obtained from periodical surveys provide not only updated accurate positions of each control point, but also information regarding crustal activities on the Japan Archipelago and its vicinity plus the state of the terrain which has accumulated in certain localities. These data are extremely important in the study of prediction of earthquakes and volcanic eruption. GSI plays an important role in the observation and analysis of the crustal activities. In this context, it has been positively promoting the establishment and operation of permanent Global Positioning System (GPS) arrays throughout the nation since 1994, leading to the world's largest GPS array network. In addition, GSI carries out various geodetic or geophysical surveys such as levelling, tidal observation, astronomical survey, geomagnetic survey, and gravity survey.

Preparation and maintenance of base maps

GSI's base map products vary in scale from 1:2,500 to 1:3,000,000. The largest-scale base map series of national coverage is the 1:25,000 Topographic Map Series, covering all of Japan in 4376 sheets as printed paper maps. This was completed in 1983. The 1:10,000 scale Topographic Map Series is prepared for urban areas, including metropolitan areas and other large cities. The 1:50,000 Topographic Map Series is compiled from the 1:25,000 scale maps and covers the entire country in 1291 sheets. Map series at the 1:200,000, 1:500,000, 1:1,000,000, and 1:3,000,000 scales are also compiled and published. They are revised periodically and after important changes occur. For example, after the Hanshin-awaji earthquake in 1995, GSI published an urgently revised edition of 1:10,000 and 1:25,000 Topographic Maps. A raster-based digital revision system has been used since 1993 for the revision of 1:25,000 Topographic Maps. GSI has produced large-scale (1:2,500) mapping only for limited areas, while local governments are responsible for preparing large-scale maps for their urban planning areas.

Reproduction and publication of maps

The printing and publication of the majority of these base maps are entrusted to the Japan Map Centre, but those which require special reproduction techniques are compiled and reproduced at GSI.

Preparation and management of Geographic Information

In order to meet recent demands for various types of digital Geographic Information on the national land, the GSI has inaugurated several database preparation projects. The earliest one was the preparation of 'Digital National Land Information', which was started in 1974 and nearly completed in 1980. Its accuracy corresponds approximately to that of the 1:200,000 scale paper maps. It consists of a Digital Elevation Model (DEM), land-use data, boundaries of local governments, major roads, railways, rivers, coastal lines, public facilities, and other features. Since

1984, preparation of 'Digital Base Map Information' has been under way. The accuracy and characteristics of this corresponds to those of the 1:25,000 mapping. Data items included are vector contour lines and polygonal areas of local governments. The 'Large Scale Map Database', captured from large-scale (mainly 1:10,000) base maps, includes all the contents of paper maps in vector form. The 'Detailed Digital Land Use Data' is a data set of grid cell land-use data (intervals of 10 m) for the major metropolitan areas which are repeatedly surveyed every five years. The 'Geographic Information Database' project, begun in 1990, is to construct an integrated database consisting of base map data (a raster version of 1:200,000 scale maps), geographic name data (extracted from paper maps), and various socio-cultural geographic data. Finally, GSI is also digitizing historical aerial photographs and storing them in CD-ROM form.

In 1995, GSI began preparations for the 'Spatial Data Infrastructure' (see the chapter in this book by Tosta). This project is designed to supply framework data for Geographical Information Systems (GIS). Existing large-scale maps prepared by GSI and local governments (analogue and digital) are collected and digitized (or converted) into common formats by GSI.

Geographical surveys and thematic mapping

One of the GSI's unique activities is its geographical surveys. Applying available data, its specialist knowledge and unique geographic, carto-graphic and photogrammetric techniques, GSI carries out a variety of applied work. This includes geographic surveys of major natural disasters, hazard mapping, active fault survey, volcano survey, land-use survey, lake surveys, ground water survey, and vegetation monitoring. The results are compiled into various thematic maps, such as land-use maps, land condi-tion maps, volcanic condition maps, tectonic maps, basic maps of coastal areas, and the national atlas. On the occasion of major disasters, GSI has carried out urgent geographic surveys and compiled special maps, then supplied the results widely to relevant organizations. For example, just after the Hanshin-awaji earthquake occurred in January 1995, GSI compiled and distributed maps showing destroyed houses/buildings, burned-out areas, damaged roads, and so on.

Research and development of surveying and mapping technology

GSI has been involved in research and development of surveying and mapping technology since its establishment. It is now engaged in such R&D as new geodetic techniques using space technology, computer-assisted mapping and map digitization, the preparation of Geographic Information and in related service systems. R&D activities by GSI are not only improving accuracy and efficiency of its survey data but are also contributing materially to earthquake prediction, disaster prevention and global environment preservation. The research results are often submitted to international societies such as IUGG (the International Union of Geodesy and Geophysics), ISPRS (the International Society of Photogrammetry and Remote Sensing), ICA (the International Cartographic Association), and the IGU (the International Geographical Union).

International co-operation in the fields of surveying and mapping

GSI has been actively taking part in various kinds of international activities. These include participation in international conferences and international academic meetings, assuming responsibility for international observation projects such as Antarctic exploration, and for technical aid to developing countries in the field of surveying and mapping. The last of these includes inviting surveyors from developing countries to a one-year group training course, sending staff experts on request, and taking part in mapping aid projects via the Japanese International Co-operation Agency.

A matter of particular importance is that, in order to cope with issues of global environmental change, it is essential to initiate such basic activities as data collection concerning the entire global environment. GSI is rigorously making efforts to clarify the state of the earth through surveying and mapping in co-operation with other countries. The Global Mapping Project, which GSI is strongly advocating, began when GSI hosted the First International Workshop on Global Mapping in 1994. In February 1996, the International Steering Committee on Global Mapping was established; its Secretariat is entrusted to GSI.

SOME EXAMPLES OF MAJOR GSI PROJECTS

Here we describe a number of major projects carried out by GSI in support of its role as set out above.

The nation-wide GPS array network

GSI has operated the world's largest Global Positioning System (GPS) array network system ('GPS Regional Array for Precise Surveying' or 'GRAPES') since 1 October 1994. This system has two main purposes: the first is to monitor and detect crustal deformation on a continual basis, and the other is to serve as an active control system for GPS surveying.

GRAPES consists of 900 permanent GPS observation stations throughout Japan and a data-processing centre at GSI in Tsukuba. Plate 5 shows a typical GPS station. A GPS antenna is mounted on the top of a 5 m stainless steel pillar. A GPS receiver, a modem or terminal adapter, and a battery are placed in the central body of the tower. The data collected at each station are transferred to the data-processing centre via telephone lines. Data are collected throughout all hours of the day and night with a 30-second sampling. These data are processed in a cluster of workstations. Precise analysis software (called GAMIT, which was developed at the Massachusetts Institute of Technology and at the University of California, San Diego) yields the position of each station with an accuracy of a few centimetres or better in a global reference frame (ITRF).

GSI monitors daily variations of station positions to detect any abnormal changes in crustal strain, which bring us important information for the prediction of large earthquakes and volcanic eruptions. The earth's crust can, however, be deformed in various ways. Tectonic events such as large earthquakes cause sudden and large deformation of the crust, whereas plate motions or magma movements deform the crust slowly and gradually. For the prediction of earthquakes or volcanic eruptions, the detection of the slow deformation is extremely essential. Because of its continuous operation and its accuracy, GRAPES is an ideal tool for detecting slow deformation.

Since GSI began the operation of GRAPES, several major earthquakes have occurred in and around Japan. GRAPES has successfully detected them. The first one was the Hokkaido-Toho-Oki earthquake of magnitude M8.1 on the Japan Meteorological Agency scale. This occurred off the east coast of Hokkaido on 4 October 1994 just after the beginning of the GRAPES operation. The system monitored how the earthquake distorted the crust of Hokkaido at the time of the main shock. Plate 6 shows the horizontal components of the displacement vectors. The station at Nemuro City, 170 km west of the epicentre, moved 44 cm to the east. Even the stations in southern Hokkaido, more than 300 km distant from the epicentre, experienced a few centimetres of horizontal displacement towards the epicentre. On 17 January 1995, the Hyogo-ken Nanbu (Hanshin-awaji) earthquake of magnitude M7.2 hit the densely populated Kobe area. GRAPES immediately detected the crustal deformation at the time of the earthquake (shown in Plate 7) and provided crustal information for earthquake studies.

These results prove that GPS is effective in detecting crustal deformation. In the case of traditional triangulation or multi-angulation methods, it usually took several months to detect coseismic deformation, and it was difficult to separate this into real coseismic and post-seismic movements. GPS gives us continuous and prompt results immediately. Moreover, while VLBI (Very Long Baseline Interferometry) works effectively for long baselines and makes clear global plate motions, GPS is suitable to detect regional crustal deformation such as intra-plate motion. Such GPS data bring us important information for earthquake prediction as well as post-earthquake displacement studies. We can calculate the strain field from the displacement data. Such data provide a breakthrough for the assessment of future seismic hazards. We are trying to calculate the velocity field of Japan in the quest to improve earthquake prediction.

In addition to all this in-house research, GSI plans to provide observation data from each station with a set of station co-ordinates. This will enable non-GSI surveyors to using GPS in public and engineering surveys to use GRAPES stations as known reference points. In this way, they can accomplish their work by placing receivers only at the points which they want to survey. Consequently, GPS surveying will be much more efficient on a national basis.

Planimetric observation of crustal deformation by SAR interferometry

Synthetic Aperture Radar (SAR) is a kind of imaging radar. Microwave radiation is emitted from a flying vehicle (usually an aircraft or a satellite) to the ground, backscattered from the surface of the earth, and received by the same antenna. This reflected radar signal is measured and recorded. SAR interferometry involves the measurement of the range (the distance between the sensor and the target) and the changes in the range by comparing phases of reflected radar signals in two or more SAR images in the same scene with different acquisition times. By analysing these together with the information of precise locations of the vehicle at the image acquisition times, topographic height and/or topographic change can be estimated. It can provide detailed spatial (planimetric) distribution of surface displacement over a large area without any field survey. Another advantage is that the data acquisition is independent of weather and daylight.

GSI has applied this method to detect ground displacement associated with earthquakes and volcanic activities using SAR data from the JERS-1 satellite. Plate 8 shows the result of SAR interferometry which reveals the crustal deformation associated with the 1995 Hyogo-ken Nanbu earthquake. The SAR data used were acquired on 9 September 1992 and 6 February 1995. The fringes in the figure indicate the amount of displacement of each spot in the direction towards the satellite. A full cycle of colour change (blue-purple-yellow-green-blue) corresponds to a displacement of 11.8 cm. This was the first study to provide a spatially continuous distribution of coseismic crustal displacement in Japan. Until then, we could have inferred the displacements only from the survey of dispersed points. To develop this method, GSI is seeking to identify error sources such as tropospheric delay from water vapour distribution and local condition of the reflection at the surface.

New technology for maintaining base maps

The first national base map series covering the entire country of Japan was the 1:50,000 Topographic Map Series. The preparation of these began in 1895 and was completed in 1925. In 1964, GSI adopted the 1:25,000 Topographic Map Series as the national base map, replacing the 1:50,000

Map Series. Encompassing the whole country of Japan, the 1:25,000 Map Series was almost completed in 1983. Consequently, the major responsibility of GSI for base maps at present is to maintain and update them.

GSI has been conducting revision surveys for and recompilation of these maps based on the following principles:

- the 1:25,000 scale maps are revised every three years for urban areas, five years for suburban areas, and ten years for mountainous areas, depending on the amount of changes in each map sheet;
- the 1:50,000 maps are revised simultaneously with the revision of the corresponding 1:25,000 scale topographic maps;
- the amount of changes are assessed by Regional Survey Departments of the GSI, which are at ten locations throughout the country.

In 1993, GSI adopted a raster-based revision method for the 1:25,000 scale topographic maps. This involves initial scanning of the previous version of the map to produce raster data. Vector data of changed parts are obtained from air photographs in stereo-plotters with co-ordinate encoders. The raster data are then revised on an EWS using the vector data of changes. Finally, the revised raster data are plotted on film ready for plate making using a laser plotter. This method gives less stress to the operator because, unlike the conventional scribing method, it permits the cancellation of edit operations. Another advantage is that it causes no degradation due to photomechanical processes even if the revision works are repeatedly performed. GSI plans to replace the conventional method completely with the new digital method by 1997.

Preparation of the spatial data infrastructure

GSI has been developing digital Geographic Information since the middle of the 1970s. In co-operation with the National Land Agency, it has developed the Digital National Land Information required for national land development planning and regional planning by the central governmental agencies and the local governments. It has also prepared the Detailed Digital Land Use Data (described earlier) to support the policy making of building land administration in collaboration with the Economic Affairs Bureau of the Ministry of Construction. However, these have not been available to the public but are used only by administrators within central and local governments and researchers in universities.

In June 1993, GSI launched the publication of digital cartographic data sets called the Digital Map Series. Since then, the variation and number of published digital cartographic data have increased year by year. At present, six kinds of Digital Map Series are available. They are Digital Map 10,000 (combined), Digital Map 25,000 (shore lines and administrative boundaries), 50 m, 250 m, and 1 km meshes of elevation data and 1 km mesh of average elevation (shown in Table 3.1). These are text files in MS-DOS format and distributed by 1.2/1.44 Mb floppy disks with simple software for quick browsing of the data. Table 3.2 indicates the level of sales of each data set. In terms of the purpose for purchasing these data sets, according to results of a questionnaire to users who purchased them, education, analysis of topography, regional planning, and assistance for administrative works are the main ones. Their use for purposes such as facility management, navigation, and marketing is small.

Since 1995, GSI has started to prepare a new type of digital cartographic data set called Spatial Framework Data for major metropolitan areas (Tokyo and Osaka). Table 3.3 indicates the contents of these data sets.

The characteristics of these data sets are that they:

- are structured by several very simple items;
- distinguish each city block as a polygon (suitable for address matching);
- contain road network structure;
- can be used on a personal computer and are easily transferred.

The data sources for these files are:

- data converted from digital maps already held by GSI;
- newly digitized data from the 1:2,500 base map for city planning which local governments have; or
- newly digitized data from the 1:500 map for road management held by some local offices of the Ministry of Construction.

Table 3.1 Different types of Japanese digital map series and their characteristics

Type/source of digital map	Number of disks available in December 1996	Characteristics
1:10,000 (combined)	235	about 5 x 5 km on each disk. Only created for major cities.
1:25,000 (shore lines and administrative boundaries)	86	About 80 x 80 km on each disk. To be revised every year
50m mesh Digital Elevation Model	2798	about 10 x 10 km on each disk. Some 4000 disks will cover Japan
250m mesh Digital Elevation Model	88	about 80 x 80 km on each disk. All of country available
1km mesh Digital Elevation Model	1	all country compressed on one disk
1km mesh Digital Elevation Model (average elevation)	1	all country compressed on one disk
TOTAL	3209	

Table 3.2 Sales of data disks from each of the Japanese digital map series

Type/source of digital map	June '93 – March '94	April '94 – March '95	April '95 – March '96	April '96 – December '96
1:10,000 (combined)	4026	7075	6543	4108
1:25,000 (shore lines and administrative boundaries)	2491	2343	3231	1865
50m mesh Digital Elevation Model	3513	5277	14,069	7713
250m mesh Digital Elevation Model	695	3689	4788	3325
1km mesh Digital Elevation Model	–	103	195	115
1km mesh Digital Elevation Model (average elevation)	–	84	99	73
TOTAL	10,725	18,571	28,925	17,199

These data sets will be published for the use of any individuals at an appropriate price, as the Digital Map Series have already been published. They are also intended to be distributed free of charge to every local government which provides source data.

The Ministry of Construction (MOC), to which GSI belongs, is currently making a major effort to develop and utilize GIS after recognizing the necessity and important role of Geographical Information Systems (GIS) in the high-information society. To establish new strategies relating to GIS, the headquarters of MOC and GSI are jointly organizing a GIS Research Committee which consists of professors from universities. The first report by the committee was presented on 2 February 1996.

One of the targets of the new strategies of MOC is the standardization of GIS. At the international level, GSI is involved in the activities of the International Standards Organization's committee ISO/TC211 with the support by other related agencies and professors from universities. Japan has also undertaken the secretarial work of two Work Items with Japanese team leaders among 20 Work Items of TC211. GSI also recognizes however that harmonization between national standards and the ISO/TC211 international standards is very important.

Many ministries and agencies in the Japanese government are concerned or interested in GIS. The Cabinet Councillors' Office on Internal Affairs is organizing a Liaison Committee of Ministries and Agencies concerned with GIS.

Table 3.3 Contents of the Japanese Spatial Framework Data

Item	Data structure	Attribute
Administrative boundary and coast line ('Cho-Chomoku' and 'O–Aza' (municipal section) as the minimum areal units	Polygon, arc, point	Administrative code, name of each municipality
Block	Polygon, arc	Block code ('Ban')
Road line network	Vector, network	Name of each road
Road centre line, boundary of road and sidewalk, boundary of road site (national highways only)	Vector	Name of each road
River centre line, boundary of each river site (only for major rivers)	Vector, polygon	Name of each river
Railways and stations	Vector, point	Name of each railway and station
Inland water area, other specific area (park, airport)	Polygon	Name of each area
Buildings (only for central districts)	Raster image, polygons of public buildings	Code and name of each public building

GSI and the National Land Agency jointly provide its Secretariat. The Ministry of Construction, recognizing its important role as a core member of government, is committed to enhancing co-operation with other ministries and agencies concerned in GIS.

Promotion of global mapping

It is now widely realized and accepted that accurate and up-to-date environmental information of the entire earth is essential to solve global environmental problems such as global warming, deforestation, and desertification. Environmental policy-makers need environmental information of at least 1 km² spatial resolution for their decision-making processes; the spatial resolution of globally available data at the moment is not sufficient for this purpose.

Although there are already in existence 1 million scale maps which cover the entire world, they do not have sufficient elevation accuracy and some of them are outdated, particularly in developing countries. In addition, thematic information such as land use and vegetation – which is indispensable for environmental studies – is not included in these maps. Consequently, none of the existing geographic data satisfies the needs for information to help solve global environmental problems: the spatial resolution and currency of existing globally available data are both inadequate for this purpose.

This recognition has driven the Ministry of Construction and GSI to propose a plan for a Global Mapping project to the international communities; the initial proposal was put forward in 1992. The following description is a draft proposal, to be further improved through discussions among professionals of mapping and environmental research communities, and to be implemented through close international collaboration.

1 The objective of the Global Mapping project is to provide a biological and geographical database useful for both global environmental studies and large-scale regional development planning.
2 The spatial resolution of the Global Map database is 1 km by 1 km to grasp environmental phenomena. This spatial resolution corresponds to a scale of 1 million for printed maps.
3 The Global Map database should be revised every five years to detect biological and geographical changes at regional scale.
4 The information content of the proposed Global Map database is as follows:
   a) Geomorphological data (terrain elevation data on 1 km grids, watershed and geomorphological units boundary data in vector format),
   b) Environmental data (vegetation, hydrological conditions, and land-use data on 1 km grids),
   c) Basic geographical data (rivers, coast lines, and administrative boundaries data in vector format). The other basic geographic data have already been provided by the Digital Chart of the World project.
5 The production of the Global Map should be accomplished by taking full advantage of data prepared by existing global programmes. If there are no appropriate data, existing maps and satellite data should be employed. The proposed production procedures for the data set are as follows:
   a) As for geomorphological data, the whole land area of the earth is already covered with digital terrain elevation data thanks to the activities of US and co-operating mapping organizations. The evaluation of these data and their update and enhancement are now the main tasks. Data quality can be improved through use of remotely sensed stereo data obtained from SPOT/HRV and/or ADEOS/AVNIR. The boundary data of watershed and geomorphological units can be produced from the terrain elevation data.
   b) Vegetation and hydrological condition data are produced for the entire land area from the NOAA/AVHRR data of 1 km resolution, terrain elevation data, and ground truth data.

c) Land-use data of approximately one-fifth of the land area, where human activities are high, can be produced by manual interpretation of higher spatial resolution satellite images such as those of SPOT/HRV, Landsat/TM, and ADEOS/AVNIR.

d) Regarding basic geographical data, rivers and coast-line data can be produced by manual interpretation of higher spatial resolution satellite images such as those of SPOT/HRV, Landsat/TM, and ADEOS/AVNIR. Administrative boundaries data must be collected from existing maps and mapping agencies in the world through international co-operation.

6 The Ministry of Construction and GSI will continue to seek every opportunity to co-operate with other countries, mapping agencies, and other related organizations for the successful implementation of the project. GSI plans to make a part of Global Map database as a pilot product study on such important issues as the information content, data format, map projection, and data production procedures.

Global mapping and Agenda 21

As indicated above, the Global Map is not something 'nice to do'. The Japanese Ministry of Construction and the Geographical Survey Institute believe that this is essential to tackle scientific and development problems of the kind described in earlier chapters and recognized by the international agreement known as Agenda 21, signed in Rio de Janeiro by most of the world's governments in 1992.

In our view, then, the surveying and mapping community should be charged with developing a Global Map of integrated geographic data with consistent specifications and at least 1 km^2 spatial resolution on the ground. This would form a key part of a Global Spatial Data Infrastructure (GSDI), analogous to the National Spatial Data Infrastructure described by Tosta (in this volume) and earlier in this chapter. It is not, however, a trivial task for, as is clear from other chapters, the organization of and funding for almost all official mapping agencies is essentially national in character. In addition, many other players would need to be involved beyond the NMOs.

To take forward the proposal for a Global Map, GSI has organized an ongoing International Workshop on Global Mapping. The first meeting of the workshop was held in November 1994. Another was held in Tsukuba, Japan, in February 1996, which led to the creation of the International Steering Committee for Global Mapping (ISCGM). It was also decided that the Geographical Survey Institute should provide the Secretariat for the ISCGM.

In November 1996, an 'Interregional Seminar on Global Mapping for Implementation of Multi-national Environmental Agreements' was held to advance the cause of, and encourage international co-operation in global mapping. It was organized jointly by the United Nations Department for Development Support and Management Services (UNDDSMS), the

University of California, Santa Barbara, and GSI. The participants at this seminar were drawn from many different nations and organizations. They agreed a number of recommendations, collectively known as the Santa Barbara Declaration. All involved urged that these recommendations should be embodied in a report to be presented to the Special Session of the United Nations General Assembly on the Implementation of Agenda 21 in 1997. The Declaration is as follows:

1 A Global Mapping Forum must be created bringing data users and providers together to facilitate creation of a Global Spatial Data Infrastructure or GSDI. A variety of national, regional, and international organizations, NGOs, private sector companies, academia, NMOs and space agencies, as well as other relevant organizations, must be involved in this effort. The International Steering Committee for Global Mapping should undertake a study to create such a Forum and determine the essential responsibilities, such as the periodic assessments of progress, the harmonization of standards, and mechanisms for the establishment of a global mapping network. Such a network would exploit the Internet and other means to facilitate communications.

2 Agencies implementing Agenda 21 accords (see Htun's chapter in this book) should precisely define their spatial data and information requirements for implementation, compliance, and monitoring with the assistance of expert groups (e.g. ISCGM). These requirements should be included as priorities of the GSDI.

3 Financial and other incentives for project partnerships within the GSDI should be devised to facilitate the participation of national institutions of developing countries and economies in transition.

4 Donor agencies and development banks should increase assistance to institutions in developing countries and economies in transition to improve the quality of spatial data products and services and facilitate access to these data for the creation of regional and global map products.

5 Issues related to spatial data policy and access need to be discussed in the UN Regional Cartographic Conferences.

6 Overall Global Map development should be fostered under the umbrella of the United Nations and should recognize existing initiatives being taken at national, regional, and global levels.

7 The UN Environment Programme's Global Resource Information Database (UNEP/GRID) and other UN programmes directly involved in GSDI activities should be strengthened to provide the necessary technical support systems and metadata services to UN agencies and to member countries.

8 Complementary efforts for the provision of technical support by a variety of national, regional, and international organizations should be encouraged and co-ordinated to strengthen GSDI activities.

9 The report embodying these recommendations, to be presented to the Special Session of the United Nations General Assembly on the Implementation of Agenda 21 in mid-1997, should make a clear and practical proposal for implementation of the Global Map proposal. This should be developed under the auspices of the UN Department for Development Support and Management Services, with the assistance of the International Steering Committee for Global Mapping.

All of the discussions held to date have demonstrated the crucial role which NMOs can and must start to play in Global Mapping if scientific, economic, and humanitarian objectives are agreed by the world's governments and international societies.

RELATIONS WITH THE PUBLIC

The Geographical Survey Institute has been devoted to presenting its information, such as results of survey, the fruits of research and development activities, to the public via various media. For instance, when the Hanshin-awaji earthquake occurred on 17 January 1995, GSI immediately made every effort to clarify what had happened. To identify the crustal movement, it urgently conducted a GPS survey, a levelling survey, and other geodetic works. A few hours after the earthquake hit, GSI's aeroplane was taking aerial photos of all damaged areas and, in the night of the same day, GSI's printing machine was printing maps of the affected area. In the afternoon of the same day, a survey team composed of specialists on active faults and geomorphological disasters headed towards Hanshin and Awaji Districts. Within a few days, maps indicating destroyed houses, damaged structures, and so on were compiled and distributed to the necessary organizations and people.

The results of these activities were all released via press conferences, but GSI has found a more effective medium. The Geographical Survey Institute launched its home page on the Internet especially to publish information related to the earthquake on 24 January, just a week after the event. In this page, a lot of 'hot' results were presented, including images of aerial photos indicating offsets along the earthquake fault, damaged structures, fires and liquefied soils, the results of crustal displacement observation using GRAPES, images of SAR interferometry analysis, the results of geomorphological field survey, and so on. The nature of multimedia in an Internet context has proved quite effective for communicating these kinds of information. In March 1995, GSI launched its 'normal' home page, including explanations of its institutional matters and projects, examples of the products, introduction for global mapping, and so on. Figure 3.1 indicates the rising number of accesses to the GSI home page.

Another major public relations effort by GSI is the establishment of 'The Science Museum of Map and Survey'. This was constructed in the premises

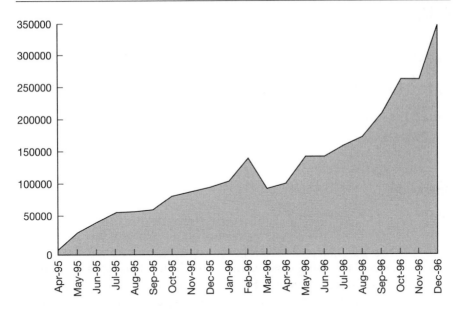

Fig. 3.1 Total number of 'hits' on GSI's home page on the World Wide Web

of the headquarters of GSI and was opened in June 1996. It is an independent, two-storey building with 4252 m² of exhibition spaces.

This museum is the first exhibition facility of map and survey in Japan. In it, the principles, the mechanisms, history, and new technology for mapping and for survey, various maps, and the relationship between our life and maps and survey can be learned. It has also the function of an information service providing data on control points, aerial photographs, various maps, and so forth. In order to familiarize the public with maps and surveys, it will be the centre for cultural exchange between researchers, associations of map makers and surveyors, and the regional residents. Some 25,000 visitors were in the centre from 1 June 1996 (opening day) to January 1997.

CONCLUSIONS

The Geographical Survey Institute is eager to widen its range of activities. We believe the public and Japanese organizations alike expect GSI to be more aggressive in collecting, analysing, and presenting various types of vital Geographic Information concerning our varied and changing national land and, beyond that, on a global scale. We are determined to meet that expectation.

CHAPTER 4

Mapping for the reconstruction of South Africa

Derek G Clarke

SUMMARY

South Africa experienced a major political change in 1994 with the first democratic government coming to power. This government has as its priority the reconstruction and development of all communities. The South African national mapping organization (NMO) has had to adapt to these new priorities and new demands for spatial information. Some examples of these new demands are discussed and the acceptance of the NMO as the authority on spatial information contained on maps and aerial photography is demonstrated. Experiences gained from working on projects of the government's Reconstruction and Development Programme have highlighted some major challenges for the NMO.

INTRODUCTION

In 1994 South Africa held its first democratic general election. This brought to an end centuries of domination by one group over the rest of the people of the nation and the start of a new government. The political change took place smoothly and has been welcomed by the vast majority of the people. The new government has committed itself to the development of *all* of the communities and has adopted various plans to achieve this, the most notable of which is the Reconstruction and Development Programme. But, unlike the political change, the consequential administrative change was not given the same amount of thought and has been slower to implement. The result is that the ambitious plans of the new government have been slow in coming to fruition; these plans required new policies to be established first before implementation could take place. The approach of the new government is to involve the communities in the policy formulation and planning stages so as to empower the communities. This in turn fosters successful implementation of the policy. The approach is a refreshing change from the previous process of policy formulation and planning which was a strictly top-down approach: communities were dictated to about what was good for them. The democratic approach is most honourable but it is liable to lead to delays in policy formulation.

The new direction of the government and, in particular, its urgent development needs have forced public sector institutions (central and provincial government departments, local governments, and public utilities) to re-prioritize their programmes and projects. This in turn has led to an urgent need for new information to support the planning and decision-making processes. In the previous dispensation, there was a bias in the development of areas and numerous 'black spots' were created: it is particularly in these areas where action is now proposed but the required information is not available. Furthermore, the approach of involving the communities ensures that there are now new users of information who were previously not considered. These changes have had a profound effect on information providers.

Much of the information required for development is of a spatial nature, indicating where 'things' are on the earth's surface and their relationship to other 'things'. The map is known to be the best conveyor of spatial information. Maps have therefore become an important component in policy formulation and the planning of projects in the pursuance of the goals of the government. As a result, the NMO in South Africa has new and substantial challenges in meeting the demands of the new users of spatial information.

HISTORICAL REVIEW

Before describing these new challenges facing the NMO in South Africa, it is necessary to put the national mapping programme into perspective with a brief historical review.

The first topographical mapping made in South Africa was, as in many countries, for military purposes. From 1899 to 1911, the Royal Engineers of the British Army carried out surveys and produced topographical maps of areas along the coast and certain other areas of military importance, such as the 1:125,000 series of the Orange River Colony (now the Free State province). After this early work, there was a break of many years before any mapping that could be considered as part of a coherent national scheme was undertaken. At the start of the twentieth century Sir David Gill made attempts to convince the then colonial and republican governments (which, after Union in 1910, became the provinces of South Africa) of the benefits of a well-mapped country and in 1904 chaired the first Topographical Survey Congress (Thomas 1982a: 78). But nothing was to come of this. However, Gill had established the basis of the geodetic triangulation of South Africa. Many people considered a good triangulation system to be a prerequisite for the national mapping coverage.

In 1920, the Trigonometrical Survey of the Union of South Africa (now incorporated into the Chief Directorate of Surveys and Land Information, the NMO) was established. The director of this survey had the authority to undertake national mapping. At this time however, the secondary triangulation of the country was receiving priority and the only mapping undertaken was experimental projects in the Cape Peninsula and surrounding areas to determine the best method to produce mapping under the unique conditions of South Africa.

It was not until 1936 that the then Minister of Lands appointed an interdepartmental committee to advise the director on the mapping requirements of the government. The 22 representatives were obviously desperate for mapping and eventually agreed on the following main points (Thomas 1982a: 84):

- the whole Union was to be covered by a topographical series of maps at 1:50,000 scale with 50-foot contour interval;
- in special areas the scale would be 1:25,000;
- owing to the sparseness of development in many areas, it was not necessary to publish the relevant 1:50,000 sheets but at least the field work should be undertaken at that scale;
- the mapping was to be based on aerial photography;
- the first [national] cover was to be completed in 15 years;
- all air photography for government departments was to be arranged by Trigsurvey.

The country was divided into 1916 map sheets, each extending 15' latitude by 15' longitude. Besides the scale, contour interval and sheet lines, the other specifications were left up to the director. Thus 1936 was the real start of the national mapping programme in South Africa.

The 15-year plan was ambitious, taking into account the resources available and the inaccessibility of many areas. In practice, very little progress was made during this period. The director was receiving little support from his surveyor-general colleagues who together made up the Survey Board: their main interest was cadastral surveys. As a result of this inaction, the director obtained ministerial approval to form the National Survey Advisory Council in 1949. This was an interdepartmental advisory body on the requirements and priorities for topographical surveying, engineering surveying, aerial photography, and cartography. Following the 1936 decision to survey but not publish complete coverage at 1:50,000, the National Survey Advisory Council considered what should be the smallest acceptable published map scale for each area. A 'Domesday Book' was compiled showing the smallest-scale map for each area. These scales included 1:25,000 in the developed areas, 1:50,000 mainly in the eastern half of the country and the coastal areas, and 1:100,000 and 1:250,000 in the more sparsely populated areas (Thomas 1982b: 179). However, in the early 1960s a decision was made, after intervention by the Department of Defence, that the entire country was to be covered by the 1:50,000 map series as published maps (Thomas 1983: 336).

By this stage, the second 15-year plan was well under way but a third 15-year plan was to be necessary because of the increased work. Production increased significantly in the 1960s with the use of new techniques and equipment. The workload, however, also increased, with additional burdens placed on the organization to produce 1200 sheets at 1:50,000 scale of the then South West Africa (now Namibia). From 1970, South Africa changed to the metric system and the maps produced from that time on were required to have the metric co-ordinate grid and a 20 m contour interval. The compilation of the last 1:50,000 scale map sheet was completed in May 1973 and the last sheet was printed in March 1976 – well ahead of the third 15-year deadline. The job now was to metricate all the sheets. The programme for metrication was fitted in with the revision of the sheets. Over the years, amendments have also been made to the specification of the map series mainly adjusting the symbolization to meet changing needs.

South Africa is fortunate then to have complete topographical map coverage at 1:50,000 scale – a series consisting of 1916 sheets covering 1.219 million km^2, or 470 700 square miles. The NMO has also produced complete coverage of the country at 1:250,000 scale (70 sheets) and 1:500,000 scale (23 sheets); 1:10,000 scale orthophoto maps covering the metropolitan and growth areas and other selected areas of user interest (approximately 25 percent of the surface area covered at present) have also been produced. All of the mapping is based on the integrated national control network of South Africa. This network is also compatible with the network in South Africa's neighbouring countries.

Requirements for mapping in the past have been determined by the interdepartmental committee, in conjunction with the NMO. The priorities for map revision, for new 1:10,000 orthophoto map coverage, and for coverage of aerial photography have been determined at the annual meeting of the National Survey Advisory Council. The council's requests form an important input into the national mapping programme for the forthcoming year, but this has to be balanced against the budget allocation – which is often insufficient to meet all the requests. The national needs have largely been determined by the projects in which user departments are engaged and the systematic revision programme of sheets as determined by the NMO. The projects of the departments have in the past been in areas promoted by the policy of the previous government. The content of the map and the symbolization used have largely been determined by the NMO. Although attempts have been made in the past to involve users in this process, the users approached have been from a select group and in most cases the response from users has been poor.

There are those who claim that the national mapping of South Africa has supported the ideology of apartheid because the maps have been biased. For example, it has been said that the maps do not show the areas where most of South Africa's people live but only the 'white' cities and towns (Human Rights Commission 1992). This mismatch is less a matter of previous policy than a consequence of a very high rate of urbanization. New settlements have sprung up over a short period of time, some of which are formal but many are informal in nature. The map revision process has been unable to match the pace of these developments. Also many black settlements developed under the apartheid system were an annexe to the main city or town and, as such, were not considered as a city or town on their own, irrespective of the population size. The depiction of such areas on the maps therefore were the same as a suburb and not as a separate city or town.

It is well known that maps *can* carry disinformation (Monmonier 1996). The NMO in South Africa has always endeavoured to reflect, as best it could, the true situation on the ground in its maps within the constraint of available resources. Nevertheless, accusations of bias and its history of being an institution of the previous government (like all public sector institutions) have made the NMO's task of arguing the case for a national mapping programme more difficult. This is all the more difficult since the attainment of the goals of the new government alone have posed significant new challenges for the NMO of South Africa.

THE RECONSTRUCTION AND DEVELOPMENT PROGRAMME

The government of South Africa which was elected in April 1994 realized that the country had to be transformed in many respects. In particular, it committed itself to addressing effectively the problems of poverty and the gross inequality in almost all aspects of South African society. It was necessary not only to set objectives of reconstruction and development but also to balance this with sustainable economic growth. To achieve its goals, the government developed the Reconstruction and Development Programme (RDP). The RDP is an integrated and coherent socio-economic policy framework. The policy document (a White Paper) sets out the six basic principles of the RDP as follows:

First, we require an integrated and sustainable programme. . . .

Second, this programme must become a people-driven process. . . .

Third, this programme and this people-driven process are closely bound up with peace and security for all. . . .

Fourth, as peace and security are established, we will be able to embark upon nation-building. . . .

Fifth, nation-building links reconstruction and development . . . an integrated process. . . .

Sixth, these first five principles all depend on a thorough-going democratisation of South Africa.   (*Republic of South Africa 1994*)

Five key programmes were envisaged in the RDP – meeting basic needs; developing our human resources; building the economy; democratizing the state and society; and implementing the RDP. Meeting basic needs involves land reform, housing, services, water and sanitation, energy, telecommunications, transport, the environment, nutrition, health care, social security, and social welfare. In developing human resources, the people must be empowered to participate fully in the decision-making process, implementation of projects and job creation.

The implementation of the RDP required public institutions to realign their objectives with those of the government. All institutions requesting funding from the exchequer (parliamentary votes for budgets) have to motivate the funding in terms of the RDP programmes. This has ensured that the public funds will be used to attain the goals of the government. A further requirement of the government is that state departments be transformed to serve the population as a whole. The government seeks to make the public service representative of the various population groups and to democratize the workplace. All of these matters have impacted on the NMO. Being a professional and technical service organization rather than one of great political significance has ensured that it has not been in the political spotlight. None the less, it has had to establish its continued existence and funding. The new politicians have had to be informed of the need for a national mapping programme. They have also had to be convinced that the workforce cannot be changed overnight from a predominantly white one because of the lack of persons from other population groups with the required knowledge, skills, and experience.

NEW DEMANDS FOR SPATIAL INFORMATION

The majority of users of the products of the South African NMO are public institutions, which includes state departments (central government), provincial government, local government, and public utilities. These institutions have been most affected by the changed priorities of the new government and are required to implement the programmes of the RDP. In many cases, the programmes address new problems and require the government to formulate new policies. Understandably this has led to the need for spatial information in new priority areas and for the information to be made available in a short period of time. New demands have therefore been placed on the NMO to deliver the required information.

It has not proved easy to meet all the demands because of the time constraints. The NMO has been experiencing a decrease in its budget in real terms and reduction of its staff numbers over a number of years. Funds have also not been available to contract out large amounts of the work. To overcome this problem, it has been necessary to enter into co-operative work arrangements with many of the user institutions. This arrangement has meant that the majority of the funding would be provided by that institution with the NMO using all available resources of its own. Work has also been contracted out but private sector organizations have not been prepared for this sudden influx of work: there has been a clear limitation in the capacity that exists in the private sector. This in turn has encouraged new contractors to spring up, but most do not have the required knowledge and skills to undertake the work successfully.

Not all of the public institutions have made contact with the NMO to express their needs. Some have decided to go their own way and have appointed consultants such as planners and engineers to provide the required information as part of the total project. There is no government regulation forcing them to make use of the NMO. Experience has shown that this approach often leads to duplication of data collection, information of dubious quality as some consultants do not have the necessary expertise, and, on occasions, the work undertaken by the consultants is unnecessary ('over- servicing'). The NMO is also prepared to advise such institutions on technical issues without interfering with their method of operation (and has done so).

The conventional paper map remains a major source of spatial information but many of the users are implementing Geographical Information Systems (GIS) and there is a growing demand for digital spatial information. South Africa's NMO had the foresight to commence a programme of converting its maps to digital form to establish a digital topographic database some years ago, but the new demand has meant that this programme has had to be accelerated. Aerial photography has also become increasingly popular, most probably because of the need for the rapid gathering of information where field inspection would take too long for most applications. Another product which is rapidly increasing in popularity is the digital orthophoto image. It is most popular with those users who have GIS and use the digital orthophoto image as a 'back-drop' onto which other information can be added or from which it can be extracted. The digital orthophoto image provides advantages over the ordinary aerial photograph because of the geometrically correct and geo-referenced image, permitting direct measurement.

In conjunction with reprioritizing its work programmes, the Chief Directorate of Surveys and Land Information has provided services to a number of other public institutions in support of their own RDP work. Some examples of the new demands for spatial information are discussed below.

Population census

The exact population of South Africa is unknown, mainly due to the fact that the previous censuses were deemed by many as being a control tool of the previous regime and therefore they did not participate. The previous apartheid states of Transkei, Bophuthatswana, Venda, and Ciskei were also excluded from thoses censuses. To provide adequate services and to target communities most in need of services, it is however vitally necessary to have a good demographic profile of the communities in the country. Many projects of other institutions rely on this information. In preparing for the first complete population census in October 1996, the institution responsible for the census had first to determine enumerator areas and to demarcate the boundaries of such areas clearly. With the short time available and the inaccessibility of many areas, the decision was taken to make use of recent aerial photography where available and to have new aerial photography flown in selected areas. The aerial photography proved most useful to depict many of the households not shown on the maps and also improved orientation for the demarcators. Once the areas had been identified and marked on the 'field copy' of the aerial photograph enlargement (usually an X4 enlargement), then the areas were transferred onto the 1:50,000 map. Approximately 80,000 enumerator areas had to be demarcated within about eight months; this required a large workforce of temporary workers. These demarcators had little or no previous experience in map reading and photo interpretation and had first to receive training.

The role of the NMO was to provide the maps, administer the contracts for new aerial photography, produce contact prints and enlargements of the aerial photographs, to provide training to the demarcators and give subsequent support in the demarcation process. This support was found to be invaluable for the successful completion of the demarcation process.

The responsible institution, the Central Statistical Service, intends to create a GIS with the enumerator areas. This information will then be available to users of the population census for their own applications. The Chief Directorate of Surveys and Land Information is assisting in the establishment of this GIS and the provision of digital cadastral and topographic information to be used for the identification of the boundaries and orientation of the locality.

Potable water for all

The government wishes to provide potable water to all. Although this exists in the established cities, towns, and villages, most informal settlements and rural households have to travel long distances to collect water. The intention is to provide water points no more than 400 m from each household. To achieve this first requires information on the location of households and the relationship of the households to existing water reticulation networks. In many areas no water reticulation exists and so requires the long-distance transport of water by canal or pipeline and, in some areas, the building of storage dams. The institution responsible for water resources, the Department of Water Affairs and Forestry, is using a GIS for the planning of this work. It has placed demands on the NMO for the supply of digital topographic information, including accurate digital elevation models, for the study of catchment areas, the location of required water points, possible location of storage dams, and the routing of canals and pipelines.

Agricultural potential of land

A major focus of the government is the uplift of the rural communities. One approach to this is to provide previously disenfranchised people with the opportunity to farm land commercially and to move others away from traditional subsistence farming to commercial farming. To utilize the land optimally, the agricultural potential of such land has to be determined. Maps and aerial photography, and the more recent digital orthophoto images, are invaluable for this work.

Housing

Proper shelter is a basic human need and providing people with it is an urgent priority of the government in order to achieve stability. The government wishes to provide 1 million houses within five years. To plan this first requires a survey of the existing housing stock and the location of houses. From this information, it will then be possible to target the areas most in need of houses. The urgency of the project has meant that great reliance has been placed on aerial photography to provide the information. Digital orthophoto images are being used to locate the houses.

Electricity and telecommunications

A further way of 'uplifting' the people is to provide electricity to each house and easy access to a telephone. The responsible institutions – namely, Eskom and Telkom – require knowledge of the location of all houses to plan and implement this requirement. To acquire this information, a combination of field inspections, aerial photography, and maps has been used.

As will be evident from this description, the needs for the census, housing, electrical supply, telecommunications, and to a small degree also water supply required similar information – namely, the location of existing houses. To avoid duplication of effort, these institutions had the foresight to co-operate. The NMO was recognized as having the required expertise to assist in these projects.

Upgrading education

The education of black communities was neglected by the previous government and has been recognized as a priority of the new government. The first requirement is to take stock of the existing schools, determine their location and the facilities available at each. Maps are proving to be invaluable in this exercise by aiding the workers to orient themselves and also to demarcate the position of each school. Hand-held Global Positioning System (GPS) receivers are being used to determine the co-ordinates of the school and these are then plotted on the maps.

Land reform

The policy of apartheid forced people off the land and moved them to designated areas, as well as reserving land for specified population groups. Furthermore, the land tenure system did not permit freehold title to land to be held by black citizens until recently and the tribal system of land tenure did not permit women to own land. To correct these inequities of the past, the RDP makes provision for land reform. This includes land restitution (giving land back to previous owners who were removed from their land), land tenure reform (providing for various types of tenure with security for all), and land redistribution (making land available to those who were previously excluded from the land market). In the case of land restitution, it may not always be possible to return the land to the previous owner because of changes that have taken place over the years. In such cases, alternative land has to be found. This need, together with the requirement to make land available for redistribution, has made it necessary for the government to locate and make suitable land available. The Constitution of South Africa protects ownership of land and therefore the normal market mechanisms have to be used. The state itself is a big landowner and the policy is first to make available state land prior to buying land from private owners.

This requirement has led to the first ever land audit of state-owned land, including unalienated state land. The first stage in this process was to create a customized GIS, called the State Land Information System. It includes three main data sets: namely, cadastral, deeds, and topographic data. The cadastral data consist of the location of each land parcel, together with its property designation, farm name where applicable, and the legal area, the administrative districts, and the Magisterial districts (in South Africa the Magisterial districts are used in many applications as a reference area). The deeds data are linked to the cadastral data and provide the name of the registered owner as well as the title deed number. The topographical data consist of the road network, rivers, dams, settlements, contours, game and nature parks, and railways. From this system, state-owned land can be located and certain information provided about it, as well as information on the topography and infrastructure. Additional to this, the state institution currently using the land, the current land use and potential land use of each land parcel must be determined, and it must be established if the land is still required for state purposes or if it is superfluous to state needs. Land that is superfluous and has potential for productive use can be made available for the land redistribution programme. Besides supplying digital topographic data for the State Land Information System, the Chief Directorate of Surveys and Land Information has also made available maps, aerial photographs, and orthophotos for the land-use evaluation. The 1:50,000 and 1:250,000 maps are also being used extensively as strategic information for the monitoring and evaluation of the land reform programme.

Economic development

The main economic activity is found in the developed areas but the government wishes to develop the rural communities as a particular target group. In certain areas, this will be difficult as the environment is not conducive to sustainable economic development. One such area is the Namaqualand district on the west coast. This area is arid with limited agricultural potential. The main economic activity has been the fishing industry and mining of diamonds from the sea bed and coastal dunes. Both of these industries have been declining in recent years and alternatives have to be developed to sustain the local communities. The development planners required recent information but found that the conventional 1:50,000 scale map was inadequate in this sparse area. Aerial photographs were required as these depicted the arid vegetation, informal tracks, and landforms in a much better way. As no recent photography existed, the NMO had to reprioritize its programme to meet this need.

CHALLENGES IN MAPPING THE NEW SOUTH AFRICA

The change to a new political dispensation took place so rapidly that little time was available to prepare for the new South Africa. The NMO has been under extreme pressure to meet the needs of the various users working on RDP projects, some of which have been described above. There has been no time to adjust map specifications or product presentation. The experience to date has shown that there are a number of issues to be addressed by the Chief Directorate of Surveys and Land Information, mainly because of the new approach to development planning and the new customer base. Some of the challenges they pose are discussed below (in no particular order of preference).

The nature of South African maps

In the work done for the population census, it became apparent that many of the users could interpret information from an aerial photograph more easily than from the conventional line map. This finding raises the question of which type of map is more appropriate for users with little or no prior knowledge of map reading, the line map or the (ortho)photo map. Further studies will be necessary to verify the early findings favouring the photo image. There are, however, many experienced users who show preference for the line map. A possible solution may be to print the line map on one side and the photo map on the opposite side of the paper.

The currency problem

South Africa has been experiencing rapid urbanization for a number of years, with the resultant formal and informal settlements springing up in many places. Given the capacity of the NMO, it has not been possible to keep pace with all the developments. Furthermore, previous priorities of user institutions led to a concentration of NMO efforts in certain areas at the expense of other areas. Constitutional matters also played a role: the mapping of the area of the former Transkei was not the responsibility of the South African NMO and this led to the maps in that area not being updated for about 18 years. In addition, the procedures used in the past of undertaking field annotation, and field checks and updates prior to finalizing the map for printing have had to be curtailed in the past ten years or so because of increasing costs.

The result of all of this is that many South African maps are out of date. The effects of this are severe, as the country is now in desperate need of information that reflects the current situation. This has been partially overcome by undertaking aerial photography in particular areas and use of orthophoto maps. Satellite imagery (SPOT) has been considered but found to be inadequate for the needs of most users. The Chief Directorate of Surveys and Land Information is currently implementing information technology and procedures to increase its map revision programme, with a target of an increase of 50 percent. This target has to be achieved without an increase in personnel. A digital topographic database is now being established which will form the heart of the whole system. This database is being updated by a variety of procedures, such as digital monoplotting using digital orthographic images overlaid with existing data, direct digital stereo-compilation, and import of digital information from other source institutions. The database is then used as the source for the computer-assisted cartographic system for the production of digital maps and the subsequent colour separates for map printing. Attempting to keep the maps as up-to-date as possible has also required the map revision cycle to be altered and realigned with the new development priority areas.

Acceptable geographical names and language

The policy of the NMO with respect to geographical names (including place names) is to use the names officially accepted by the National Place Names Committee and gazetted in the Government Gazette. Many of these names were given by the institutions or communities influenced by the previous government and may not be widely accepted by the people. This is particularly relevant to the names of settlements. It has now been found that many settlements have names which are not 'official': the local inhabitants are using different names. In some cases a settlement can have two or three different names, caused often by different political or place of origin groupings in the community using different names. This has created a chaotic situation as far as national mapping is concerned. It will be necessary to make contact with the various communities in each settlement where names are a problem in order to reach consensus on an acceptable name. Some of the cities may also be subject to name changes. Names that were previously assigned to geographic features and farm names which are now considered racially offensive have also been banned and are being removed as quickly as poss-ible from maps.

Prior to 1994, South Africa had two official languages; namely, English and Afrikaans. Official maps were designed to be able to provide for these two languages. There are now eleven official languages. Incorporating all eleven languages onto the maps will be a major challenge, but has not yet been considered. It will be too expensive to produce different language versions of the same map.

The growth in need for digital information

An increasing number of users are using GIS and associated technology for analysing data, planning, and decision-making. These users require digital data, which are often obtained from outside data suppliers. At present there is a limited amount of digital data available but this situation is changing. Problems that are being encountered are similar to those in other countries, mainly because it is not a trivial task to exchange digital data between institutions and between systems. Different systems use different data models, and some exchange formats do not permit transfer of the full data model specification. Also, data standards are required, including those for metadata. Currently there are some attempts in South Africa to achieve such standards, but most institutions are too engrossed in their own systems to make any significant move on the standards front. What is required is strong leadership, with enough power to obtain acceptance of the need for standards and to ensure their widespread implementation. The NMO certainly stands to gain from such a move as it will make the supply of data a lot easier.

Enlarging the user base for maps

It is estimated that the NMO sells approximately five maps per 1000 of the population per annum. While it can be assumed that many more persons use the maps because of institutional access to maps, the figure is still extremely small. Possible reasons for this are that the South African people, whether as individuals or in their work, are not aware of the availability of the maps and/or are map-illiterate and therefore cannot benefit from maps. With the poor education system in the past, especially of the black people, spatial concepts and sources of spatial information have not been adequately taught, if at all. These are the very people who are now being targeted for development – but they are not yet empowered to make proper decisions for themselves because crucial information, such as that contained on maps, is not available to them. These people are recognized as the new customer base of the NMO, together with the development professionals. To address the problems of the lack of awareness of the availability of maps and the high level of map illiteracy, the Chief Directorate of Surveys and Land Information has embarked on a Map Awareness/Map Literacy Project. Community leaders, development planners, and non-governmental organizations involved in development are the main target groups. This project has been designed as a multi-pronged approach to deal with each group in the best possible way.

As can be seen from many of the challenges above, there is an urgent need to determine the current and future needs of users. The official maps still have the content and are designed with symbology determined some years ago. With a new user base, it is imperative to review the design of the maps. It may also be necessary to repackage them and to provide the user with a more flexible product. In the past, little attention has been paid to the needs of the customer, but this has to change if the NMO is to remain relevant and be effective. In a multi-cultural society such as South Africa, it is also necessary to determine what impact cultural differences have on the national mapping. Are the current map and the current national map series appropriate for the wider South African community? This question must be answered.

IN CONCLUSION

The South African NMO has been in existence since 1920 and had a slow start in life. Throughout most of its life it has had to cater for a user community that was largely white and to work on projects to meet the objectives of the white-dominated government. In 1994, this situation changed with the first democratic government coming to power. The priority of this government was to redress the inequities of the past and to develop the previously disadvantaged communities. At first it was necessary for the NMO to prove the necessity of its continued existence to the new politicians. This has been a relatively easy task because of the new demands for spatial information required for reconstruction and development projects. There are, however, still many challenges that lie ahead for the NMO.

There is a new map user who did not exist before. These users are both from government institutions charged with new priorities and from the communities now involved with making decisions and planning their own development. The future of the South African NMO will depend largely on how it adapts to meeting the needs of these users. It is essential for the organization to become more flexible in its products and services, to provide the users with solutions to their individual needs. It will be necessary to get closer to the users so as to be more sensitive to their changing needs.

To some degree the situation in South Africa is unique, but some of the experiences gained in mapping seem likely to be relevant to NMOs and related bodies in other developing countries. In such countries, the imperative is not so much to raise revenues by sale of maps or data, but rather to help meet the needs of people who have long suffered problems far removed from those in the developed world.

REFERENCES

Human Rights Commission 1992 *The two South Africas. A people's geography.* Johannesburg, August 1992

Monmonier M 1996 *How to lie with maps.* 2nd edn. Chicago, IL, University of Chicago Press

Republic of South Africa 1994 *White Paper on Reconstruction and Development.* Pretoria, September 1994

Thomas PW 1982a Topographical 1:50,000 Series of South Africa, Part I. *South African Journal of Photogrammetry, Remote Sensing and Cartography* 13 (2) June 1982

Thomas PW 1982b Topographical 1:50,000 Series of South Africa, Part II. *South African Journal of Photogrammetry, Remote Sensing and Cartography* 13 (3) December 1982

Thomas PW 1983 Topographical 1:50,000 Series of South Africa, Part III. *South African Journal of Photogrammetry, Remote Sensing and Cartography* 13 (5) December 1983

An application of new technologies: the National Geographic Information System of Mexico

Carlos M Jarque

SUMMARY

The transformations that have taken place in recent years around the world and in Mexico, as well as the challenge posed by the globalization and interdependence of economies, emphasize the need for more and better information in Mexican society. INEGI is Mexico's official statistical and mapping organization. It has implemented a Modernization Programme to develop and consolidate the National Statistical and Geographic Information Systems and to provide timely and efficient answers to the users' requirements in this field.

Within this framework, INEGI initiated a process to convert topographic and natural resources maps into computer form. These maps were produced by manual methods over the previous 25 years and were stored in analogue (namely, paper) form. This project also included the updating of the resulting data through the use of new methods and tools which offer a greater diversity of products created from the resulting database in a shorter time. Currently, INEGI is in the initial stage of the digital production and updating of Geographic Information on several subjects, leading to what will be a large geographic database. In addition, and as a result of the new agrarian legislation, a Rural Cadastre Programme (PROCEDE) was instrumented. This required a large purchase of advanced technology for field measurements and processing.

Through the modernization of these geographic activities, INEGI generates information which contributes to the definition of policies. In turn, this leads to the adoption of measures which contribute to the better use of the natural resources and, consequently, to the sustainable development of the country.

INTRODUCTION

The transformations that have taken place in recent years – around the world as well as in Mexico – and the challenge posed by the globalization and growing interdependence of economies have had a strong influence in Mexican society. They have enforced the need to have more and better information. Such information is a prime concern of the Instituto Nacional de Estadística, Geografía e Informática (INEGI), Mexico's national statistical institute and mapping agency. Facing these needs, INEGI decided to implement a Modernization Programme. This has been orientated towards the development and consolidation of the National Statistical and Geographic Information System (SNIG) and to provide timely and efficient answers to the users' requirements in this field.

INEGI started the geographic modernization programme in 1992. The primary objective is of course to define and display the characteristics and descriptions of the national territory for use in a multiplicity of tasks. Since 1992, however, an important objective of the process has been to update and accelerate the production of such geographic information by means of new methods and tools in order to offer products and services with higher quality, of greater variety and higher precision with better coverage – all in a shorter time. The MNGIS (Mexican National Geographic Information System) transformation process consists of the application of new methodologies and the adoption of 'cutting-edge' technologies to a variety of products using information on natural resources, the physical environment and the national territorial space. In combination, these produce a wider knowledge of the landscape than previously existed in any coherent and useful form.

THE EXISTING CARTOGRAPHY

INEGI's cartography of Mexico was produced between 1968 and 1992 by conventional methods and covered the national territory of some 2 million square km. At 1:50,000 scale alone, it comprises over 2400 topographic maps and 3600 other, rather diverse thematic maps. This required the creation of a vast geodetic network, the operation of an aerial photography fleet, the photogrammetric restitution of hundreds of thousands of photographs, the compilation of millions of toponyms and the publication of thousands of topographic and natural resources maps. There is also complete coverage of topographic and natural resources maps at 1:25,000 and 1:1,000,000 scales.

THE TECHNOLOGICAL TRANSFORMATION

This has various components, each of which is now discussed in turn.

The challenge of updating

The first task was to meet the needs of users for mapped information across the whole country. The main updating phase was postponed since the priority was on completing this national coverage in the minimum possible time, even though some maps were updated during that period.

In 1992, it was decided to face the challenge of updating the maps and to incorporate the latest technological advances. The magnitude of this problem led to a decision to carry out an intense internal study and a search abroad for the state of the art. The purpose of all this was to evaluate the pros and cons of the Mexican National Geographic Information System (MNGIS) and to diagnose the most appropriate conversion and production processes.

The result of this diagnosis was as follows:

- updating was extremely difficult to achieve in a reasonable period with the processes then being used;
- the existing production capabilities were constrained by various factors, notably the limitations of the equipment used for almost 25 years;
- there was an accumulated and growing demand for new products: for maps in other scales, for diversification of the existing thematic coverage, and for products in new presentation forms. Many of these demands were driven by the necessity to support high-priority national projects;
- there was a need for effective means to promote and distribute the products and services; and
- it was essential to update the methodologies used. More specifically, it was essential to adopt digital technology in order to have the information in a geographic database which allows the handling of large volumes of information in a fashion congruent with contemporary demands and the requirements of any user.

All of the cartographic information represented by the traditional maps printed on paper, as well as other information from documents generated by INEGI, were in analogue format. Such a format, the only one available for decades, has serious limitations so far as handling large volumes of data are concerned and also in combining them in a geographic information system (GIS) environment.

The advent of INEGI's modern computing system allows the input, processing, and storage of the geographical objects represented in maps as well as alphanumeric data in a digital format. The implementation of the system involved conversion of the analogue information from maps and documents into a digital format. This was achieved through scanning and digitizing under established standards and specifications.

Conceptual scheme of the modernization

Two premises underpinned the creation of the modernized MNGIS. These were that society's rapidly evolving needs imply a substantial change, qualitative as well as quantitative, in the way we generate geographic information. Parallel to this, the second premise was that the advent of new technologies and processing resources, which offer greater speed and precision and the possibility of updating the information, solve critical problems and open new ways to information diversification.

Thus digital technology was seen as a way to achieve the Modernization Programme of the Geographic Activity in INEGI. Under this concept, the MNGIS comprises all the capture, production, organization, integration, analysis, and presentation processes relating to Mexican Geographic Information. The ways in which these processes are implemented are all part of the application of advanced and specific technology within the integrated framework of the Geographic Information production in INEGI. Hence, the system contains analytical tools to allow the maximum benefit to be gained from the existing data that is being integrated. This is in accord with our Statistic and Geographic Information Law. It occurs within a predefined conceptual structure embracing economic, demographic, and social phenomena, their relations to the physical surroundings and the territorial space and their interdependence.

Implementation of the technology

The decision to make a new cartography was followed by the definition of the conceptual scheme for the database modelling and for the construction of national standards and specifications, followed in turn by the acquisition and installation of the 'system'. The latter includes advanced equipment and software; the adaptation of the infrastructure; the start-up, acceptance and performance tests; training, technical advice, and the modification of the basic structure of the geographic part of INEGI itself. Thus the effects of the new approach go far beyond a simple technological replacement and have resulted in an organizational transformation. The system adopted represents the integration of a group of resources in a manner which is at the vanguard of technological progress and within a scheme which is unique world-wide. Table 5.1 shows the progress which has been made in creation of the core database.

From analogue to digital

One vitally important element in the Modernization Programme was the change from analogue to digital format. Geodetic work and aerial photographs are still used, photogrammetric procedures and image analysis are also applied as well as fieldwork, editing, and printing. These

Table 5.1 Some digital results of the MNGIS, December 1996

Cartography	Conversion	Updating		
Topographic 1:50,000	450 sheets (20%)	240 sheets (11%)		
Topographic 1:250,000	national OK	national OK		
Topographic 1:1,000,000	national OK	national OK		
Topographic 1:4,000,000	national OK	1995		
Land use and vegetation 1:1 million	national OK	national OK		
Ground hydrology 1:1 million	national OK	national OK		
Other Digital Results	1:20,000	1:50,000	1:250,000	1:1,000,000	1:4,000,000
Digital Elevation Models		240	national OK	national OK	national OK
Spacemaps			national OK	national OK	national OK
Anaglyphs Spacemaps			national OK	national OK	national OK
Orthophotos	1440				

processes are modernized under the new conceptual framework or as support components and they form part of the system as a whole. The Global Positioning System (GPS) has been implemented, a new National Geodetic Network has been designed, and the ITRF 92 geodetic reference system has been adopted. Aerial photographs have been improved, with the incorporation of advanced cameras and airborne GPS. The photogrammetric processes used are digitally based. Photo-interpretation capabilities have been broadened through the use of satellite image processing.

The modernized system has six basic components. These are: conversion; production; updating; visual display and automated reproduction, spatial analysis; and geographic databases.

Conversion

This is the first operational process and it is the most time-consuming one. The basic purpose is the preparation of the information for the updating component. Digital terrain models are obtained as derived products from the digital conversion of the contour lines from the 1:50,000 topographic series.

Production

This component has two purposes. These are production of 1:250,000 scale 'space maps' and of 1:20,000 scale orthophotos. The space maps are also used for the production of 1:250,000 thematic maps as well as for the updating programme for the 1:250,000 scale topographic series that will be updated about 12 months, finishing in November 1996. The orthophotos support updating tasks, rural cadastral mapping, and other user requirements.

Updating

Updating constitutes the central issue of the Modernization Programme in Geography. It necessitates complex processes, aimed at decreasing production times under different priorities for each subject and map scale. The topographic cartography at 1:250,000 scale has the highest priority. This is because it is Mexico's medium-scale map series, and is the base for thematic and derived cartography. Next in priority are the topographic maps at 1:1,000,000 scale and land use and hydrological themes. The programme of topographic maps at 1:50,000 scale is running only for urban areas over the biggest 100 cities.

The basic input data are structured digital files from conversion, digital elevation models, orthophotos, and field information. Updating is done in each of the ten INEGI regional offices across the country.

Visual display and automated reproduction

This area performs cartographic editing from updated vector files linked to the database. Visual display generates the digital files for the automated reproduction section where the colour separation is done, proofs are generated, and the printing originals made.

Spatial analysis

The spatial analysis component is charged with image processing, geostatistical analysis, the production of specific information dealing with GIS; geography, methodology and applications studies and related activities, and the generation of prototypes. Due to the strong relationship between these aspects and the users, this area constitutes the communication link between the users and the MNGIS. It largely comprises technical advice and technology transfer when required.

Geographic Database

The Geographic Database is the core of the system. It contains the sets of data organized in vector, raster, and alphanumeric files produced by the different components described above. All the system activities and the users have access to this database. MNGIS's Geographic Database will include all the geographic data already generated by INEGI, properly customized and updated. It will also include all new data, including those produced by other sources if they meet the national standards and specifications. The conception is integrated and global; thus it requires a great effort to gather, organize, and analyse the huge amounts of data involved.

Training

Technological change implies a new way of performing cartographic production processes. It requires highly specialized personnel. The Modernization Programme has involved a large training effort which has allowed the personnel to adapt to and apply modern technology for increasing the quality of the products and to develop cartographic production and updating methodologies.

Basic training

In the first stage, the training was basically aimed at the operation of equipment and the use of software. A group of 73 specialists, all with some computer knowledge and broad experience in their own areas, was selected to receive it. One hundred and sixty-nine courses over a nine-month period prepared them to operate the system.

Cascade training

After basic training, a cascade training strategy was implemented. This ensured the transfer of knowledge to a second group of technicians, whose trainers were the personnel qualified in the first stage. Within seven months, this strategy permitted INEGI to train 91 additional specialists, who were incorporated in different production and management areas.

Curricular modalities

Training for the system does not stop at the operating level. INEGI has an Integral Training and Research Programme aimed at satisfying institutional needs in different areas. This programme includes diplomas, modular courses, short courses, and permanent courses.

International participation

With the purpose of having permanent contact with the development of modern technology, INEGI has built relationships with international institutions and organizations related to Geography. In this context, several educational events have been carried out, sharing the training staff and our facilities. For instance, over 100 technicians from Latin America and the Caribbean have been trained at INEGI on modern methodologies for Geographic Information production and updating.

FINAL COMMENTS

The modernization process described above has involved a deep change in INEGI, both at the conceptual and in the instrumental levels. It has required change both in viewpoints and in the ways of doing things. Changing mentalities and assimilating new schemes and processes, meeting new requirements, the training of personnel, the introduction of new management styles and techniques are just some of the manifestations of its impact. All these elements have been and are being achieved within the framework and expectations of the Modernization Programme.

As a conclusion, we can state that INEGI is generating information that contributes to the definition of government policies. This is also leading to the adoption of measures helpful to the better use of natural resources and hence to the sustainable development of the country.

CHAPTER 6

Mapping in Russia: the present stage of development

Nikolai Zhdanov

SUMMARY

According to the Constitution of the Russian Federation, geodesy, cartography, and naming geographical features are carried out under the jurisdiction of the state. Surveying and mapping of federal importance are executed by the federal service of geodesy and cartography of Russia (Roskartografia). Tasks set by the government before the creation of Roskartografia are defined in a number of legislative and normative documents issued over the last five years. The most important of these is a federal law 'On Geodesy and Cartography' published in 1995 to regulate surveying and mapping activities in the Russian Federation. To meet the requirements of current development in the country, Roskartografia is charged – in addition to its conventional tasks – with various new ones. These are to provide coverage of the territory of Russia with revised topographic maps and plans by using digital technology and satellite methods. It is also charged with providing surveying and mapping for the delimitation, demarcation, and control of the national border line of the Russian Federation. And Roskartografia is required to provide support of land reform, designing electronic maps and Geographical Information Systems (GIS), and with providing educational institutions and the population with cartographic products.

The most urgent tasks are being realized within federal and regional programmes. One of these, considered as a directive to Rokartografia, is a federal multi-purpose integrated programme running until the year 2000 entitled 'Progressive technologies of surveying and mapping of the Russian Federation'. This programme is aimed at eliminating any lag of national surveying and mapping as compared with the world level by speeding up technical and technological re-equipment. Achieving this programme will meet national demands for topographic data and cartographic products. This chapter describes how Roskartografia has gone about meeting the programme objectives, notably through the development of new techniques based on extensive research and development projects. It also demonstrates the priority placed on international contacts.

INTRODUCTION

According to the Constitution of the Russian Federation (article 71, item'p'), geodesy, cartography, and the naming of geographical features are carried out under the jurisdiction of the state. Surveying and mapping of federal importance are executed in the country by the federal service of geodesy and cartography of Russia (Roskartografia). Tasks set by the government for Roskartografia are stated in a number of legislative and normative documents published during the last five years. The most important of these is a federal law'On Geodesy and Cartography', issued in 1995 to regulate surveying and mapping activities in the Russian Federation. The draft of a federal law'On the naming of Geographical Objects' is under consideration in the Federal Assembly at the time of writing (mid-1996). The putative law gives a legal basis for naming and renaming geographical objects and for the use, registration, and storage of geographical names as part of historical and cultural heritage of the peoples of the Russian Federation.

Consequent upon the changes in the political and economical situation in the country, Roskartografia has new tasks and problems to solve. The most urgent of them are dictated by the current development of Russia and are being carried out within federal and regional programmes. One of these is considered as a directive and forms a multi-purpose, integrated, federal programme running until the year 2000. Entitled'Progressive technologies of surveying and mapping in the Russian Federation', it includes a number of special-purpose sub-programmes: these are described below. The federal programme is aimed at eliminating any lag of national surveying and mapping behind the world level by speeding up technical and technological re-equipment. Achieving the programme will meet national demands for topographic data and cartographic products.

PROBLEMS BEING SOLVED BY THE FEDERAL SERVICE OF GEODESY AND CARTOGRAPHY OF RUSSIA IN TOPOGRAPHIC SURVEYING AND MAPPING

Since January 1966 – when the Federal law'On Geodesy and Cartography' came into force – surveying and mapping activities in the country have, for the first time in the history of home geodesy and cartography, been regulated on a single legislative basis. According to this law, the federal service of geodesy and cartography of Russia is a federal governmental body of executive power charged with functions of an executive, directorial, permissive, and supervisory nature to provide surveying and mapping over the territory of the Russian Federation. Roskartografia includes air surveying and geodetic agencies, Geographical Information centres, cartographic factories, optical-mechanical plants, research and development institutes, regional divisions of the state supervision service, and other organizations. It employs some 20,000 staff.

Roskartografia' s surveying and mapping activities have a multi-aspect and multi-purpose character, depending on the different objectives of national, regional, or local significance. It conducts surveying or provides mapping to meet the demands of governmental institutions, of local organizations of the Federation subject-states such as municipal bodies, and of citizens or lawyers. Surveying and mapping activities considered to be of federal importance are as follows:

- compilation, production, and revision of national topographic maps and plans in graphical, digital, photographic, and other forms to solve problems in the economy, science, education, and defence;
- surveying and mapping to support federal and regional programmes – for instance, ecological and land reform programmes;
- the remote sensing of the earth for mapping;
- creation and maintenance of federal and regional topographic data archives;
- development and maintenance of GIS for various applications;
- design, compilation, production and revision of geographical, thematic, reference, educational, political, and administrative-division maps and atlases;
- standardization, registration, and the consistent use of geographical names;
- surveying and mapping to support delimitation, demarcation, and control of national land and water border lines;
- research and development, design and project work at federal level;
- facilities for the full-scale production of mapping.

Special-purpose surveying and mapping activities also under the responsibility of Roskartografia are as follows:

- topographic surveys for engineering, construction, and other works, for land management, the cadastre, and other specialist applications;
- compilation and revision of topographic plans designed for construction site lay-outs of industrial projects, underground networks and structures, and for other particular specialist applications;
- design and maintenance of GIS for special applications;
- compilation and production of thematic maps, special-purpose plans, and atlases in graphical, digital, and other forms;
- special-purpose research and developments, design and project work.

In accordance with the federal law'On Geodesy and Cartography', Roskartografia is also responsible for licensing and supervision of all other surveying and mapping activities in the country.

TOPOGRAPHIC SURVEY COVERAGE OF RUSSIA

One of the main objectives of the national surveying and mapping service is to provide topographic coverage of the country. Russia is a vast territory covering 17,075,000 square km, i.e. almost twice the size of the USA, 31 times the size of France, and 46 times the size of Japan. Detailed topographic surveys have permitted country-wide production of topographic maps and plans at all scales adopted in the country. In this regard, Russia has reached the level of the major advanced nations in the world. Topographic maps at 1:25,000, 1:50,000, 1:100,000, 1:200,000, and 1:1 million scales cover the national territory. All the industrial and agricultural regions that occupy one-third of the territory of Russia are provided with maps at 1:10,000 scale. Towns and town-like settlements are covered with topographic plans at 1:5000, 1:2000, and larger scales.

One of Roskartografia's vital concerns and a matter of federal significance is the continuous revision of topographic maps and plans to make the content correspond to the current situation of the terrain. In connection with recently launched land reform, demands for large-scale topographic maps will certainly increase. Roskartografia is therefore facing a need to speed up rates of topographic map revision through use of new technologies, notably the use of satellite-based, remotely sensed information and digital maps.

THE FEDERAL PROGRAMME'PROGRESSIVE TECHNOLOGIES OF SURVEYING AND MAPPING OF THE RUSSIAN FEDERATION'

This major federal programme integrates a number of special-purpose sub-programmes. The first of these is'Digital mapping of the Russian Federation'. This programme provides for production of maps of 1:10,000 to 1:1 million scales, and, based on them, formation of digital map data archives at federal and regional levels. It includes development of GIS of various applications such as GIS for state government bodies, for national borders, and regional, municipal, and territorial GIS.

'Provision of educational institutions and the population of the Russian Federation with cartographic products' is the second sub-programme. Its successful completion will meet the national demand for maps, atlases, relief maps, and plastic globes. The programme will take full account of all geopolitical changes in the country and in the world, revise all of the cartographic products issued before 1991, and produce maps and atlases of a new kind – namely, electronic ones.

The third sub-programme is entitled'Surveying and mapping for delimitation, demarcation, and control of the national border line of the Russian Federation'. Under this, national vertical and horizontal control networks will be densified to a required level, boundary marks will be positioned in the field, boundary demarcation maps at 1:10,000, 1:25,000, and 1:50,000 scales will be compiled, and these maps and demarcation documents will be published.

The'National research and development sub-programme' is designed to support all aspects of the main'Progressive technologies for topographic survey coverage of the Russian Federation' programme. Implementation of the sub-programme will involve intensive research and development activities aimed at developing new technologies and facilities with respect to satellite positioning, digital and electronic maps design, database creation and maintenance, and the improvement of technologies for map-plotting and map-printing procedures. Such R&D is based on digital methods applied to all types of surveying and mapping activities. Thus for surveying, GLONASS/GPS methods will be used and for topography, electronic tacheometers; for mapping, the new technologies will include digital maps, scanners, and analytical photogrammetric instruments of the SD-20 type. Devices to produce automatic colour-separation of diapositives, colour copies of maps, and digitally produced plans ready for printing are under development at Roskartografia.

Today, then, Roskartografia stands at the threshold of a transition to automated technologies for surveying and mapping operations, all based entirely on digital methods. It is important to appreciate that these efforts are highly focused: all of the surveying and mapping agencies and research organizations of the federal service of geodesy and cartography of Russia contribute to the accomplishment of the federal programme. Having described the aims of the various sub-programmes, it is now appropriate to review progress in some of the key components of the overall programme.

Progress in the'Digital mapping of the Russian Federation' sub-programme

In the second half-year of 1992, Roskartografia began mastering a new kind of cartographic product – namely, digital maps. In 1992-93, several Roskartografia centres of geographical information were set up to solve problems of digital mapping and GIS design. These were the Russian science production geoinformation centre in Moscow (Rosgeoinform) and regional centres of Geographical Information in St Petersburg, Ekaterinburg, Novosibirsk, Irkutsk, and Khabarovsk. In 1994, a state centre for GIS applications (GosGIScentre) was established in Moscow. The centres of Geographical Information are responsible for designing digital and electronic maps, creation of geographical databases, supply of users with digital terrain information, and for development and application of GIS.

Research institutions in Russia, at the behest of Roskartografia, have developed a technology for design and construction of digital maps and plans for use in the centres of Geographical Information. This technology is highly automated, utilizing efficient image recognition methods.

In designing digital topographic maps for Russia, the main requirement is to make them fully comparable in their content to conventional topographic maps and plans; that is, features and objects in the digital map should have a sufficient number of attributes associated with them to represent all their 'real world' characteristics. This requirement calls for great efforts and causes high production costs since traditional topographic maps in Russia are information-rich.

At the end of 1994, the year after the work had started, a digital topographic map at 1:1 million scale for the whole territory of Russia was completed. At present a digital map derived from 1:200,000-scale materials covering all of the country is being created. Over half of the Russian territory had been already covered with this map at the time of writing this chapter. The completion of the map is scheduled for the end of 1996.

The main characteristics of digital topographic maps made in Russia are as follows:

- the content, mathematical basis, and map sheet divisions are identical to those of the reference (or source) cartographic materials used for digitizing;
- the system of classification and coding of features and objects fully corresponds to that accepted in conventional cartography;
- the objects are identical to those in reference cartographic material;
- relief is represented by contour lines with conventional contour intervals;
- various levels of data access are available. These are at the level of an elementary object, for a compound object, a net of objects, a map sheet, and a defined territory. In addition, information enquiries may be made about data at any access level.

In digital topographic mapping, special attention is paid to information quality control. At each one of the centres of Geographical Information engaged in creating digital maps a strict quality-control system is in operation. It involves appropriate software and hardware and specific control procedures to provide detection and elimination of errors of different types: sheet margin deformations, errors in codes assigned to objects and their characteristics, errors in vertical and horizontal positions of objects, and so on. Some of the characteristics of Russian digital maps are set out in Table 6.1.

Digital maps have found their practical applications in the needs of different ministries and departments: for instance, digital maps of 1:1 million scale are used by the ministry of emergency situations of the Russian Federation. It has concluded with Roskartografia an agreement for the

Table 6.1 Main characteristics of Russian digital topographic maps at 1:1 million and 1:200,000 scales

	1:200,000 scale	1:1 million scale
Data sources	Stable based film	Stable based film
Number of map sheets in series	3543	138
Number of digital maps	All in digital form by end-1996	138
Map sheet dimensions	40′ x 60′	4 x 6 degrees
Data structure	Vector	Vector
Average data volume per map sheet	2.0 Mb	2.5 Mb
Maximum data volume per map sheet	3.5 Mb	6.5 Mb
Average number of objects per map sheet	15,000	20,000
Layers	8	8
Object codes used	320	170
Relief representation	contours with conventional intervals	contours with conventional intervals
Technology used in digitizing	scanning	scanning
Co-ordinate System	CS 1942	CS 1942

design and construction of decision-support GIS to warn, localize, and liquidate the consequences of disastrous hazards of natural or technological or biogenic character. In addition, GIS are being created for state government bodies to provide them with actual and full information to support management decision making and other applications such as a cadastre. Thus Roskartografia's agencies and organizations have produced a number of digital maps of 1:10,000, 1:25,000, and 1:50,000 scales for various regions. Several municipal administrations (in Kaliningrad, Tyumen, and in other towns) are using now GorGIS, a GIS designed for municipal management.

To co-ordinate the inter-branch activity on GIS developments and applications, a Joint Committee on Geographical Information Systems has been established by government decree. It is headed by N D Zhdanov, the president of the federal service of geodesy and cartography.

Progress in the'Providing cartographic products to educational institutions and the population of the Russian Federation' sub-programme

The task of providing the country with sufficient quantities of high-quality cartographic products, including general-geographical, educational, and reference maps, plans, and atlases as well as standard topographical maps, is being fulfilled by the various mapping agencies and enterprises of Roskartografia. At present, there are three map-printing plants in Omsk, Novosibirsk, and Ekaterinburg and one mapping production association (PKO) Kartografia in Moscow. Former map-printing plants in Riga (Latvia), Vinnitsa (Ukraine), and Tbilisi (Georgia) are now on the other side of various borders. Roskartografia's mapping agencies compile and print maps, plans, charts, and atlases at all scales, for different applications and with different contents (including relief maps), depending on the application; they also manufacture plastic globes. The mapping association'Kartografia' is a specialized enterprise that is engaged in compilation and publication of maps and atlases designed for mass use; in experimental work, and in the development of automated technologies for compilation and printing operations. It also publishes some special-purpose cartographic products.

Before the USSR' s disintegration, the Soviet cartographic industry met the needs of the national economy, science, and defence by producing cartographic materials and manufacturing plastic globes in large organizations at plants in Vinnitsa and Tbilisi. Despite economic difficulties, mapping agencies and map-printing plants preserved the main profile of their activities and, over the last few years, have begun enlarging their capacities and increasing production rates. In 1995, mapping agencies of Roskartografia produced 67,000 copies of educational maps, 2.877 million copies of school atlases, 741,000 reference maps (including thematic maps), 129,000 reference atlases, and 15,000 topographic map sheets at different scales. The following new map series are under development:'General geographical maps of the Russian Federation','Topographic maps of Russia','Administrative division maps of the Russian Federation', and'Maps of towns of Russia'. Production of plastic globes with a diameter of 210 mm and of one-sheet relief maps of Russia at the scale of 1:16 million have begun; many-sheet maps of 1:8 million scale are under development. Over the 1992-95 period, over 200 of cartographic product titles were developed and published. Despite all this achievement, in order to meet fully the country's demands for mapping products it is planned to increase production rates further, to modernize old equipment, introduce new technologies and facilities for the compilation and publication of maps, and to adopt map printing with a reduced number of printing inks.

To work out the single approach to geographical names and their agreed use in cartographic products, a Joint Committee on Geographical Names has been formed by government decree. It too is headed by N D Zhdanov, president of the federal service of geodesy and cartography of Russia.

Progress in the'Surveying and mapping to support delimitation, demarcation and control of the national border line of the Russian Federation' sub-programme

Roskartografia will continue to carry out work of political significance in providing surveying and mapping support for delimitation, demarcation, and control of the national border line of the Russian Federation. The total length of the national border, including the outer line of territorial waters with islands, amounts to 7.2000 km. Of these, only 5.3000 km have been demarcated and officially documented according to international law: these are the borders with Norway, Finland, Poland, Mongolia, and the Korean People's Democratic Republic. Roskartografia provides historical information on the border territories and participates in governmental commissions on delimitation and demarcation of the border with Latvia, Lithuania, Estonia, Georgia, and Azerbaijan.

Under the federal programme of 1992, the surveying agencies and organizations of Roskartografia began topographic surveys for delimitation, demarcation, and control of the national border line of the Russian Federation. Demarcation topographic maps at 1:25,000 and 1:50,000 scales have been compiled on the basis of survey data. To provide the border delimitation and demarcation with revised topographic maps. Roskartografia executed 1:10,000-scale surveys over the area of 15,640 square km. It is essential that there is a full correspondence of topographic map content to the terrain situation and the agreed border line in such territories, so topographic maps of this type should be continuously revised. Radically new technologies and facilities are urgently needed to comply with the requirements.

Progress in the'National research and development programme'

As indicated earlier, the objectives of this scientific and technical programme are to transform radically the technologies now used in the Russian surveying and mapping industry, and to effect a change to the most advanced methods of digital mapping based on GIS technologies and global satellite systems.

Main research efforts to accomplish the urgent digital mapping programme are focused on:

- raising the level of automation in design and creation of digital maps;
- improvement of digital processing methods for remote sensing (RS) data;
- integrated processing of digital maps and RS data to revise topographic maps, to compile maps for regions difficult of access, and to produce image maps, thematic, and special-purpose maps;
- automation of RS data interpretation and map generalization methods;
- automation of stereo-photogrammetric procedures using aerial and space images and the development of new instruments;

- development of design and adaptation methods for use with map databases and with video data;
- design and adaptation of GIS of different levels of complexity and for different purposes;
- development of special-purpose software and hardware for various sub-systems of map and image processing;
- the marketing and social conditions in which Roskartografia will operate after its transition to use of digital methods.

The federal programme requires Roskartografia to provide mass production of cartographic works of art. The specific R&D activity to facilitate achieving the goal involves various actions. The first of these is the development of new types of maps and atlases: a many-volume *National Atlas of Russia*; general-purpose geographical and thematic maps and atlases (some of them based on space-based survey data); thematic maps and atlases for educational institutions; and regularly revised ecological maps (including the *Ecological Atlas of Russia*). Another activity centres on the improvement of map-publishing facilities and technologies. It includes the revision and improvement of standards for design, editing, compilation, and preparation of maps and atlases for publication; the development and improvement of technologies for compilation and preparation for publication of small-scale maps and atlases, the use of new materials and facilities; automation of certain operations; and standardization of geographical names. Parallel to this is the development of facilities and technologies for manufacture of plastic globes and relief maps; the development of new materials; development of new technical facilities and methods of creating colour proofs without the use of offset lithographic proof-printing machines; and automation of the printing of cartographic products by transferring an image directly from the computer onto a printing machine. Finally, to increase the efficiency of surveying, this programme supports R&D in the design of devices for independent positioning, such as satellite receivers for the Russian GLONASS and US GPS positioning systems.

Key objectives in the implementation of the federal integrated programme'Progressive technologies of surveying and mapping of the Russian Federation'

Solving the tasks given to Roskartografia will enable it to speed up the technical and technological re-equipment of surveying and mapping agencies. More importantly, this will also enable it to meet wider objectives:

- to foster the creation of a new information industry in Russia through development of digital databases and GIS and use of'state of the art' information technologies;

- to meet the demands of the national economy, of the defence and education sectors, and from the population of the country for maps and atlases for various applications;
- to promote the beneficial use of satellite-based technology in surveying;
- to provide surveying and mapping support for delimitation and demarcation of the national borders of the Russian Federation.

INTERNATIONAL CO-OPERATION

Roskartografia participates in a number of international projects for the development of GIS, based on digital topographic maps. In 1995, it completed the development of an ecological GIS, called'GIS-Sever', for neighbouring territories of Russia and Finland. This was designed on the basis of digital maps at the scales of 1:200,000 and 1:1 million. Joint work was carried out by Roskartografia and the National Land Survey of Finland in accordance with a Russian–Finnish agreement signed on 21 January 1993. Aside from the international dimension, the project was agreed with the ministry of environmental protection in Russia. 'GIS-Sever' was developed within the framework of the national programme'Ecological safety of Russia'. Other states of the Russian Federation have shown a great interest in GIS-Sever. In particular, the government of the Republic of Karelia intends to use GIS-Sever as a basis to develop a regional multi-purpose programme called'GIS-Karelia'.

Taking into account the importance of geoinformation to support activities aimed at the protection and sustainable development of the Lake Baikal region, the federal service of geodesy and cartography of Russia, the ministry of nature of Russia and the National Mapping Division of the US Geological Survey jointly have proposed a collaborative GIS-Baikal project. This is designed to provide ecological monitoring based on space photography. The project was also approved at the meeting of the Russian governmental commission on Baikal.

In addition to these specific projects, the federal service of geodesy and cartography develops and improves business contacts with a variety of foreign partners. Roskartografia participates as a member in some non-governmental international organizations, notably the Fédération Internationale de Géometres (FIG), the International Cartographic Association (ICA), and the International Society for Photogrammetry and Remote Sensing (ISPRS). It also develops economic co-operation with advanced countries to study and adapt their technological achievements, to adopt their experience to define a legal basis for surveying and mapping activities, and so on. Roskartografia collaborates with other countries and foreign companies in joint research and developments and in joint instrument production. Thus close contacts have been established with the Swiss firm Leica AG. These have resulted in joint production of the SD-20 analytical photogrammetric instrument (a Russian analogue of the SD-2000 equipment), of the PUG-4 stereo point marking instrument for field processing, and of the ST-4 mirror stereoscope. Roskartografia intends to develop further the co-operation with foreign partners in the field of surveying and mapping.

CONCLUSIONS

Roskartografia, the NMO of Russia, has been set formidable tasks to help the development of the national economy, enhance national defence, and foster the knowledge of the peoples of the country. It is meeting these tasks through the rapid transition to use of digital techniques for mapping, many of these created in Russia. This transition is being planned through one major programme and a series of contributory sub-programmes, all carefully planned and carried out within Roskartografia. In addition, however, the importance of international contacts is well understood and Roskartografia is widening its networks with like organizations world-wide.

SECTION 2

The global framework and user needs

The previous section was focused largely on national frameworks and how these were being created, modified or up-dated in the light of changing circumstances. Some organizations – a growing number – have a need for consistent framework information on a regional basis (e.g. the Americas or Europe) or even a global one.

One such organization is the American military. Two influences account for this situation. The first is the role which the USA has increasingly come to play in international humanitarian aid and in various armed conflicts around the world. The second is the shift from a scenario of large-scale potential conflict with one or two other 'super-powers' to a situation where action may be required on a smaller scale anywhere on earth, thereby requiring a much greater range of information, often at short notice. A complicating factor is the partnership between different nations in many of the operations, bringing problems of interoperability of equipment and data. Lenczowski describes how, to help meet the growing need for data, the US National Imagery and Mapping Agency has embarked upon an initiative called Global Geospatial Information and Services (GGI&S). This effort follows upon the successful design, production, and distribution of the Digital Chart of the World (DCW) but extends it greatly. She describes the background to NIMA's role, defines the nature of global geospatial information and the concept of GGI&S plus the architecture and components (such as data security and value-adding) which form the basis of current and future NIMA efforts to realize GGI&S. The importance of achieving interoperability through a commitment to community standards for the data model, encapsulation, and distribution are emphasized, as is the extreme importance of high-speed networks for dissemination of data, and the growing reliance on commercial systems is demonstrated.

In contrast, the two other papers emphasize the need for global framework data for development and scientific purposes. Htun, a senior member of the United Nations staff, describes how good-quality and comparable 'core data' – especially the geographical framework – are needed to attain sustainable development which takes account of human health and welfare considerations. As he points out, these data do not yet exist for many areas of the world and it is highly wasteful to expend further funds on duplicating it where they do already exist. He issues a challenge to National Mapping Organizations (NMOs) to collaborate in order to create a truly global framework which can be used routinely to improve the quality of life of the billions of people on earth.

Collins and Rhind stress the scientific needs for framework data on a more consistent and affordable basis. Working from a non-profit organization charged with maintaining databases of the world's fauna and flora and warning of threats to the survival of species, they are particularly concerned with the issue of maintaining biodiversity. They point out that the intergovernmental commitment made under the Rio 'environmental summit' as Agenda 21 has specific provisions for the availability of environmental data and contrast these with their experience in assembling data from around the world on top of what framework data are available. The two authors suggest improvements which, if enacted, would permit the World Conservation and Monitoring Centre and other organizations to concentrate on the delivery of information and services to decision-makers, rather than devoting scarce resources to basic data gathering and duplication of activities.

CHAPTER 7

The military as users and producers of global spatial data

Roberta E Lenczowski

SUMMARY

In the past, geography and cartography joined forces to provide paper-constrained geospatial information in the form of maps and charts. The lithographic product is no longer the exclusive source for reliably positioning things or activities relative to the earth. As sources for geographic data have expanded, synergistic uses have also grown and can be expected to continue to broaden. Adaptive computer technology has accommodated powerful analytic applications that consume vast digital stores of geographic, cartographic, socio-economic, geophysical, and political data to feed decision-enhancing tools. Nowhere is this more marked than in the military domain, where there is increasingly a need for a world-wide capability to mount operations, whether these are to counter insurgency or support humanitarian operations. Many of these operations will involve partners and hence involve multiple sourcing and sharing of data.

To help meet the growing need for data, the US National Imagery and Mapping Agency (NIMA) has embarked upon an initiative called Global Geospatial Information and Services (GGI&S). This effort follows upon the successful design, production, and distribution of the Digital Chart of the World (DCW) but extends it greatly. This chapter describes the background to NIMA's role, defines the nature of global geospatial information and the concept of GGI&S, plus the architecture and components (such as data security and value-adding) which form the basis of current and future NIMA efforts to realize GGI&S. It discusses the importance of achieving interoperability through a commitment to community standards for the data model, encapsulation, and distribution. The extreme importance of high-speed and wide-band networks for dissemination of data and the growing reliance on commercial systems is demonstrated. NIMA's activities to bring about these plans are summarized in various case studies.

INTRODUCTION

On 1 October 1996, the Defense Mapping Agency (DMA) in the United States joined the Central Imagery Office, the National Photographic Interpretation Center, the Defense Dissemination Program Office, and the imagery exploitation, dissemination, and processing elements of the Defense Intelligence Agency, National Reconnaissance Office, and the Defense Airborne Reconnaissance Office to form a new agency named the National Imagery and Mapping Agency (NIMA). NIMA has the mission to provide timely, relevant, and accurate imagery, imagery intelligence, and geospatial information in support of national security objectives. The agency's vision is to guarantee the 'information edge'. By providing comprehensive management of US imaging and geospatial capabilities, NIMA will improve support to national and military customers alike. In the paragraphs which follow, description of past work will generally refer to the Defense Mapping Agency or DMA, and current work or future vision will reference the National Imagery and Mapping Agency or NIMA. The focus of this chapter is not on the broad mission objectives of NIMA but specifically to emphasize the agency's need for and production and the provision of geospatial information.

Recent, unprecedented changes in the global political and technological environments provide complex challenges for the producers and users of mapping, charting, and geodesy information. In the United States, many local, state, and federal agencies share responsibility for ensuring the availability of this geospatial information, as described by Tosta in this book. For defence purposes, improved responsiveness depends upon NIMA's ability to populate a massive database or federated databases and to broker others' data stores, within a 'data warehousing' architecture. Appropriate standards for the entire spatial reference model must frame the structure. A 'technology-extensible' approach in an open-systems environment can provide to spatial data consumers the most current and appropriate knowledge, at the right time, and with the needed accuracy. To achieve this vision, DMA proposed the Global Geospatial Information and Services (GGI&S) initiative in 1993. This received endorsement within an independent study conducted by the Defense Science Board in 1995. The initiative encompasses an agency commitment, passed on from DMA to NIMA, to information production, information management, information dissemination, and information servicing. This commitment will be realized within an enterprise architecture which articulates customer and system requirements, which defines the data environment, which places commercial software and hardware into an efficient production environment, and which offers data exploiters certified tools and intuitive interfaces.

As used by the military, the term 'Global Geospatial Information' (GGI) comprises world-wide, precise, spatially co-referenced information about the earth, arranged in a coherent structure to support measurement, mapping, visualization, monitoring, modelling, terrain evaluation, and spatial reasoning applications. Linked either with sophisticated GIS technologies or with network-transferable application modules, the 'services' aspect of the GGI&S initiative promises 'desktop' import and export of geospatial data sets. Standardized exchange formats and documented content definition, coupled with currency, accuracy, and completeness descriptions, are designed to assure interactive and reliable data manipulation, update, and value-adding. Gateway connections, to and from consumers with certified use-profiles, into multi-level secure networks will promote rapid access to and distribution of needed data.

BACKGROUND

NIMA, like other government mapping organizations, produces multiple series or versions of maps and charts, as well as other well-defined digital or hardcopy products. The agency has published voluminous military specifications, military standards, and handbooks to specify the content and format of those products. Despite the advances in handling of digital geospatial data, the utility of the traditional paper or digital product as an aid to decision-making during mission planning or mission execution will not be obsolete for some time. Over the past 20 years, however, the accelerating demand for digital products has reflected the improved speed of data processing, the increased complexity of software applications, and the decreasing cost of high-powered hardware within the users' exploitation environments.

Most existing product specifications were derived from the information needs of specific customer systems. Consequently, even digital products have frequently satisfied the data needs of only one customer, or one system, or a limited suite of applications. Other users or uses transformed or adapted the standard product or turned to providers elsewhere with no foresight about any eventual need to share information. The myriad users of spatial data built 'stovepiped systems', with tailored applications and unique transformations of the standard digital products.

The 'lessons learned' reviews of the Desert Storm experience revealed the importance of what the pioneers in the spatial standards community had proclaimed for years. Without common understanding or taxonomy, without collaborative agreements on structure definition, data elude interoperable use. In the most fundamental sense and for both strategic and tactical planning or execution, shared information multiplies defensive and offensive power. Since information is understood to be data with meaning, mastery of rudimentary information technology, including standards development and their application, came to be understood as essential to successful operations.

The civilian map-makers have been reaching comparable conclusions as Geographic Information System (GIS) applications began to proliferate to meet concerns such as urban planning, environmental monitoring, and socio-economic analyses. Thus, throughout the geospatial data community, traditional digital data sets are being re-examined to determine with what reliability they can be used for a variety of information needs. The data must be robust enough to support extensible use. At the same time, with the global community's drive towards multi-functional, multi-media terminals providing information fused together to produce an integrated spatial picture, the data must be consistent enough to support the integrated global 'infosphere'.

Another powerful sculptor of information infrastructure has been the pervasive effect of the Internet and the World Wide Web (see Calvert et al, Tosta and Warita and Nonomura's chapters in this book). Providing increasingly broad and cost-effective physical telecommunication lines was merely the initial technological thrust of this dominating influence. What travels the lines is no longer limited to pre-staged files or e-mail. 'Net-surfers' have graduated from browsing various web-sites in search of information to querying files interactively from afar, while exercising data-to-information applications supplied remotely. Production and consumption are less easily distinguished. Defining and implementing measures of trust for data, for information, and for tools challenge all participants.

The growing ubiquity of geospatial information, supported by global connectivity, will continue to change the primary uses of the information. Geographers and cartographers, as map producers, have hitherto enjoyed an eager market among those who are strangers to an unknown space and who needed to understand where they are in relation to where they need to be. But other disciplines increasingly recognize that Geographic Information has value far beyond positioning or navigation into foreign territory. The flexibility of digital geospatial data allows rapidly changing visualization perspectives and, accompanied by mature GIS applications, analysis of political, social, economic, and environmental topics. Today knowledge fused from multiple disciplines is used to predict and influence behaviour by effectively presenting issues referenced to a geospatial foundation.

COMPELLING MILITARY NEEDS AND NEW APPROACHES

Four issues influence the military approach. The first is the emerging world order, with its minimally predictable regional cacophony, involving multinational military operations that range from succour to counter-proliferation. Relationships between the great powers have surged and retracted during the past two centuries. The future world order will be shaped by economic, political, cultural, and technological alliances and splits. Among the technologies contributing to understanding this complex world are the advances in GIS. NIMA will therefore support use of those technologies. Its working groups routinely gather to examine models for database management design which will support real-time and mission-critical information processing and dissemination. In principle and practice, then, data providers of the larger nations (like NIMA) must design, populate, and manage user-accessible databases of global geospatial information.

The scale of the technical challenge across the spectrum of commercial, academic, and government R&D encourages joint doctrine to enforce common views of those data or information. Although the common view may require common tools or applications, it is attainable only with consistent data input. It follows that data providers, like NIMA, must invest in the development or adoption of standards which are confirmed by the joint community which assure data content, meaning, quality, encapsulation, and delivery (see Salgé's chapter in this book).

Conscientious life-cycle management within any organization's information infrastructure forces evaluation of all existing and planned production and exploitation systems. The complexity of systems and recent technical developments ensure that data providers, like NIMA, must migrate to open and flexible architectures: in principle, these permit effortless ability to add hardware and software improvements and allow routine modification of production processes as customer requirements change. An open architecture commitment furthers the goal of a common industrial base by invoking commercial practices, processes, and products.

Global communication networks have traditional cable, fibre optic and/or satellite links world-wide connecting all facets of the private and public sectors. Current political leadership of the world's technically advanced nations seeks harmonization of the world's telecommunications infrastructure in order further to influence multi-national economic, environmental, and political endeavours and help advance world order. NIMA must therefore travel the information highways, especially in support of navigation safety and crises. In such cases, accurate and complete geospatial information is needed quickly.

Those four issues are used to focus this chapter's discussion of the GGI&S concept. NIMA has a mission-defined responsibility to support a defence and federal community with mapping, charting, and geodesy. That support must be relevant to the present requirements and must anticipate the future refocus. The nature of contemporary technologies challenges the realization of the GGI&S initiative.

DEFINITION OF GLOBAL GEOSPATIAL INFORMATION (GGI)

GGI is world-wide

The National Imagery and Mapping Agency's strategic plan for digital data production contains global objectives. Because the military can, have been, and will be sent to all parts of the world on missions ranging from battle defence to humanitarian succour, NIMA must be ready to respond to crises anywhere – although not necessarily to have data sitting ready everywhere. Some responsibilities for services and data are inherently global. Continuous global attentiveness is mandated at all times for safety of navigation, both maritime and aeronautical. Thus Notices to Mariners, Notices to Airmen, and Charting Update Manuals are services designed specifically to maintain currency and to ensure safety. Certain traditional map series, like the Operational Navigation Charts (ONC), and standard digital products like Digital Terrain Elevation Data are world-wide to enable global aeronautical planning and training.

In the late 1980s, DMA began converting its maps and charts into raster digital products as a first step to support newer computer-base systems with as much digital mapping data as possible. Currently, NIMA is completing conversion of its lithographic holdings to a raster format and has begun distribution of the standard compressed version.

Vector data, even from digitized maps and charts, is more costly to produce and more difficult to format. DMA, with Canada, the United Kingdom, and Australia, collaborated in the design and production of the Digital Chart of the World (DCW), which was vectorized from the ONC source. A new version of that product, identified as Level 0 of the Vector Smart Map (VMap) series, reflects a decision to standardize the layers or coverages among various scales of source. A Level 1 product in the series will correspond to the content and density of the Joint Operational Graphics, traditionally published at 1:250,000 scale. Production, both under commercial contract and in-house, began in 1995. The higher-density content of a Topographic Line Map, at a scale of 1:50,000, will be found in the Level 2 product. The content and density of features in the VMap series might have relevance for some of the scientific needs defined elsewhere in this book by Collins and Rhind as well as military ones. In addition and before the year 2000, NIMA will have completed the world-wide, vector-formatted Digital Nautical Chart (DNC) program, corresponding to its paper coastal approach and harbour maritime products. The DNC – by design – maintains consistency between the coverages derived from the various scaled charts and accommodates the tools in the ship's electronic bridge to navigate coherently from open water towards the shore and into the harbour.

New vector sets are under design, prototype, or review which do not originate from an existing paper product. These reflect user needs based upon use requirement studies. They have the advantage that resolution of information, not scale of an existing product, dictates the level of detail stored and available. Thus, if a global vector data set is claimed to be needed, the cost in time and resources for specific amounts of detail can be factored against the global need. NIMA is querying customers to determine if certain themes, like transportation routes, have higher intrinsic priority than other themes when seen from a global perspective. Reducing time-costly compilation to only the essential vectors within the first critical hours of a crisis would improve responsiveness.

Another new product called Controlled Image Base (CIB) is orthorectified, mosaiced, and radiometrically balanced geocoded imagery. It can provide an initial, immediate response to crises and will provide global readiness. Tools to allow its fusion with either raster maps or with a minimum essential set of vector information permit users to interrogate the digital data set to obtain a level of geospatial understanding.

In addition to all of the above, GGI&S has broader objectives. These are to improve the pace of production and global population, improve the accuracy and thus the fusibility of the data sets, refine and discipline the content of the data by standardizing data models and definitions, leverage technology advances in new data architecture, and management by co-operative efforts with industry, academia, and other government agencies.

GGI is accurate, precise, and current

Geospatial information suppliers like NIMA must provide user accessibility to accurate data. Moreover, these data must already be processed into the information designed to support the users' application or which users can themselves leverage into trusted information for various needs. As the geospatial information infrastructure expands with more demanding users who have increasingly powerful analytical tools, their concern about the geo-extent and the reliability of available data sets is broadening. By specification, NIMA data sets carry auxiliary information describing absolute and relative accuracies. As data sets are extended to new uses, different 'measures of trust' are emerging to fit different applications. This situation forces an obligation on the producer to provide more data about the data: their source, currency, lineage, completeness, and like elements.

In 1994, by executive order, US government agencies were obliged to participate in the advancement of a National Spatial Data Infrastructure (see Tosta's chapter in this book). The Federal Geographic Data Committee provided recognized leadership and sponsored the development and implementation of a metadata standard, precisely in anticipation of the recognized need to 'brand label' data. NIMA has specified use of the Federal Geographic Data Committee's metadata standard for its data delivery. This standard has been accepted as part of the Australian geospatial information strategy and, as other countries participate in its refinement, it is expected to be of invaluable assistance to global data use.

Although documenting data sets with metadata allays concern about the level of risk attendant on its use, it does not reduce the need to improve the data. Accuracies needed by NIMA's future customer require nearly a magnitude of improvement over the present to match the higher granularity of data. The accuracy of elevation, feature, and attribute data extracted from imagery sources relies upon the robustness of the photogrammetric process, particularly in the elements of absolute orientation. That process determines resultant error estimation. The Global Positioning System (GPS), used with the data-collection platforms or in providing ground control, promotes the most accurate photogrammetric solutions. NIMA, working with academic researchers and government laboratories, continues to refine the World Geodetic System (WGS 84) which, in turn, improves GPS state vectors. Delivery of the WGS 84 World Height Datum will reduce the uncertainty of vertical positioning relative to the geoid.

As practised in many countries in the initial phases of populating digital databases of geospatial information, digitization of existing maps and charts ensures that the positional accuracy of features is constrained by the limitation of the scale and size of the paper product. For NIMA, the first production of the medium resolution vector formatted products, like the Digital Nautical Chart (DNC) and Vector Smart Map (VMap), is from existing cartographic sources. NIMA will migrate production to photogrammetric sources to ensure that cartographic displacement is eliminated. During the possibly lengthy transition period between the delivery of data that are exclusively cartographically derived and only later photogrammetrically compiled, conflation tools to accommodate inevitable placement discrepancies for adjacent or overlapping data sets will be provided.

GGI is spatially co-referenced

The spatial accuracy and precision promised by GGI with its spatially co-referenced data sets rely upon exploiting geodesy. All current NIMA products are referenced to a common datum: the WGS 84. Modernizing procedures for collecting photo-identifiable, first-order surveys would expedite an extensible, global control network for photo-triangulation.

The more accurately data are produced, the more likely data sets – even those collected at different times or for different uses – will fuse. Geocoded raster and vector data will align for visualization and will support consistent analytical evaluation, especially if the metadata accompanying those data sets is comprehensive. The spatial integrity of this framework geographic data – as stressed in many other chapters in this book – provides the foundation for the other data sets that may be overlaid or integrated, like meteorology or demographics.

GGI is arranged in a coherent structure

As the Department of Defense (DoD) supplier of mapping, charting, and geodetic data, the NIMA has leadership responsibility in the definition of geospatial models and elements. Adherence to a suite of standards, whether developed or espoused and adopted, is essential to give the structural coherency needed in fully interoperable environments which military operations demand. A general data model, applicable horizontally and vertically among all users of varying-resolution geospatial features, must be collaboratively completed. In the past, discussions about standards have focused almost exclusively on producer and distributor perspectives. Fortunately, the acknowledgement of user influences is continuing to prosper. Provider and user, for example, need to speak with a common taxonomy and set of definitions. NIMA has been engaged with other agencies and organizations to provide standard data definition for terms used across the defence community.

Similarly, NIMA will henceforth use standard media, including the standard conventions for directories and indices, to forward deploy its data sets. Magnetic tape, whether 9-track or cartridge, CD-ROM, or newer industry-standardized media solutions will be used consistent with customers' capabilities. When communication networks are used, NIMA will prepare its digital data to be compliant with necessary transmission protocols.

GGI&S supports varied applications

In an era of reduced budgets, the military is 'training as it will fight' without actual physical presence. Data sets with high degrees of authenticity for geographically remote locations are demanded in order to carry out reliable exercises. Because high-resolution compilation is production-intensive and costly, the database may not be fully populated when an actual crisis flares. Part of the GGI&S strategy is to recognize that dispersed sites, at the command level and below, will have authority to populate, to manage, and to distribute specific features or attributes within virtual and redefinable local databases.

NIMA will therefore distribute stable foundation data upon which the consumer can build reliable inferences. NIMA's digital data will be accompanied by importers and display tools. To assure that the market place encodes mapping, charting, and geodesy (MC&G) algorithms satisfactorily, NIMA will warrant tools to be catalogued in the Defense Information Systems Agency (DISA) software re-use archives. These tools will also be found in the Global Command and Control System's Interoperable Map Software as it evolves to its maturity. These and other MC&G-warranted tools may also be used by collaborative producers for reliable value-adding in the deployed environment.

Only a few years ago, the modelling and simulation community was almost entirely a defence enterprise. But, as commercial interests have seen the potential for combining GIS technology with imaging and graphics technologies, modelling has migrated from weapons trainers to arcades. The simulation contractors use virtual reality techniques, with associated data management capability, operating in real-time on very high resolution geospatial information, and with analytical derivation of inferences or deductions. These approaches dominate mission rehearsals and planning but can also have far broader application. The military employ artificial intelligence and decision-support systems to ingest and rapidly fuse multiple intelligence sources. They have flexible planning tools, war-gaming, simulation, and multimedia technology.

Architecture

Across the face of the earth, physical 'things' are being built, sustained, improved, and removed. This very tangible activity, with its myriad levels of complexity, becomes captured in the concept of architecture. Transferring that conceptual term into a geospatial information discussion warrants preliminary explanation. The term 'architecture' has theoretical, system, and operational implications which are discussed below. It also carries through the postulated analogy that geospatial (framework) information is the foundation data and the structural framework for multi-disciplinary analysis of earth-referenced data.

From the theoretical architecture standpoint, a move towards open systems necessitates development of a complete reference model, with all the linkages and interfaces logically captured in a codification accepted by the community as a whole (see Salgé's chapter in this book). Partnerships between industry, academia, and government can foster development of and commitment to the standards required by the theoretical architecture.

From the system architecture perspective, the components assembled in the design and engineering of the physical environment should abide with the guiding principles of the theoretical architecture. By rigorously pursuing disciplined approaches to system engineering, like those advocated in capability maturity models and embedded in leading engineering-consulting companies, greater confidence can be placed in the up-front estimates of expected return on capital investment.

From the operational architecture viewpoint, the built-to-design physical environment should be relevant, functional, and sustainable. Tasks to be accomplished are defined in the operational architecture. Roles and responsibilities relative to those tasks, however, continue to evolve. Distinction between producer and consumer, as both logically and physically separate operations, continues to blur. The physical environments for each operation are dynamically interchangeable. Collaborative tool sets and remote control of workstations and servers are no longer novel or pilot efforts.

Today's considerations

NIMA's inventory includes over 230 geospatial products, each described in a published specification. More than 70 of these are digital products. For over two decades, DMA followed a planned programme based upon meeting the regional precedences and product priorities established by the military services and commands. For the most part, the digital products were tracked with library and card-catalogue database management techniques, employing a simple databasing approach in which location of media and minimal descriptive information about the data sets was retained on-line.

Distribution of these data sets was on standards-compliant hard media: 9-track magnetic tape, CD-ROM, and 8 mm cartridge tape. CD-ROM production mimics the usual model of producing and warehousing map sheets. For several years, some data have been distributed across existing communication link-ups. However, except for the Notice to Mariners and the Electronic Charting Update Manual (ECHUM), DMA did not provide routine electronic transmission of products.

In 1995, significant change occurred in both the identified requirements as well as the data delivery processes. Satisfying the documented operational needs of the military community became the paramount consideration in a 'responsive today, ready for tomorrow' production and distribution strategy. DMA initiated organizational and process change in order to:

- ensure better understanding of what customers need to do with data or information;
- appreciate the relative merit or value in specific applications of different aspects or attributes of the data or information;
- distinguish the time-significance of the level of attribution and resolution required at different stages in the planning and execution of an operation; and
- learn where and when data-push or data-pull are most appropriate.

Embedded in NIMA's modernized digital production process is a massive MC&G database, which can be progressively populated to satisfy validated requirements. By design, it manages feature and terrain data extracted primarily from photogrammetric sources prior to its transformation into several of the standard products. The limiting architectural feature of this database, however, was the design consideration that the 'finished' paper or digital product was the primary objective. Permanence of the data, for the data's sake, was not a primary consideration. Retaining all the metadata, consequently, has been of only secondary importance. Remedies, although costly, exist for that flaw. By 're-architecting' any necessary links between information management and 'finishing', producers like NIMA can avoid constraining the data to fit only one representation of information called a product. Eliminating or relaxing those constraints, which may have been set by media limitations or which may have been decreed by specific, non-interoperable systems, will require on-going re-education of both the producer and the consumer communities.

Working to achieve the vision of the future

There are substantial pressures upon NIMA from its customers and from developments in information management generally which make it essential to identify the technical architecture for geospatial information, to use sound information-systems engineering approaches, and to support operations which are demanding of geospatial information. The following are among NIMA's expectations of future capabilities:

- eliminate inconsistent multiple representation of features;
- move without ambiguity from the topographic view of the shoreline to the hydrographic view of that shoreline;
- 'feather' without gross abruptness from one resolution of spatial data to another;
- accommodate time-varying characteristics of some spatial features in databases;
- embed each object with all its topological relationships so that 'decluttering' and generalization is robust or, as a minimum, define each object with very accurate 3-D geometry so that topology can be rapidly computed;
- invest each element of the geospatial domain with as much integrity as is appropriate, balancing consumer demands with production realities;
- 'package' agency expertise for the spatial information users.

Nearly all aspects of the current picture will experience change as NIMA moves towards realizing the GGI&S. Military customers' requirements will continue to reflect regional precedence but the regions of interest may not be as reliably predictable as in the past. Content of the features and attributes will be more carefully defined in future. The geospatial information, as used by future GIS, may cease to be viewed from thematic or layered perspectives and may be dependent upon object descriptions embedded with functionalities. A 'one size fits all' product definition will be replaced by performance specifications and a data-tailoring capability, although the standard product can be delivered as long as users' legacy systems or new ones require it. NIMA will explore through a series of 'pilot' projects the methodologies best suited to providing a service which allows consumers to be better users and to feed back important field-gathered data to the core databases successfully.

Internally, NIMA has accelerated its focus on a data environment rather than on product finishing. Finishing digital data into lithographic products may well require a 'just-in-case' minimum stock level and a 'just-in-time' crisis printing capability. Traditional uses of standard products, as taught in military doctrine, will not be neglected although efforts to update the doctrine have been initiated. Recognizing the inherent value of the digital data itself, irrespective of its compliance with product specifications, NIMA can assemble its digital working-files and its legacy databases to support various clients through a distributed and hierarchical server design. Those databases may be relational, hierarchical, object-oriented, or flat, but the database management system for the data warehouse must be able to manage this broad-base data resource and present it to the user as a 'federated' accessible system. User-accessibility to the valuable spatial data store, with on-demand 'pull' capability, is a critical design consideration. Appropriate interfaces, complying with standards in the Common Operating Environment (COE), must be clear and concise presentations of quite complex information.

The logical architecture for the data warehouse can overcome the liabilities inherent in legacy physical data stores by allowing access to virtual partitions, if so designed. Any data type partition may be built with the appropriate genre data from databases distributed in heterogeneous environments. Within the feature partition, for instance, the full population of all attributes could tap multiple sources from varied production environments accessed through some distributed processing. To satisfy the requirements of the more robust GIS applications, assembling the data into topologically reliable tiles or units presents a considerable challenge. Although singular representation of the feature with all its attributes may be theoretically desirable, subsequent spatial operations on the data cannot violate topological integrity. They must allow decluttering (that is, reducing the amount of information in either relational or object-orientated archives) and generalization (that is, less resolution or more collapsing of information).

This is an era of joint and coalition forces for military operations. Interoperability for planning and weapons systems, whether initially designed or 'kluged together' for joint use, will demand that system profiles be established so that the right information – but only the needed information – is distributed. Users can specify the data they need by designating features and attributes or by defining the geographic extent. They may wish to define a geographic area by using a bounding rectangle, a user-described polygon, a stored definition of a region of interest, user-designated country codes, or standard tiles. In such an environment, geo-packaging of several types of geospatial data could be handled. As an example, a particular system may require an orthorectified image in raster form, transportation vectors, and a variable density elevation grid within a defined geographic area.

Value-adding

Architectural design of new information systems will be influenced by the emphasis placed upon value-adding, which may be broadly examined from the viewpoints of maintenance, updating, and augmenting. Traditionally, the producer assumes responsibility for the maintenance plan and confirms with the customer community that the cycles are appropriate. Updating, however, may involve only part of the data included in a complete product.

Although there may be cyclic releases like Notice to Mariners or Flight Information Publications to assure safe navigation, an update could be pertinent irrespective of any schedule. The latter situation is quite relevant to the populating of the GGI&S data warehouse. A field-deployed, carefully trained individual with a GPS receiver could provide highly accurate geographic co-ordinates for a natural or man-made feature which is otherwise well described in the database. Just as production focus changes from product finishing to population of a database, maintenance focus must change. Updates to the database need to be incorporated whenever new relevant source is available. Updating is GGI&S maintenance. The technology infusion of Internet activity both helps and confounds the issues. Updating can come from multiple sources, almost simultaneously, and certainly at unscheduled times. Traditional solutions to handling this timing contention, like 'database lockout' and evaluating the provider through lengthy certification practices, are not amenable to such real-time activity.

Undoubtedly the first opportunity to effect the updating strategy for the vector- product-formatted information will be in the deployment of the Digital Nautical Chart. Prototypes of three methods have been reviewed by the Navy and assessed for ease of use, for cost to the producer, and for method of distribution.

From the augmenting or supplementing perspective, value-adding allows creation of additional layers or attributes or the replacement and enhancement of deployed data with more current data. Those value-added data may be forwarded to be incorporated into the primary data set because they represent updates. For some customers, that forwarding of new data may be simply notification that it is available to be pulled or it may be a push of the data to a customer known to expect automatic distribution of updates. Sometimes, as with weather or intelligence overlays, the augmenting data are not part of the foundation data holdings of the geospatial information producer. In that case, the primary concern will be provide help in geo-referencing the augmenting data to the framework.

Data security and integrity

The integrity and security of any information archives are of paramount concern in considering how to incorporate user feedback, such as updates. Multiple levels of security classification and access restrictions must be uncompromisingly maintained and inherently supported by the database design, the database management approach, and the operating systems, as well as the network protocols. Appropriate procedures and requirements for a user to be certified as a *bona fide* contributor will be implemented in the NIMA system. The process by which data are validated and incorporated into the database must be as clearly established for the 'value-adder' as for the primary production component. Data that fail validation may be maintained separately and provided to the user with the appropriate caveats. The associated metadata must be as complete and thorough for value-adding as for standard production. They should describe not only the content and format of the data itself, but also provide relevant information about the 'value-adder' and the conditions under which they were captured.

Gateway interface services

The growth of the telecommunication options and NIMA connectivity to a varied, and interested, geospatial market require that any gateway connection is usable by both the novice and the expert. The interface rides on electronic network backbones and serves as a network geospatial information manager as well as the mechanism for geospatial information exchange using appropriate and standard communication protocols. Three data files are seen as essential to this interface: general information about NIMA and its inventory; hierarchically structured data about the data (metadata); and customer profiles. In scenarios, which will continue to be tested by pilot projects like those described below, the customer will gain access to the interface gateway via a user profile which will be defined by access privilege, security level, pertinent data/product requirements, and level of expertise.

Working with its customers, NIMA has refined the preliminary requirements for its initial gateway services. These are the customer interface, customer profile, query, order, and administrative support. A limited operating capability established in late 1995 fused the interface and profile components by building three separate communications links, constraining the access privileges by separating the network links. This approach forces replication of files and exacerbates the up-date and synchronization responsibilities of the distributor. Lacking sanctioned multi-level security switches, a distributor must resort to physical separation of the lines. NIMA caches the most frequently sought files with on-line servers and keeps the remainder of the digital data on retrievable CD-ROMs in a large capacity tower. Querying the data and metadata stores remains rudimentary, as both provider and consumer determine what constitutes a meaningful interface and which graphics presentations are unambiguously comprehended. A softcopy catalogue of DMA product information, which appeared initially on CD-ROM, will be an on-line tool that allows a user to browse and select products and to submit orders. Newer tools will allow the user to mine into the digital vector and raster products, to retrieve only certain thematic coverages, or to define a geographic footprint of interest which is within or crosses current product boundaries. Customer help desks are staffed to respond to on-line mail or to answer telephone questions.

Several hardware and software platforms owned by the customers are already supported. Despite the push towards the Common Operating

Environment in the Defense Information Infrastructure, more – or at least different – applications are expected in the future. The conduit will be the network linkage but the flow will be supported with data format converters or translators into standard data models, the interface or front-end processors for applications, and an associated set of application program interfaces (API) to allow software to function in the platform environment. Since data are platform-independent, the interface gateway must be able to utilize APIs for multiple platforms. Network enablers, like Netscape, and approaches to tool-sharing, like JAVA, continue to alter the local environment's basic needs.

Communications backbone

GGI&S is being brought on-line in an environment that continues to grow richer with communication capabilities. Significant deployments of Synchronous Optical Network (SONET) equipment by the domestic common carriers will create a transmission network of 2.4 Gbps (Gigabits per second) pipes. This network will cover much of the USA as well as the major US trading partners. The Asynchronous Transfer Mode (ATM) service set will be provided on these SONET facilities. ATM will support a wide range of commercial service offerings including 'virtual private lines' at speeds of 46, 155, and 622 Mbps and switched, on-demand virtual circuits at the same set of speeds. These commercial, off-the-shelf service capabilities will be integrated into DoD networks as the Defense Information Systems Agency (DISA) up-grades those networks. ATM 'feeders' at lower speeds (1.544 Mbps) will also be available.

Transportable satellite terminals accessing commercial transponders already provide the capability of extending 46 Mbps ATM-based services into operations theatre. Narrowband ATM (1.5 Mbps) are at the early stages of deployment both in the tactical arena and to naval units afloat. While all these commercial facilities will be able to operate in an encrypted mode to prevent interception, most will not be jam-resistant. Modems over the various commercial and government voice networks will perform well over most connections at 9.6 kbps and 14.4 kbps. Modem connections between major business centres will run at 28.8 kbps or higher.

For initial operations, it is assumed that any customer will have a fixed base of operations (designated individuals at pre-known organizations) that can be networked by cable and satellite transmission. As the customers become increasingly field-based, moving quickly and often from location to location, then communication considerations must be able to span a range from limited radio to high-speed, broad-band transmission.

The set of other information vying for space on the limited amount of available bandwidth to reach into theatre and to forces afloat is such that, in some crisis situations, little or no capacity may be available for geospatial information. It is therefore necessary to adopt a GGI&S Electronic Data

Delivery strategy that is conservative of bandwidth and can suffice even in an off-line mode. Data transfers must be prioritized so that vital geospatial information is delivered expeditiously and that non-critical data transfers do not interfere with priority message traffic over communication networks. The basic approach to the electronic delivery of global geospatial information is to implement a 'Take and Update' strategy. Under this strategy, softcopy versions on standard media containing appropriate sub-sets of GGI files, which contain these data that remain fairly stable once compiled, will form the 'take' portion of the delivery system. The 'update' portion of the system allows access to the GGI&S gateway(s) over DoD-selected commercial telecommunications networks for critical safety of navigation data, for that portion of the geospatial information for which currency is operationally essential or for time-critical large data sets.

Another approach to bandwidth conservation is data compression that facilitates the transfer of large data sets, like raster imagery and map products. NIMA will take advantage of whatever technology advances occur in this field. The current 55:1 compression of the ARC-Digitized Raster Graphic (ADRG) to the Compressed ADRG (CADRG), although dramatic, may not be sufficient for future needs.

Testing the GGI&S vision

The Department of Defense (DoD) annually provides its members and their contractors with the opportunity to assess current technical capabilities in a series of risk-taking stress tests with the intent of leaving-behind promising capabilities. These events are called the Joint Warfighting Interoperability Demonstrations (JWID). NIMA staff recognized this as a perfect opportunity to evaluate some of its GGI&S concepts and to allow *bona fide* operators some voice in the progress towards the GGI&S vision.

For JWID 95, DMA provided both terrain and feature data to support a ground-level mission planning effort. A quick response non-combatant evacuation scenario was supported by direct link to DMA production teams. DMA terrain data, digitized map graphics, and orthorectified imagery were broadcast to tactical users during a test of the Global Broadcast System. A collaborative point-positioning task, using 'white board' telecommunication tools and remote programme control, took advantage of some World Wide Web 'know-how'. The latter activity was sufficiently successful to be a 'leave-behind' candidate.

JWID 96 leap-frogged the previous year's endeavour. NIMA shared workstations with another agency and took advantage of cartographers already deployed in the field as part of NIMA's GGI&S implementation. Data were retrieved from the forward-deployed libraries to illustrate the principles of the 'take' aspect of the 'take and update' data distribution strategy, from NIMA's limited operating capability server, from the co-operating agency's image products archive server, and from real-time reports inward-bound from the field. Cartographers and imagery analysts assisted Joint Task Force personnel using available data and readily available commercial GIS applications. During the shared sessions, requirements were refined or redefined, telementoring occurred to share knowledge, data sets were tailored, updates were incorporated, and revised data redistributed to appropriate users. An adjunct to this digital exchange is support of the generation of hardcopy, when and where it is needed and tailored to be what is appropriate. The Remote Replication capability fielded to several sites in 1995 and 1996 allows deployed tactical units to scan hardcopy, to receive digital files, to modify various elements of information, and to print resultant maps in limited quantity. This system, initially designed for on-land operation, now also operates afloat.

The quest for standards

NIMA's objective in advocating geospatial technology standardization is to seek global interoperability that will enable:

- military use of geospatial data from multiple sources with minimal need to transform or preprocess data into useful information;
- joint, combined, and coalition-sharing of a common view of the operational area;
- certified endorsement of commercial information technology for accessing, storing, processing, and displaying standard geospatial information;
- reduction of costly production duplication so that resources are directed to reduce costs and timelines in populating global databases.

US defence policy mandates the use of non-government standards whenever they are capable of supporting military requirements. DoD Directive 8320.1 further advised its agencies to use standardized data elements and established the Defense Data Dictionary System (DDDS) as a central repository. Under the direction of Dr Jack Teller, a collaborative group of experts from vested interests began in 1995 to model the structures found in the Feature Attribute Coding Catalog (FACC) or the Digital Geospatial Information Exchange Standard (DIGEST). The resulting DMA Feature Data Model (D-FDM) provides an overall definition, the relationships between and among, and the structures for all geospatial feature data. Objects to be modelled are those currently found in DIGEST. By mid-1996, 11 models were completed: air routes, airport, DMA management, hydrographic aids to navigation, inland water, port and harbour, power generation, railroad, road, shore and shoreline, tunnels and bridges, and parking areas. As other models are completed for the remainder of the DIGEST objects, more consideration is being directed to including the dynamic and functional aspects of geospatial data, additional detail, and more objects.

This work builds upon over a decade's investment in pursuing interoperability for both NIMA co-producers and NIMA customers. Since 1987, DMA's R&D programme included initiatives to develop a comprehensive suite of standards for the consistent co-production, exchange, manipulation, and display of digital geospatial data. In March 1993, Mil-Std-2407, Vector Product Format (VPF), was issued and approved for use by all DoD Departments and Agencies. VPF is an exchange standard based on a geo-relational data model. Its DIGEST counterpart is the Vector Relational Format (VRF). As another exchange standard for customers of raster geospatial information, the Raster Product Format (RPF) also completed its review and endorsement cycle. NIMA customers are assured that digital deliveries of raster graphics and imagery products will employ an encapsulation compliant with the US National Imagery Transmission Format Standard (NITFS). This further promotes access to geospatial data sets from the distributed servers within the US Imagery System (USIS) architecture. For digital text format standards, industry efforts – as well as government-funded work on authoring software and retrieval engines – will lead to an acceptable standard which employs Continuous Acquisition and Life Cycle Support (CALS) and Standard Graphics Markup Language (SGML) and takes advantage of the success of HyperText Markup Language (HTML) in the Internet environment. This latter example, where an industry lead, rather than a government development, sets the pace will more frequently become the 'best practices model' as future standards evolve and emerge.

To the extent that the existing geospatial commercial market is currently dominated by proprietary software and (often) proprietary data models or formats, this has been unacceptable for defence use when interoperability across platforms is required. Government and private sector organizations have formed the Open GIS Consortium (OGC) in response to similar demands, from sectors other than defence, to change from monolithic GIS solutions to an environment that allows transparency of access and processing of information. Both the defence and civil government mapping organizations have pro-active membership to help facilitate the restructuring of the GIS market and the integration of advanced information technology into geo-processing.

As Salgé shows elsewhere in this book, standards work is not a 'one-time' effort to trim and divest and then entrench inflexibly. The necessary first, and sometimes faltering, steps toward comprehensive life-cycle management of data means some efforts will be more productive than others. Consequently, NIMA participates across the spectrum of on-going efforts and represents defence interests in a variety of forums. The agency is a member of the Steering Committee, as the designated DoD representative, for the Federal Geographic Data Committee (FGDC) and shares its technical expertise in the subordinate working groups and sub-committees. In 1993, the American National Standards Institute (ANSI) approved the establishment of a Spatial

Data Transfer Standards Subcommittee (X3L1) under its Information Technology Standards Committee (X3). ANSI intends to align all information technology into a National Information Infrastructure. One goal is to bring geospatial information into agreement with imagery, video, and other geo-referenced data at the national level. The International Hydrographic Organization (IHO) has already established standards for the exchange of digital hydrographic information and for the display of that information on the 'electronic bridge'. The embedded feature and attribute coding scheme, S-57, of the DX-90 standard differs from the FACC of DIGEST. With DMA support, the Canadian Hydrographic Service has led the effort to harmonize the DIGEST and DX-90 standards as a transition measure to ensure maritime interoperability. In 1994, the International Standards Organization (ISO) chartered the Technical Committee for Geographic Information/Geomatics (TC 211) from which will emerge standards for the complete geospatial reference model (see Salgé's chapter again). Several participants are promoting a collaborative working relationship between the TC 211 and the Open GIS Consortium in the release of standards accepted across the international geospatial information community.

Assuredly, much work completed over the past decade may only be a prelude to future international development. During the next decade, various standards will emerge. Some will be complementary; others will be conflicting. Where possible, harmonization efforts – which may include translators between exchange formats and which will abet migration towards common definition of data elements – will be tolerated by NIMA as a risk-management alternative to information highway blockades.

A SAMPLING OF RELEVANT DEVELOPMENTAL WORK

The Global Geospatial Information and Services (GGI&S) initiative will develop the data warehouse architecture and gateway infrastructure to realize this substantive vision. Just as important, however, this effort integrates several relevant developmental activities, some of which have been mentioned earlier. These contribute to the data-sensitive environment sought by the GGI&S initiative. Among those are the following: a Modernized Catalog System, the Remote Replication systems, the Defense Hydrographic Initiative, the Controlled Image Base, the Joint Mapping Tool Kit, Terrain Modelling and Simulation, and global Digital Terrain Elevation Data. Each is now described in greater detail.

The Modernized Catalogue System

This enables NIMA to provide its customer community with a more usable, more reliable catalogue of the available inventory of products. Both a soft-copy and a hardcopy version have been released, although the objective is to eliminate hardcopy production. In addition, the initial release of a soft-copy catalogue is CD-ROM-dependent, rather than interactive 'dial-up'. The inventory information is focused on standard products that can be ordered using stock number accounting. The computer interface (a commercial package) for the softcopy version begins to prepare the user community for browsing and querying on the availability of data in a paper-less and on-line, 'dial-up' environment. Once this type of interface becomes familiar, adding features like tailored ordering from a data inventory, rather than a product inventory, should be a natural progression.

Remote Replication

Remote Replication allows in-theatre scanning and printing of hardcopy in addition to providing some standard GIS applications that allow data manipulation, update, or overlay. By working in the digital environment, new information from various sources can be rapidly incorporated into available raster and vector files. Some systems and some users can remain in that digital environment; however, no one should naïvely believe that paper products will rapidly become obsolete. Technology today makes it possible to print small quantities of less-than-lithographic-quality maps in a deployed environment. In a variety of circumstances, this capability can be quite timely and the most cost-effective approach. Fewer copies of a map need to be pre-deployed, saving costly warehouse space. On-hand stock can be scanned to create a good resolution raster file from which exact copies can be duplicated. Digital data sets deployed on CD-ROM, or transmitted electronically in a crisis, can be printed only when and where required. Furthermore, the design of the vector graphic permits decluttering by accommodating visualization of desired themes only. The consumer has the option of printing only what is needed and only when it is needed.

The Remote Replication system demonstrated its operational utility and flexibility in support of the Dayton Peace negotiations where preliminary results could be quickly conveyed to traditional map representation and rapid revisions could be effected. Large-quantity printing was neither necessary nor desirable. Several systems were deployed in 1996, including first tests afloat, where space limitations and dynamic motion were new challenges.

The Defense Hydrographic Initiative

The Defense Hydrographic Initiative (DHI) includes, in addition to multiple improvements to the collection, management, and distribution of hydrographic data, the Hydrographic Source Assessment System (HYSAS) and the Master Seafloor Digital Data Base (MSDDB). MSDDB was designed to be delivered as a operational system, but in many ways it can be viewed as a verifying pilot of the GGI&S vision. The database architecture includes distributed processing and distributed storage with network connectivity for transferring data, upon demand, from one node to another. HYSAS provides a processing engine that informs those accessing its files about inventory status, metadata, and the status of documented requirements.

The Controlled Image Base

In 1996 DMA began to populate what has been designated as one aspect of the image layer of foundation data. The product, made available either by electronic transmission or on CD-ROM, is an orthorectified, radiometrically balanced data set named the Controlled Image Base (CIB). The original design uses commercially obtained SPOT images. However, the imagery source is not restricted to SPOT. Nominally, the geo-extent of each data set will be a 1° by 1° geocell that aligns well with DMA's traditional Digital Terrain Elevation Data (DTED). Each pixel of CIB will have horizontal coordinates and, fused with DTED, will allow interpolation of the mean sea-level height value. CIB permits NIMA to respond rapidly to its customer base with a standard and reliable data set within only a few hours of request if the image source is available.

This product was also very useful during the Dayton Peace talks when, linked to a commercial application and system called PowerScene, negotiators could see the effect of the projected zones and boundaries by 'flying through' the image on which the relevant vectors were overlaid.

Joint Mapping Tool Kit

In 1994, the Chairman of the Joint Chiefs of Staff issued the directive that there would be 'only one (Joint) Command and Control System'. To that end, the Global Command and Control System (GCCS) was designated to support all joint Service requirements. It provides the core command, control, communications, computers, and intelligence functions required by the military to plan, execute, and manage their operations. One of NIMA's cooperative roles is to support data exploitation. The Joint Mapping Tool Kit (JMTK) started as a loose collage of nominated tools from existing Service packages. The spatial database management portion of the Air Force Common Mapping Toolkit was identified, as were the visualization modules from the Navy's CHART system and the Terrain Exploitation Module from the Army. Some tools were drawn from the DMA MC&G Utilities Software Environment (DMAMUSE) and from the National Security Agency's OIL-STOCK. The early versions of JMTK convey a federated rather than an integrated approach. Additional efforts will incorporate commercially available tools, will comply with the standards for software re-use as defined in the Interoperable Map Software documentation for software technical architecture, and will be adaptable to systems beyond the scope of the GCCS.

Terrain Modelling and Simulation

In an era of reduced government budgets, the military must train as they will fight and will fight as they have trained. Modelling and simulation includes 'live' training through operational exercises in the field using real equipment in simulated combat and rescue missions; virtual simulation which exercises personnel and equipment on synthetic battlefields using simulators or trainers; and constructive simulation which involves a suite of war-gaming and analytical models, tools, and systems that are found in a 'world' where forces, weapons, and sometimes even the decision-makers are synthetic. To bring standardization to this effort, a Defense Modelling and Simulation Office (DMSO) was established in 1991. The representation of the earth's surface is a major component of these simulation activities since the geo-referencing foundation and the framework allows constructive coherence of data and activities. For this reason, DMA was identified as the executive agent for terrain modelling. Standards for the 3-D representation of objects on the surface of the earth and methods to promote the rapid generation of terrain and feature data are the two primary focuses of the agency's work. Both are essential to the success of the GGI&S initiative by seeking compatible standards and by promoting the population of the user-accessible data warehouse.

Global Digital Terrain Elevation Data

Digital Terrain Elevation Data (DTED) exists for approximately 65 percent of the earth. Various military and civil applications consume this product, whether in support of hydrological studies that analyse ground-water flow or to provide safer approach routes over terrain around airports. It has taken over 20 years, using various production methods including high-cost stereographic extraction, to acquire this data store. Different sources and methods contribute to inconsistencies and sheer within the data. In many cases the data are not releasable due to bilateral agreements between co-producing organizations.

To overcome some of these integrity and availability constraints DMA and the National Aeronautics and Space Administration (NASA) finalized an agreement during summer 1996 for a space shuttle mission using the

Shuttle Radar Topographic Mission (SRTM). The mission is expected in late 1999 and will collect sufficient data during an 11-day period, between 60° north and 56° south, to cover over 80 percent of the land surface with interferometric synthetic aperture radar sensing. Accuracy of the elevation information is expected to exceed that of the existing data, with 90 percent horizontal accuracy of 20 m and vertical accuracy of 15 m with reference to the WGS 84 geoid. The release policy will allow public access, through a civilian agency like the United States Geology Survey (USGS), to the near-global elevation data at 100 m post-spacings. Elevation data at 30 m post-spacing, over the United States only, will also be available. Comparably dense elevation data elsewhere will be released on a case-by-case basis over small areas, primarily to assist researchers.

GEOSPATIAL INFORMATION INTEGRATED PRODUCT TEAM (GIIPT)

Discussion of the GGI&S vision originated in remarks made in late 1992. Work continued thereafter on articulating the details of the vision and generated enthusiastic technical support, but it struggled to catch and maintain the attention of the primary customer. A report from a respected group of industry leaders, published in 1995 by the Defense Science Board, corroborated DMA's vision but noted the absence of end-to-end community involvement and saw real opportunity for improvement in the defence mapping process.

To ensure that the vision for GGI&S is realized, one recommendation from this report was to establish a special team to prepare a master plan for action and to work all the related issues through the co-operative exchange between defence and civil government agencies, the military, academia, and industry. Four focus teams are tackling specific aspects of the programme: requirements, information production, information management and dissemination, and information application. Within 18 months of start-up, the team will have tested, either through pilot projects or through exercises, various operational concepts. New joint doctrine for the military execution of a mission will be in use; a viable data population scheme into a mature data warehouse design will be realized; the geospatial information data dictionary for a hardened data model will be near completion; and the geospatial gateway will have reached state-of-the-art functionality. By the year 2000, a fully operational but not globally complete data warehouse will be easily accessed by consumers, populated by traditional and non-traditional contributors, and will carry rich metadata to direct users to the appropriate servers existing in a world-flung distributed architecture.

CONCLUSIONS

Global geospatial information underpins and describes the next generation of mapping, charting, and geodesy support. To satisfy its customers in the near-, mid- and long-term, NIMA must direct its powerful production engine to populate more extensive, higher-resolution, and consistently accurate databases and, at the same time, reduce the production timelines. The GGI&S initiative is fundamentally a data management and information delivery endeavour. Its architecture is achievable. It can be implemented with proven and emerging technology. New database and network technologies will allow the geospatial community to accomplish tasks that only a couple of years ago seemed unattainable. However, the work to develop the necessary standards required for the reference model of the notional architecture demands strong leadership and collaborative effort.

On-going changes in the customer environments will require NIMA to pursue the migration from a product-orientated to a data-attentive posture. Revealing the multi-dimensioned utility of global geospatial information for the future environments will expose brand new vistas for data exploitation that need not be limited by today's insights. Terminology such as 'value-adding' and 'tailoring' point to the way geospatial information will be exploited, stored, enhanced, and distributed in the future, as it is presently perceived. This is a dynamic era and that perception itself will evolve as technology offers even more incentive for producers deftly satisfying customer needs.

The delivery of GGI&S data sets and services will employ a full range of existing US Department of Defense communications networks in a 'Take and Update' strategy, with appropriate media for digital data dissemination comprising the 'Take' element of the strategy. The National Imagery and Mapping Agency will pilot several gateway interfaces and will test the connection of those gateways to the network. Results of all these ventures will help NIMA develop its readiness to support traditional and tailored requests for military support and to respond to crises.

REFERENCES

Clinton WJ 1994 Executive Order 12906 *Co-ordinating geographic data acquisition and access: the National Spatial Data Infrastructure.* Washington, DC, April 11

DIGIWG 1994 *Digital Geographic Information Exchange Standard (DIGEST).* Digital Geographic Information Working Group, Edition 1.2, January

DISA 1993 *Department of Defense Technical Architecture Framework for Information Management (TAFIM),* Version 2.0. Washington, DC, Defense Information Systems Agency, Center for Architecture, 1 November

DMA 1994 *Strategic direction for the Defense Mapping Agency – a vision for the 21st century.* Fairfax, VA, Defense Mapping Agency, February

DMA 1996 *DoD Geospatial Data Standardization Project Report*. Prepared by the Defense Mapping Agency for the Defense Information Systems Agency. Washington, DC, Defense Information Systems Agency, 15 March

Joint Staff 1993 *Committed, focused, and needed: C4I for the warrior*. Prepared by the C4 Architecture & Integration Division (J6I) J6. Washington, DC, The Joint Staff, June

Mapping Science Committee, National Research Council 1993 *Toward a co-ordinated spatial data infrastructure for the nation*. Washington, DC, National Academy Press

National Defense University 1995 *Strategic assessment 1995*. Prepared by the Institute for National Strategic Studies of the National Defense University. Washington, DC

OUSDAT (1995) *Report of the Defense Science Board Task Force on defense mapping for future operations*. Published through the Office of the Under Secretary of Defense for Acquisition and Technology. Washington, DC, September

The need for basic map information in support of environmental assessment and sustainable development strategies

Nay Htun

SUMMARY

A major goal of the United Nations is to promote and facilitate the integration of economic, ecological, and social parameters to attain people-centred sustainable development. Increasingly, this must also pay heed, for example, to resource consumption and depletion, wasteful and polluting production patterns, increasing population, poverty, soil degradation, fresh water, biodiversity, and disasters. The United Nations Development Programme (UNDP) is focusing on four areas: poverty alleviation and elimination; productive employment; enhancing the role of women; and protecting the natural resource and environment base.

In any area of the world, a number of core data types are required to assess environmental conditions and develop strategies that can lead to long-term sustainable human development. For many areas of the world, these data do not exist at the scales required to support these activities. Development of such data sets is labour-intensive and costly and, although these data sets could support a wide variety of applications, no single use can generally justify the full cost of development.

One of the leading questions to ask here is this: with the need so great for appropriate scale data products to support environmental assessment and sustainable development, how can the mapping organizations of the world support the broader need of the world community for up-to-date information in spatial format? This is the challenge that should be a primary concern of national mapping organizations (NMOs). A start has been made through the Japanese proposal for a Global Map but there is much still to be done.

INTRODUCTION

Policy-makers need access to the right types of data in order to make appropriate decisions that can increase standards of living and improve the quality of life. Maps are one important example of the type of data needed by resource managers and public policy decision-makers.

Today, adequate maps that can assist in environmental assessments and sustainable development strategies, do not exist in many areas of the world. Depending upon scale, thematic content, and timeliness, this lack of maps is equally true in both developed and developing countries. Yet, many people – including research scientists, policy decision-makers and the general public – find this hard to believe. They assume that the maps they require exist, contain the information they seek, and are accurate. Even where maps do exist, the features often depicted are dated. Some mapped information is more perishable than others; e.g. forest clear-cutting as opposed to continental outlines. The value of data is related to its currency. Mapping is an important, complex, expensive, and time-consuming task that many in the international community feel is not being carried forward in an adequate fashion.

The four major goals of the UNDP are:

- poverty alleviation and elimination;
- generating productive employment;
- increasing and enhancing the role of women;
- protecting and conserving natural resources and the environment.

These are key to improving the quality of life and living standards world-wide. Attainment of these goals requires a variety of accurate up-to-date information, much of which should be geo-referenced or documented in map form.

The first goal is to alleviate and eventually eliminate poverty. One and a half billion people around the world still live in abject poverty. The capability to improve global standards of living exist and efforts to do so need to be undertaken at the national, regional, and global level.

The second goal is to ensure jobs, or more appropriately, livelihoods, that are empowering and enabling. Much of the information needed to support the creation of such livelihoods will need to be developed in a geographical or spatial format.

The third goal is to strengthen the place of women in the world. Half of the world population is made up of women, many of whom are marginalized and disenfranchised. Many do not have access to the facilities needed for development.

The fourth goal is to enhance natural resources and our environmental base. There is a great need to manage and conserve environmental capital prudently for the benefit of present and future generations.

Until recently – and in particular prior to – the United Nations Conference on Environment and Development (UNCED) held in Rio in 1992, most development programmes dealt with only economic issues. There are, therefore, abundant statistical databases to deal with'GNP per capita'. The addition of environmental and social issues to the equation to support the goals of sustainable human development greatly increases the need for additional information in a spatial format.

It is still believed that economic development is one of the necessary elements to address these goals. But, while past attempts to increase economic capital were legitimate, it has become increasingly clear to the international community that ecological capital must also be preserved. These two goals are not necessarily in conflict with each other and they must be integrated in future strategies. Integration will lead to an increased potential for an overall improvement in environmental conditions and greater sustainability of the global resource base.

At the 1992 Rio summit, there was recognition that improving these two types of capital alone would not be sufficient. There is a growing acceptance that a third component, the preservation and enrichment of social capital, is also important. It is only when there is a balance of economic, environmental, and social issues that a more stable, environmentally sensitive, and sustainable human development can be achieved. The world community met in 1995 in Copenhagen to consider the means by which social capital can be increased. The results of that meeting will have significant implications for future development strategies. The meeting, the World Summit for Social Development, was attended by more than 120 heads of states or governments. The meeting adopted ten commitments; these included the four UNDP goals. In addition, the other commitments also call on states to:

- ensure that structural adjustment programmes include social development;
- create an enabling environment;
- promote social integration;
- promote and attain universal and equitable access to quality education and health.

It is important that the global development community (and those who provide information to the policy-makers) now, more than ever, take an integrated view of the factors that impact the sustenance of these three types of capital.

Because the linkages among these three capitals are complex, there is a need for more reliable databases if better integration is to be achieved. The challenge is to identify the types of economic, ecological, and social data that are critical for guiding policy-makers towards greater sustainability and greater harmony at scales from local sites to regions of the whole world. Locally, better data are required in support of siting technology installations, such as water-treatment facilities, electrical power generation plants, and highways. On a regional scale, we need databases which can help ensure equity and improve social stability. In the past, development planning did not always consider the potential for the creation of social conflict. What we need to practise more of is what the United Nations refer to as preventive development – development that takes into account region-wide cultural, social, economic, and political conditions; development that is sensitive to the need to benefit, as equally as is practical, all the peoples in the area. This is the type of development that UNDP believes can help to create a more peaceful and sustainable community of nations.

The compilation and dissemination of the data needed to accomplish what I have laid out here is complex and expensive. Much of the data needed to address these issues may not even exist at present. Once the required data are identified, their current availability as well as the capability to collect and use them must be assessed. This is a task of great interest to the UNDP.

IDENTIFICATION OF CORE DATA NEEDS

To address the global adequacy of core data sets needed by environmental planners, resource managers, and public policy decision-makers, the UNDP and the United Nations Environment Programme (UNEP) sponsored an international symposium in November 1994 in Bangkok, Thailand, to:

- seek consensus on priority environmental assessment and sustainable development issues and the core data sets needed to respond to these issues;
- define the minimum characteristics of these data in relation to national and trans-national purposes;
- establish collaborative mechanisms to foster the harmonization of core environmental data; and
- examine the barriers to general access to and use of these data.

In addition to UNDP and UNEP, the symposium was supported by the United States National Aeronautics and Space Administration (NASA), US Environmental Protection Agency, US Geological Survey, and Universities Space Research Association. Sixty-five individuals from 28 nations participated in this symposium. Included were policy-makers, scientists, and researchers from developing and industrialized countries. Also included were representatives from the United Nations, industry, aid-to-development agencies, and data suppliers.

The realization of the need for this international symposium grew out of discussions held at an Aspen Global Change Institute Workshop on Early Detection of Global Change in August 1993. Six priority issues of global concern were identified in Aspen:

- biological diversity or biodiversity;
- consumption and production;
- demography;
- desertification;

- fresh water; and
- poverty.

There are more areas of global concern which could be listed for which accurate, up-to-date information is required. Given the overlap in these issues and their impacts at scales from local to global, what key variables must be documented to establish a baseline, to monitor changes in status, and to identify improvement or deterioration? While priorities of categories of economic, ecological, and social information can be debated endlessly, there can be no doubt that this type of information is required for analysis, assessment, planning, and management decision-making with respect to global change.

At the Aspen workshop, attenders were challenged to identify key environmental data sets that could serve as baselines from which change could be monitored. Although the scientists, educators, and policy-makers identified several data sets that were adequate in some parts of the world, they were hard-pressed to identify any globally consistent data sets. It was very informative to realize that the participants, many of whom were from industrialized countries, realized the inadequacy of the current state of global databases. This is a problem which is constantly faced by the international environmental assessment and sustainable development community.

Participants were then asked to identify data sets considered most critical for their particular area of investigation. One hundred and five specific data sets were identified. This list was subsequently aggregated to a list containing 17 key data sets. This aggregation was accomplished by examining the longer list and looking for those data sets that had to exist if the data set in the shorter, key list was to be developed. The 17 data sets listed were land cover, climate, population, economic activity, topography, land status, biological diversity, human health, soils, atmospheric chemistry, trace gases, water quality and quantity, ocean physical parameters, paleo-climatology and paleo-ecology, education levels, stakeholders and decision-makers, and future climate scenarios from global change models.

One of the findings of the Aspen workshop was that the lack of data sets providing even the basic information needed for developing plans and policies should be brought to an international forum. The preliminary plans for the International Symposium on Core Data Needs for Environmental Assessment and Sustainable Development Strategies were developed by a small group of the participants and subsequently held in Bangkok.

To provide focus to the Bangkok symposium, a series of plenary presentations provided background information, international case studies, and information on selected UNEP programmes. Panel discussions and working group sessions also were held. For the purposes of these discussions, a core data set was defined as'a consistent set of basic data that can be used in the analysis of a variety of environmental assessment and sustainable development issues'. Participants exchanged views on critical environmental assessment and sustainable development issues, on core data needs, and then developed recommendations related to five key topical areas:

- land use change and degradation;
- fresh water and coastal zone management;
- sustainable use of natural resources;
- human health, pollution, waste management, and natural and environmental disasters; and
- food and energy for an increasing population.

Finally, to ensure that no major issues were missed and that region-specific issues were identified, core data needs also were examined from a regional viewpoint for the five regions comprising Latin America; Asia and the Pacific; Africa; Middle East, Eastern Europe, and Russia; and Western Europe and North America.

Sixty-six data sets were identified as important to individual areas of interest. These data sets, identified by individual panels, were then discussed in open plenary and aggregated into summary tables to illustrate graphically those 'core' data sets identified as important by more than one panel. Based upon plenary discussion, a core of 16 data sets was aggregated from the total. After clarification of terminology, this list was further aggregated into 10 high-priority core data sets central to the conduct of many types of studies that produce environmental assessment information and sustainable development strategies.

These ten priority core data sets are:

Topography	Land use/land cover
Hydrology	Soils
Infrastructure	Air quality
Climatology	Water quality
Demographics	Economy

Having identified the above list, the participants then agreed that ways must be found to develop, maintain, and make accessible these core data. The participants also concluded that:

- these core data sets are essential for environmental assessments and sustainable development strategies;
- adequate representations of these types of data do not exist for many countries;
- these core data sets support a wide variety of uses specific to given locations, but often no single use can justify the cost of their development;
- development of these core data sets is often labour- and technology-intensive and, as a result, expensive; and
- a variety of factors restrict the availability and accessibility of core data sets, including costs, national security/sovereignty, lack of knowledge of existence, and lack of standardization/harmonization.

Availability and accessibility were key concerns of the symposium participants. Some participants at present often must acquire core data sets from sources outside their own countries because of access restrictions. Methods to improve data exchange, including improved networks and open data policies, need to be developed. Concentrated efforts are needed to help users gain efficient and effective knowledge, access, and delivery. Metadata, including descriptors of data type, location, structure, and quality, should be developed for core data sets and made easily accessible whenever possible.

Participants noted that it is often difficult to justify the long-term costs of collecting and maintaining data and that decision-makers are often surprised at the associated expense of collecting high-quality spatial (geographically referenced) data. It is likewise difficult to measure the benefits of such data use. Those taking part concluded that the assessment of benefits from use of spatial data should be done by creating a set of case studies, rather than solely through econometric studies. One approach suggested was to focus on satellite remotely sensed data and study examples of its use. However, participants also noted that parallel case studies combining both remote sensing and non-remote sensing data are essential to convey the benefits of spatial data to governments, international agencies, community-based organizations, and the people.

It was argued that many nations are not creating national-level core data sets and that, in some countries, there is no agency responsible for the creation and maintenance of some at least of these data sets. Participants were concerned, however, that, whereas attention was focused on this'limited and manageable' number of core data sets, there are a variety of other important data sets specific to particular topics and/or region, such as public health, consumption patterns, or species locations, which also must be generated for specific projects. There was a strong agreement that more should be done to facilitate the funding and production of core data sets. Capacity building, education, and training were considered essential to the production, maintenance, and use of these core data sets; simply making available the data sets would not be an adequate response.

Based upon these findings, symposium participants agreed the following recommendations:

- a forum should be established to provide follow-up and develop action plans to carry out the recommendations of this symposium;
- the forum, under the sponsorship of UNDP and UNEP, should have a standing core membership and should link with other forums that are addressing core data-related issues to avoid duplication of efforts;
- the forum should provide focus to all core data issues related to awareness, availability, access, use, education, and training;
- UN agencies and donor organizations should co-operate with national bodies to provide local funding for the creation and maintenance of core data sets by:

- developing funding policies and mechanisms which encourage national organizations to acquire and provide core data sets;
- encouraging national organizations to consider participation in co-operative programmes that purchase/share core data and their products;
- national governments, donor agencies, and international organizations should:
  - support the development and maintenance of core data sets;
  - conduct surveys to document the status of core data sets;
  - work towards decreasing cost, increasing availability, and improving access to core data sets;
  - expand communications, networking, and metadata efforts to increase knowledge of existing databases;
  - work towards the development of guidelines for standardization and harmonization of core data over a defined time period.

In addition to these recommendations, symposium participants felt that more should be done to publicize the fact that the creation and maintenance of core data are essential to assess the status of the environment and develop resources, both human and natural, in a sustainable fashion. They also felt that UNEP and UNDP should evaluate on a case-by-case basis the need to fund the creation of national and regional specific data sets that are key to understanding significant environmental assessment and sustainable development issues. It was also recommended that international assistance projects should incorporate strong capacity building, education, and training components that enhance the basic skills of users and the utility of the data products, and facilitate information exchange between producers and users. Where possible, a co-ordinated approach to such projects should be encouraged, so that multi-national data purchases and technical assistance facilitate the most cost-effective and productive use of data sets and resources available.

CONCLUSIONS

Governments engage in programmes of systematic mapping and spatial data collection in response to a wide variety of national, regional, and local needs – military, administrative, socio-economic, and environmental. However, the general and specific needs for such information are not yet recognized adequately enough to generate the resources necessary to produce the information required by resource planners, managers, and the scientific community. Existing indexes of map coverage differentiate areas according to the relative degree of importance that governments have attached to them. In general, the areas most intensively mapped are those areas of greatest interest and concern, not only to governments but also to society at large.

But there are many unmapped areas and there are many inconsistencies when nationally-focused mapping is assembled for global or regional purposes.

It has therefore become essential that the public, policy-makers, government agency personnel, the science community, and private industry understand that:

- spatial information currently needed fully to support environmental assessments and sustainable development studies are lacking in most parts of the world;
- economic, ecological, and social issues are critical to global security;
- there is still much to do to improve understanding of mapping spatially specific, environmental development, and resource management information;
- improved mapping of baseline environmental information remains a difficult but essential task; and finally,
- new ways can be developed to help improve the current level of understanding of what is required to create a truly sustainable future.

The challenge before NMOs is to sort out what can be done collectively by the map-making organizations of the world to improve the quality, availability, and accessibility of basic map and related environmental information. The two expert meetings described above have demonstrated that this information is rarely available at present on any consistent basis yet it is critical to resource management, environmental planning and assessment, and sustainable human development. The Japanese proposal for a global map (see the chapter by Warita and Nonomura in this book) will be an important step forward if implemented. But NMOs can contribute much more to the improvement of the quality of life on this planet if they can come together to create trans-national data sets to tackle problems which recognize no national boundaries.

CHAPTER 9

Developing global environmental databases: lessons learned about framework information

Mark Collins and Jonathan Rhind

SUMMARY

The status of the world's biodiversity has become an increasingly important scientific and political issue. The World Conservation Monitoring Centre (WCMC) is a non-profit organization whose aim is to provide information services on species and ecosystems globally, and to help others build information systems of their own. In carrying out this remit, the WCMC has necessarily been involved in assembling topographic framework and many other types of data at a variety of different scales and classifications and from many parts of the world. Based on its 18 years of experience and the Centre's knowledge of the requirements of scientific research for biodiversity and associated data, this chapter describes the shortcomings of the present situation. It suggests improvements which, if enacted, would permit the WCMC and other organizations to concentrate on the delivery of information and services to decision-makers, rather than devoting scarce resources to basic data-gathering and duplication of activities.

INTRODUCTION

Environmental issues have come to much greater prominence in the last 20 years. In the 1990s, particular attention has been paid to the loss of species and conversion of natural habitats mainly due to development activities of people. This concern for biodiversity was a primary reason for holding the 'Earth Summit' in Rio de Janeiro in 1992. This meeting resulted in the creation of Agenda 21, the intergovernmental agreement on sustainable development and protection of the environment. The summary report from Rio and the text of the Convention on Biological Diversity highlight the significant role that collection and analysis of biodiversity information has to play: unless we appreciate the real situation with regard to the numbers of species and types of ecosystems and their distribution across the world – together with changes to these parameters – national and international action is impossible on any rational basis. Through the collection and analysis of biodiversity data at a country and global scale using a 'bottom-up' collection approach, the WCMC attempts to provide a scientific evaluation of the state of the world's biodiversity. The collection, management, and integration of these data provide many problems which are discussed in a later section. Initially, however, a brief description of the WCMC and its work is given to demonstrate the Centre's experience and to summarize the type of work which is now routinely being carried out in environmental conservation. In many respects, this scientific work underpins many of the ideas and action plans set out in Htun's chapter in this book.

THE WORLD CONSERVATION MONITORING CENTRE

The WCMC is widely recognized as a centre of excellence in the handling and management of information on the conservation of biodiversity. The Centre has more than 18 years' experience in this field, providing technical data management support to its three founder organizations – the World Conservation Union (IUCN), the World Wide Fund for Nature (WWF), and the United Nations Environment Programme (UNEP). In addition, it provides information services to development aid agencies, other UN agencies, international convention secretariats, government and non-governmental organizations, the World Bank, the European Commission, and other intergovernmental organizations, the media, commerce, and industry.

The Centre is an independent non-profit organization, currently employing some 60 professional staff, with a wide range of international experience. In addition to providing 'raw' data on demand, the WCMC also has experience in the development of information services required by different users of biodiversity data. For example, it provides data management services to:

- the Convention on International Trade in Endangered Species (CITES) Secretariat and several Contracting Parties including the European Union;
- IUCN and UNESCO on World Heritage sites; and
- IUCN's expert networks on species and protected areas.

In addition, the WCMC has collaborated with British Petroleum plc and now with the International Petroleum Industry Environmental Conservation Association (IPIECA) to develop an advanced map-based information management system – the Biodiversity Map Library. This system aims to facilitate access to computer maps and the databases linked to them, providing non-expert users much of the power of a Geographical Information System (GIS) without requiring them to be familiar with GIS software and technology.

Many years of corporate experience have been gained in the creation and management of extensive biodiversity databases. Each of the units within the WCMC – Habitats, Species, and Protected Areas – has specialized in collecting data on a particular aspect of biodiversity. For instance, the Centre maintains a database of some 60,000 national parks and protected areas throughout the world which is the basis for *The United Nations List of National Parks and Protected Areas* (IUCN 1994). Thus the large data sets resulting from this long-term activity contain some of the most accurate and detailed inventories of the world's biodiversity, a summary of which was published in *Global Biodiversity: Status of the Earth's Living Resources* (Groombridge 1992), updated in the *Biodiversity Data Sourcebook* (Groombridge 1994).

Finally, whilst its databases are held in Cambridge, the World Conservation Monitoring Centre has been very active in supporting development of in-country information management. It is the hub of a network of organizations preparing guidelines and materials for capacity building. These activities build on an earlier collaboration between the WCMC and UNEP on the development of *Guidelines for Country Studies on Biological Diversity* (UNEP 1993). These guidelines provide the support necessary for developing and implementing the national biodiversity strategies and action plans called for by the Convention on Biological Diversity.

Geographical Information Systems (GIS) – Spatial Data Management

Information affecting biodiversity, such as the details of protected areas, habitat complexity, and species distribution, is very often spatial in context. Much of the data collected since the early 1980s have therefore included spatial information. However, until the development of accessible GIS software and affordable hardware, these data were usually stored as point locations within a standard Relational Database Management System (RDBMS). Since the late 1980s, the WCMC has developed many large databases either linked to a GIS or residing entirely within one.

Like those of many other organizations, the World Conservation Monitoring Centre GIS capability was developed in a series of steps. The initial installation of a single 286-based Personal Computer running PC ARC/INFO was carried out in 1989. This extremely limited facility has been replaced by progressively more powerful facilities amounting in late 1996 to many powerful PCs and workstations linked in a client/server manner with a Sun Ultra server. The main software packages include both the UNIX and PC versions of ARC/INFO, ArcView, Ingres, and FoxPro. The choice of these systems was partly because they are widely used by collaborating bodies world-wide, thereby minimizing the problems of data transfer. As GIS software and computer hardware have become more affordable, the development of the system has switched from one based solely on in-house data collection to increasingly greater co-operation with and support of organizations based in the country of study and with other international conservation groups.

In addition to the production of scientific reference materials, many of the GIS data sets have been used to produce 'glossy' conservation atlases.

Maps for the IUCN conservation atlases on tropical forests of Asia and the Pacific (Collins, Sayer and Whitmore 1991), Africa (Sayer, Harcourt and Collins 1992) and the Americas (Harcourt and Sayer 1996), and wetlands (Dugan 1993) were managed entirely within the GIS system.

WCMC data policy and practice

As an organization involved with the building and maintenance of global databases derived largely from many separate sources and then subsequently with disseminating these data widely, the WCMC has had to pay much attention to many aspects of data policy.

Data collection

The collection of much data has proved to be considerably more difficult than was first envisaged. The lack of available data has led to collection of data from numerous sources that vary greatly in scale and quality. Data sources range from textual descriptions of a particular site and hand-drawn maps produced by local experts to satellite imagery. The great variety of data and the limited knowledge of the reliability of some of it can make spatial or temporal comparisons difficult to carry out.

The most commonly observed discrepancies are in the age of source map sheets, definition of map projection details (which are very often missing), and the resolution of the information. These discrepancies become apparent when viewed alongside adjacent data sets. As a consequence of this lack of metadata or the variety of data characteristics, in some cases the data are deemed too poor to be included in the database – despite this being the only information available.

In general, the WCMC aims to collect data at a national level broadly based around 1:1 million scale, although this will vary according to the size of the area under investigation and the purpose of the project. For example, information for small countries such as Rwanda or Belize is typically collected at a much larger scale. In addition, for those projects concentrating on important globally distributed but locally small features, such as many coral-reef outcrops, the map scale for data collection is also much larger.

Data validation

All of the WCMC's data are validated by expert consultation. In some cases, this makes use of formal networks such as IUCN's Commissions on National Parks and Protected Areas, and Species Survival. Where these networks do not exist, validation is carried out by direct correspondence with experts. The repeated use of data and their dissemination results in much useful feedback from users, which in turn leads to correction of most of the remaining errors.

Data standards

The Centre has long recognized the need to apply accepted standards to data development, management, and documentation. In many respects therefore, the WCMC's approach has been more sophisticated than the focus on transfer standards common in the 1980s and early 1990s, now being replaced as described in the chapter by Salgé. The Centre has undertaken an exhaustive analysis of standards applicable to environmental information, including those in the fields of mapping, field sampling, and database design. These standards have been documented and are being distributed to WCMC partners throughout the world in a capacity-building initiative managed by UNEP.

Data documentation

The WCMC has adopted standard documentation procedures based on the DIF metadata format. However, it was found necessary to extend this format to incorporate more detail which in turn necessitated development of a tool for metadata entry. This tool supports the production of metadata records in a number of standard formats, including UNEP/GRID, CIESIN/DIF, and NASA/DIF.

Data availability

Examples of GIS data sets currently available from the WCMC include:

- a global tropical forest data set collected country by country at a nominal scale of 1:1 million. The classification of the constituent data sets has been simplified and merged with other data to enable the creation of a global forest data set (see WWF 1996). The country-specific 'unsimplified' data sets in their original classification scheme are also available for most tropical forest countries;
- global coverage for wetlands of international importance. This was collected regionally due to the inconsistencies of wetland type classification schemes;
- the protected areas of the world. This is the largest and most comprehensive data set of such areas for the entire world;
- endemic bird areas produced by BirdLife international, with whom the WCMC co-operates in many projects;
- coral reefs of the world. This project is being run in conjunction with the International Center for Living Aquatic Resource Management (ICLARM) in the Philippines;
- mangrove forests. This is being used as the basis for maps in a conservation atlas;
- nesting and feeding sites for seven species of sea turtle; and
- centres of plant diversity, the data having been collected by IUCN and its associates.

For non-commercial use, the WCMC has a policy of free distribution of data and only seeks to recover the costs of disseminating them. Restrictions imposed by copyright or stipulations made by the original provider of the data may limit the ability to distribute raw data but metadata are always freely available. The WCMC has adopted the CIESIN Catalogue Server as the primary mechanism for distributing such metadata: the metadata records associated with ten of the Centre's major data sets are already available from this source, and additional metadata records will be created both for WCMC data and for those created by our collaborators. In all cases, the source and subsequent treatment of the data are fully documented and any restrictions on distribution are indicated.

Data distribution

Where substantial, coherent data sets have been compiled, these are published on CD-ROM. The first of these was the topographic data set of Antarctica published in 1993, now available at a nominal price (Scientific Committee on Antarctic Research 1993). In 1996 a second CD-ROM, Tropical Moist Forests and Protected Areas version 1 was published (World Conservation Monitoring Centre and Center for International Forestry Research 1996). Other data sets being developed for production include those on mangroves and coral reefs. In collaboration with the World Resources Institute, thematic data for all African countries have been formatted on 3.5 inch diskettes and made available in 1995 (World Resources Institute 1995); they are primarily designed for use in-country on PC platforms. The same data but for the whole continent are available on CD-ROM.

The Internet is another frequently used mechanism for distributing data. The WCMC operates servers for e-mail, anonymous FTP (ftp.wcmc.org.uk) and the World Wide Web (http://www.wcmc.org.uk). This means of delivering data, documentation, and other information has superseded the more traditional communication links such as the postal service, fax, and telephone. On average, the World Wide Web (WWW) site responds to over 100,000 requests per month, with more than 15,000 of these being queries of the online databases. This represents a far greater number of requests than could have been handled by traditional postal queries. In many respects, the WCMC use of WWW and the Internet generally is as significant as for other organizations cited in chapters by Warita and Nonomura and by Calvert et al. It is no exaggeration to say that the Internet has changed the way in which the whole of the WCMC operates and vastly improved communication facilities between the Centre and its collaborators – all at minimal cost.

FRAMEWORK DATA PROBLEMS ENCOUNTERED BY THE WCMC

These fall into different categories but all can best be resolved by National Mapping Organizations (NMOs) and by national governments.

Inconsistency between framework data of the same resolution

As indicated earlier, the collection of spatial data commenced at the WCMC in the late 1980s. At that time there was only one standardized global data set of coastlines and countries at a scale relevant to the work that the WCMC was undertaking. Mundocart, produced by Petroconsultants Ltd, contained hand-digitized coastlines, country boundaries, and named rivers derived from the Operational Navigation Charts (ONC) 1:1 million scale map series. Where relevant, data collected by the WCMC were matched to this data set to ensure consistency between data collected from different countries. Subsequently all the features from the same ONC charts have become available in digital form as the *Digital Chart of the World* (DCW) (US Defense Mapping Agency 1992). This latter product was primarily produced using scanned data and subsequently vectorized. Not surprisingly, the two data sets are very similar but there are significant inconsistencies between the two sets of coastlines and country boundaries. As DCW has become a *de facto* base data standard, it becomes increasingly important that WCMC's data correspond to it. However, to revisit every data set would involve a huge and rather unproductive expense. New data sets will therefore be fitted to DCW but data already collected will be left matching the Mundocart boundaries for the foreseeable future.

Inadequate and inconsistent resolution of framework data

The DCW and Mundocart provide very useful base information at a scale of 1:1 million. However, they are neither detailed enough nor are the data accurate enough for many applications. The lack of accurate information is particularly acute in many of the regions in which the WCMC is particularly interested; for example, hypsographic information is sparse in much of South America. The DCW was derived from ONC charts which were in turn designed as high-altitude navigation charts, therefore detail is at its best in those areas underneath major flight paths. Larger-scale maps (e.g. 1:250,000) are frequently not yet available in computer form. With the poss-ible exception of the World Vector Shoreline (WVS) (US Defense Mapping Agency), standardized data for the entire world at a larger scale than 1:1 million are very difficult to acquire. An accurate base data layer is essential for projects carried out at much higher scales than 1:1 million and the WCMC welcomes the plans by the US military (see Lenczowski in this book) and hopes that public dissemination of the resulting databases will again become the practice.

Inconsistency between low- and high- resolution base maps

Some biodiversity sites are comparatively small and work on them requires more detailed base mapping in order to provide appropriate detail. This must be placed in a context of wide-area mapping at lower resolution. A good current example is the WCMC coral-reef mapping project. Our work demonstrates substantial misfits between the more detailed and the less detailed base mapping owing to manual generalization of the latter maps which have subsequently been digitized. This results in detailed biodiversity data being plotted in the sea and, in the coral-reef mapping project, corals apparently crossing over land areas at smaller scales. Again, the many non-GIS experts not unnaturally regard this with suspicion.

Pricing policies and restraints on data dissemination

Even where framework and other core data sets do exist, they are often charged for and their distribution is restricted under copyright terms. For organizations of charity status and for those in the developing world, the levels of charging which are being introduced by many NMOs are prohibitive. The problem is reduced where national mapping agencies have two tiers of charging, one for educational/research purposes and another for commercial ones, but even so the education charging levels may still be prohibitive for some users. The difficulties are compounded in two ways. The first is that often only a small fraction of the data is needed (e.g. the outlines of one or two coral reefs in the example above): payment for use of the entire data file is therefore inappropriate for the user. The second complication arises from constraints on dissemination. In a scientific and research organization like the WCMC, exchange of knowledge and data is central to our activities; it is – as pointed out in Agenda 21, the intergovernmental agreement – also central to the improvement of environmental conditions world-wide.

SOLUTIONS TO THE FRAMEWORK DATA PROBLEMS

The problems that face the WCMC and other bodies are those of data availability, data cost, and the standardization and harmonization of base data layers. To enable the WCMC and similar environmental and scientific organizations to continue to collect information on biodiversity and to support the building of in-country capacity to manage their own biodiversity information, changes in the information economy are required.

Accurate, up-to-date data, made available at costs which can be met by charities and without confining distribution restrictions, are required. Existing copyright issues need to be clarified, particularly with the use of a small part or only a few types of features from a much larger complex map series or data set. The best solution to minimize the problems of generalization and misfit described earlier is to derive smaller-scale data automatically from larger- scale source data – assuming it is available world-wide. Idiosyncratic, manually produced cartography is an anachronism as the basis for consistent global databases.

The first step forward in all this is the recognition of the problem. *The International Symposium on Core Data Needs for Environmental Assessment and Sustainable Development Strategies,* held in Bangkok in November 1994, identified the need for core data sets (including framework data) to be made available. A key recommendation (Estes et al 1995, vol. 1: 4) arising from this meeting was:

> Recognising existing differences in national policies on government-provided data, but work toward decreasing the cost, increasing the availability and improving access to core data sets for scientific, environmental assessment and sustainable development purposes.

CONCLUSIONS

Environmental non-profit agencies such as the WCMC play a pivotal role in achieving what governments world-wide have agreed to pursue in relation to sustainable development. They also support developing environmental information strategies. The tasks they face in building global and local area data sets on which rational decisions can be made are daunting because of the variety in availability and quality of the framework data available. But these tasks are complicated immensely by the cost of the geographical framework data sets needed to establish and use biodiversity information. If data cannot be provided free, then the status of the user and the end use of the data should be considered when pricing. NMOs and their parent governments have an interest in maximizing the beneficial use of their data.

ACKNOWLEDGEMENTS

Thanks are due to the Environmental Systems Research Institute (ESRI) and Sun Microsystems for their generous donations of GIS software and workstation hardware respectively. Without these donations, the GIS work of the World Conservation Monitoring Centre would not have been possible.

REFERENCES

Collins NM, Sayer JA, Whitmore TC (eds) 1991 *The conservation atlas of tropical forests: Asia and the Pacific.* Compiled by World Conservation Monitoring Centre and IUCN. London, Macmillan

Dugan P (ed) 1993 *A Mitchell Beazley world conservation atlas: wetlands in danger.* Compiled by IUCN. London, Mitchell Beazley

Estes J, Lawless J, Mooneyhan DW (eds) 1995 *Report on the International Symposium on Core Data Needs for Environmental Assessment and Sustainable Development Strategies.* New York, NY, United Nations Development Programme/United Nations Environment Programme

Groombridge B (ed) 1992 *Global Biodiversity: status of the earth's living resources.* World Conservation Monitoring Centre (Comp). London, Chapman & Hall

Groombridge B (ed) 1994 *Biodiversity data sourcebook.* Cambridge, World Conservation Monitoring Centre (Comp), World Conservation Press

Harcourt CS, Sayer JA (eds) 1996 *The conservation atlas of tropical forests: the Americas.* Compiled by World Conservation Monitoring Centre and IUCN. New York, NY, Macmillan

IUCN 1994 *1993 United Nations list of national parks and protected areas.* Prepared by World Conservation Monitoring Centre and IUCN. Cambridge, International Union for the Conservation of Nature

Sayer JA, Harcourt CS, Collins NM eds 1992 *The conservation atlas of tropical forests: Africa.* Compiled by World Conservation Monitoring Centre and IUCN. London, Macmillan

SCAR 1993 *Antarctica Digital Database.* Compiled by Scientific Committee on Antarctic Research, British Antarctic Survey and World Conservation Monitoring Centre. Cambridge, available from SCAR as CD-ROM and User Guide

UNEP 1993 *Guidelines for country studies.* Nairobi, UN Environment Programme

US DMA 1992 *Digital chart of the world.* Available as 1,700 Mb database on four CD-ROMs. Fairfax, VA, Defense Mapping Agency

US DMA *World vector shoreline.* Specification: DoD MIL-W-89012. Available as ASCII coded data written on ANSI standard magnetic tape. Fairfax, VA, Defense Mapping Agency

World Conservation Monitoring Centre and Center for International Forestry Research 1996 *Tropical moist forests and protected areas: version 1.* Compiled by World Conservation Monitoring Centre. Available as 550 Mb database on CD-ROM. Cambridge, World Conservation Monitoring Centre

World Resources Institute 1995 *African data sampler.* Compiled by the World Resources Institute in collaboration with the World Conservation Monitoring Centre and PADCO, Inc. Available from the World Resources Institute as a database on CD-ROM and User's Guide

WWF (1996) *The world-wide fund for nature world forest map 1996.* Available on WWW at *http:// www.panda.org/forests4life/forest_map.html*

SECTION 3

Beyond mapping: international trends affecting national mapping organizations

The dramatic changes in technology affecting those who create the geographical framework have already been mentioned in previous chapters. This is often seen as 'computerization' but is manifested in many different ways. The first chapter of this section considers four different examples of technological change which have already had great effects upon national mapping organizations (NMOs) and other organizations and will continue so to do. Calvert, Murray, and Smith describe developments in global satellite positioning systems, remote sensing imagery (especially that derived from satellites), Geographical Information Systems (GIS), and the Internet. In their view, the inevitability of continuing technological change ensures that the very nature of the framework will change. Moreover, they argue that the role of many NMOs will have to mutate from production organizations which are 'the experts in high quality cartography and geodesy to being data integrators and exploiters, certification agencies, reconciliation authorities and the like'.

Salgé describes the need for standardization of geographic information if wider and safer use is to be made of it. He summarizes the different approaches of the European standards body and the International Standards Organization, which are both actively involved in this area, and sets out how they are collaborating. Finally, he sets out a vision of the future situation, based on the spread of National Spatial Data Infrastructures (NSDIs) and regional and global versions of them, plus the European Commission's concepts on a European policy framework for a geographic infrastructure.

Nancy Tosta played a leading role in setting up and facilitating the original notion of an NSDI which subsumes the geographical framework, along with many other matters. These concepts have spread and evolved in many other countries since its original formulation. She describes how, in the early 1990s, the US mapping community began discussions about development of an NSDI to promote geospatial data sharing. This NSDI involves all levels of government as well as the private and academic sectors. It has contributed to a changing role for the National Mapping Division (NMD) of the US Geological Survey, the NMO. Actual data production activities by the NMD are likely to decline in future, whilst its co-ordination efforts increase. The challenges are likely to be to achieve consistent framework and other data on an acceptable basis.

Mooney and Grant also discuss the development of NSDIs, drawing on the pragmatic experience gained during the building of a 'first pass' national data infrastructure for Australia. Issues that have emerged from this initiative, including standards, pricing, national co-ordination, the pressures from competing infrastructures, and infrastructure responsibility, are described. The benefits of the provision and use of this framework are documented, and the chapter concludes with comments on the issues that will affect the NSDIs of the future.

The following two chapters describe wider, regional initiatives to tackle NSDI-like matters. The European views, at least at the end of 1996, are summarized in a document drawn up by the European Commission with input from many individuals. The aim of the Commission staff was to describe what is happening in the field of Geographic Information in Europe and elsewhere and indicate the need for Community actions to ensure that Europe was competitive in this area, that the private sector prospered and citizens had the maximum possible access to data consistent with privacy and commercial confidentiality issues. The document argues that a European policy for Geographic Information is needed by the European information society. The policy will contribute to providing better and more efficient government, more effective management of scarce resources, and new business opportunities. The policy is also necessary to ensure that important cross-border initiatives are nurtured and managed cost-effectively.

Finally, Majid Mohamed describes the various aims and activities of the Permanent Committee on GIS Infrastructure for Asia and the Pacific. A number of nations within this region have recognized the changing needs of their governments and peoples in terms of Geographical or Spatial Information. They have set out to create an Asia and the Pacific Spatial Data Infrastructure (APSDI) through the formation of the Permanent Committee on GIS Infrastructure. Majid Mohamed concludes that there are many parallels with work in the USA and Europe, not least in the changing roles of NMOs and in the way in which framework data will evolve.

CHAPTER 10

New technology and its impact on the framework for the world

Carl Calvert, Keith Murray, and Neil Smith

SUMMARY

New technologies are changing the way in which Geographic Information is captured, handled, and used. This chapter looks at four of the most influential technologies connected with Geographic Information in the latter part of the century and assesses how they will affect geographic framework data provision and its use.

Global positioning systems are tools for identification of position anywhere on the globe; the result can be employed not only to locate people or assets relative to one another but also to provide ever more up-to-date contextual information. As a consequence of the latter, this technology has major impacts even on the traditional – let alone new – activities of a national mapping organization (NMO). Soon-to-be-available satellite imagery has the potential to provide high-resolution (1 m) mapping from space on a continuing basis. The characteristics and likely uses of such imagery are examined, with some examples of opportunities and threats to NMOs.

The Geographical Information System (GIS) market is changing; it is no longer the domain simply of the specialist or corporate user equipped with large workstations. It is increasingly seen as a general-purpose tool available to all. However, this scenario is changing the roles of players in the market, and some of the implications of all this for NMOs and for the exploitation of the geographical framework are described. Finally, the growth of use of the Internet since the early 1990s, driven largely by development of the World Wide Web by the European nuclear research organization CERN, is coming to have a very substantial impact upon GIS and cartography. Already data are available for transfer from organizations such as the US Geological Survey. Metadata services are being defined to allow users of GIS to identify information and data sources, and new services are being developed which exploit GIS to provide part of a more general information service.

INTRODUCTION

Many other chapters in this book indicate that the advent of new technologies has changed dramatically the way and form in which the geographical framework is created, kept up-to-date, disseminated, and used. This chapter considers the four most crucial elements of the new technologies. It sets out, in a more detailed and comprehensive way than could any one other chapter, how these have changed the practices of NMOs and users of the framework and of mapping. All four have only proved feasible because of the huge increase in computer performance at constant prices – by about a factor of 10,000 since the launch of the first civilian remote sensing satellites in the early 1970s. The four elements considered are:

- global satellite positioning systems for surveying and for route guidance;
- remote sensing imagery, especially that derived from satellites;
- GIS;
- the Internet.

Many books are written about each of these four topics. Inevitably then, this chapter will simply be a brief summary of each technology and of its consequences for those involved in mapping and Geographic Information generally.

GLOBAL SATELLITE POSITIONING SYSTEMS

The principle of these systems is that, by calculating the distance between a point on the surface of the earth to at least three satellites, the location of that point in latitude, longitude, and height can be determined nearly instantaneously and to a very high accuracy – without the need for traditional instrumental surveying. The distances are derived from signals sent by each satellite and received by each survey receiver (Plate 3). The ability to observe satellites from anywhere on the earth at any time and, from them alone, produce highly accurate locations is a revolutionary concept: it changes the way in which survey has been carried out for two centuries or more. Instead of the control points being on the ground, they are in the sky – but the principles are the same. The traditional way of setting out fixed ground control points treated each as the vertex of one or more triangles, from each of which the angle to at least two others was measured, together with the length of at least one side of one triangle (often extending over many kilometres). From this network or web, the position of all control points was calculated in relation to all others and more detailed mapping of features (such as rivers and roads) was collected and positioned based upon this knowledge. Such fixed control points were often indicated by monuments (Plate 4). Satellite global positioning systems not only remove the need for so many control points in the field; in principle, they enable almost anyone – not just NMOs – to carry out survey and hence de-skill land surveyors of their traditional skills. In addition, the world-wide reference system on which they are founded provides a new harmonized basis for the framework. That such systems also engender some complications will become clear below.

Two satellite positioning systems exist at present, each initially funded primarily for military purposes but now available for universal civilian use. The American one is termed the Global Positioning System (GPS) and has been in use for solving geodetic problems since 1983 (Seeber 1994). It is based upon 24 satellites, including three active spares, all in orbit some 20,200 km above the earth. This is the *Space Segment*. At least four satellites are above the local horizon at any time of the day or night. To track the satellites and manage the system there are five stations spread around the globe. These are the *Control Segment*. The equivalent Russian system, Global'naya Navigatsionnaya Sputnikovaya Sistema (GLONASS) has the same number of satellites but slightly lower (19,100 km) orbits and an orbital period of 11 hours 15 minutes instead of the 12 hours for GPS. The fundamental difference between GPS and GLONASS is that all GPS satellites transmit on 1.575 MHz (L1) and 1.228 MHz (L2) whilst each GLONASS satellite has its own frequency in the range of 1.602–1.615 MHz and 1.246–1.256 MHz. This means that different receiver technology is required to receive signals from each system. Some manufacturers are now able to combine both receiver types on a single board, and combined receivers will soon be available (Shreenan and Becker 1996).

All GPS and GLONASS satellites have atomic clocks and the receivers also have clocks, so the journey time of the signal transmission between satellite and receiver can be measured. The speed of propagation of the signal is known, so the distance between satellite and receiver can be calculated. Without subsequent adjustment, however, there will be an inevitable error as the two clocks are not perfectly synchronized. Thus, because of this clock offset and the alterations to the speed of the signal as it passes through different layers of the atmosphere, the distances measured are not true ranges between satellite and receiver but are called *pseudo ranges*. Measuring the whole number of wavelengths and the fractional part of a wave between the satellite and receiver gives far better accuracy. These *carrier phase* observations can produce millimetric accuracies in both height and plan position whilst the pseudo-range positions provide accuracies of about a metre at best (see below).

By measuring the satellite orbits with respect to ground control points, information can be gained about the earth's shape, size, and gravitational field. Before the advent of satellites, this information was determined by astronomical observations of the stars and ground measurements over hundreds of kilometres. In the eighteenth and nineteenth centuries many attempts were made to obtain the earth's dimensions as the basis for topographical mapping, but the accuracies achieved were good locally, not globally. Partly as a consequence, there are now some 139 different local models of the shape and size of the earth used around the world. The World Geodetic System 1972 (WGS72) was designed as a single, consistent global system capable of being applied anywhere and everywhere. It was first used for the TRANSIT Doppler satellite system; its successor, WGS84, is designed for GPS. The differences between the two is small in comparison to the differences between a local system, such as Ordnance Survey 1936 (OSGB36) datum and either of the satellite systems. Large amounts of mapping and framework information are described in relation to these local systems. It is obvious therefore that one of the necessities of modern geodesy and surveying is to determine the relationship between the satellites' defining geodetic system and the local geodetic system used for mapping. From this knowledge – at least in theory – information in one system may be converted into the other.

Shortly before the Gulf War, in 1990, the United States as owner of the GPS (the Department of Defense) realized that users were able to refine positions to produce accuracies much better than a metre in a very short time. To prevent this being achieved by the opposing forces, they issued *Selective Availability* (S/A) which degrades the standard signal to civilian users. Consequently the *Standard Positioning Service* (SPS) is given as 100 m horizontal and 156 m vertical position with a 95 percent probability of being within this tolerance. GLONASS has no S/A and positioning accuracies of 30 m are commonplace. Such actions by the GPS owners undermined the case for relying on the system in the eyes of the users world-wide. One result was that the European Union formulated plans for a European system since its member states felt unable to rely on continuity of access to high-accuracy GPS in the long term. Many commercial vendors (including American businesses) also regarded S/A as impeding business opportunities. However, these barriers to wider use were recognized, and, in March 1996, the President of the USA issued a statement of policy, which is summarized below:

- the Standard Positioning Service will be freely available world-wide;
- the USA will discontinue Selective Availability (S/A) within a decade (with an annual review after 2000);
- GPS will continue to be run by the USA but in future this will be with input from international organizations;
- use of GPS will always be possible with commercially available products;
- there will be no denial of access except for reasons of national security or public safety;
- an interagency GPS Executive Board drawn form various federal government agencies will be set up.

Trade-offs between cost and accuracy and some surveying applications of GPS

Apart from the military, the initial users of GPS were physicists, geodesists, and other earth scientists. As receivers became cheaper (less than US$60,000), they came to be used in engineering applications (Calvert 1988), together with other terrestrial measurements.

With the appropriate equipment, skill, and knowledge, the accuracy in use of GPS is now extraordinary. The accuracies achieved in 1996 between terrestrial stations were better than 1 part per 10 million and accuracies in the order of 1 part per billion look possible. In 1996, the International GPS Service for Geodynamics (IGS) provided precise orbits, earth rotation parameters, and station co-ordinates which were routinely derived with the expectation of making the International Earth Rotation Service Terrestrial Reference Frame (ITRF) readily accessible (Beutler et al 1996). The use of these IGS products has enabled a greater consistency of results to be obtained with GPS than hitherto. All of these very high-accuracy results are derived with the use of post-mission processing using sophisticated software based upon many geophysical models, such as earth tides, tropospheric delay – and the number of electrons in the atmosphere!

At the other end of the accuracy scale from these extremely precise techniques for geodetic purposes is the hand-held, single-frequency receiver costing less than US$300. These deliver the standard positioning service accuracies of 100 m at the time of observation. Between these two extremes, however, are various intermediaries, including high-accuracy, continuous reference stations, with post-processing of the data and lower accuracy, stand-alone systems, producing immediate results.

Thus far, we have only described the calculation of the location of single points on the earth's surface. The alternative to such point positioning is differential GPS (dDGPS). This is a method whereby the detrimental effects of unknown signal path delay between satellite and receiver and clock offsets can be eliminated. The basic method is to have a continuously operating reference station which broadcasts its received GPS signal to the user's receiver, with the position of that receiver being computed instantaneously. Modifications to this basic system enable either longer ranges between reference and user receivers to be used or greater accuracy with post-processing.

A summary of the accuracies and methods of different ways of exploiting GPS is given in Table 10.1 below.

Kinematic GPS is a sub-set of differential GPS and has been used successfully for precision farming – the guidance of agricultural equipment and control of spraying for the optimum application of fertilizers on specific parts of a field, depending on soil type, drainage, salinity, topography, and so on. Structural monitoring of high buildings such as the Calgary Tower is now done with kinematic GPS and has demonstrated north–south motion of ±15 mm and an east–west movement of ±5 mm. Water-level profiling for tidal studies and the establishment of Chart Datums is another example of kinematic GPS use. An accurate geoid model is necessary for this work, and the studies in Canada by the Canadian Hydrographic Service have shown that adequate (less than 10 cm) accuracies for charting can be achieved.

Table 10.1 Best available accuracies from different GPS techniques (Cannon and Lachapelle 1996)

Mode	Accuracies achievable			
	0.01 m	0.10 m	1.0 m	10.0 m
Point Positioning (geodetic)			****	**
Differential (C/A code)			****	**
Differential (Carrier Phase)	****	****	**	

More generally, kinematic GPS is now being widely used by NMOs and by commercial map-makers alike. For instance, Sweden (Hedling and Jonsson 1996) has an Active GPS Network of continuously recording GPS receivers at reference stations. This is designed to provide single and dual frequency GPS data collection, dGPS, high-precision control, and integrity monitoring. This model is becoming commonplace for national surveys, either in support of NMOs' own activities or as a commercial service. Seeber et al (1996) have given an example of using kinematic GPS for photogrammetry in Lower Saxony, Germany: the differences between the perspective centres of the photographs determined by classical methods differ by about 5 cm from those determined in the air with GPS. The main problem seems to be between the strips of photography and along the edges of blocks of photography obtained at different times where accuracies fall to 20 cm. Warita and Nonomura describe elsewhere in this book the use made in Japan of 'fixed' GPS stations for monitoring earth movements.

More generally, there has been a development of Global Navigation Satellite Systems (GNSS) encompassing GPS, GLONASS, INMARSAT, and other complementary technologies. The objective of GNSS is to provide safe and precise navigation throughout the world on land, sea, and air. Fixing position is only one factor in the argument: reliability and integration with other complementary systems is necessary to achieve the objectives. The use of GPS for aircraft navigation has led to world-wide agreement that WGS84 (realized as the European Reference Frame – EUREF – in Europe) will be the common datum for all air navigation aids before the start of the new millennium.

There is no shortage of new applications being suggested for GPS. One potential vehicle navigation application is the Instant-Rent-a-Car (IRAC) concept (Chisholm 1996), whereby the position of a rented car can be determined at any time. Current experiments indicate accuracies of 30 m are possible using single frequency (i.e. cheap) GPS receivers. The concept enables a car to be picked up by anyone with a personal computer and a mobile phone. Authorization is gained using the mobile phone, the hirer is given the location of the nearest available car, the charges are calculated, and the location of the car's end-of-hire parking relayed to the central bureau. Inclusion of GPS technology in mobile telephones for use in calling breakdown assistance and emergency services is also being evaluated in the USA. At the other extreme, more than 20 spacecraft now have GPS receivers and 40 more will soon have them built in (Mitchell et al 1996).

Some problems to be resolved

The accuracy, ease, and low cost of use of global satellite positioning systems have led to a huge expansion in their use over the past five years. As shown above, many new applications are being devised almost daily. But a number of problems remain to be resolved, some of which will require considerable investments.

Much routine use of such systems relies on their being integrated with other systems or information. In the first instance, the relationship between WGS84 (World Geodetic System 1984) used by GPS and PZ-90 (Parameters of the Earth 1990) used by GLONASS have only just been derived (Rossbach et al 1996). More fundamentally, defining the relationship between these systems and other, previously employed geodetic data is still a current activity in many countries: as indicated earlier, this is a fundamental issue since information on existing maps is based on the latter. In practice, relating high-resolution GPS co-ordinates to existing information is often not a simple matter, though transformations built into many GPS receivers imply that the conversion is routine. Moreover, existing customers who have built sophisticated GIS and much of their business on the previously available, map-based frameworks may have real disincentives to convert all their data to a geocentric-based datum such as WGS84. Despite this, a number of NMOs – notably in Australia and the USA – have announced that they will convert all their mapping onto such a basis. The practical consequences of this may be that NMOs may have to maintain two different versions of their own national framework, with implications for consequent cost and complexity.

REMOTE SENSING IMAGERY, ESPECIALLY THAT DERIVED FROM SATELLITES

Images of the earth taken from the sky above have been widely used since at least the First World War. Until the late 1960s/early 1970s all these were collected as photographs, using light-sensitive emulsions and lenses in camera systems familiar at least in principle to the public. From the 1920s onwards, such aerial photography became a routine way of collecting information used for defining the geographical framework, though it still required many control points on earth to establish the correct geometry.

Stereoscopic use of such photographs, ensured by overlapping successive photographs simulating different eye positions, became the basis of much three-dimensional mapping and, in particular, the drawing of contour lines.

Observation of the whole earth or large sections of it first attracted public attention with the US Apollo space programme of the late 1960s and early 1970s. Even before this time American and Soviet military missions were active. Following the changed political situation at the end of the Cold War, some of the early US military images and technologies have been released. The history of the then secret CORONA programme and the images, based on the Keyhole series of photographic cameras, can be accessed at the EROS Data Centre World Wide Web site (http://edcwww.cr.usgs. gov/dclass/dclass.html).

Expense and continuing logistical difficulties with film recovery from space initially led the technologists to process the film on board and then scan and transmit the image back to earth before moving finally to develop digital image sensors. The data from weather and almost all other satellites are now collected, stored, and sent back to earth in digital form by telemetry. The image is composed of the amount of radiation (e.g. visible light) reflected or emitted by a small area of the earth's surface. The size of the area is represented by a pixel (a picture element) and defines the basic resolution or detail of the system (though several pixels are generally required to recognize any one 'real world' feature). The US NOAA sensors and European satellites have been particularly successful, delivering digital images on a regular production basis for meteorological purposes. One of the most successful has been the TIROS-N AVHRR Imager, providing 1 km resolution pixels and a 3000 km-wide image swath of the planet on a continuous basis. All of these systems have delivered hundreds of millions of images but none have been of sufficient spatial resolution to provide a suitable basis for mapping or for constructing and updating the geographical framework.

The first major step forward in routine, wide-area high-resolution imagery available to civilians came in July 1972 with the launch of ERTS (Earth Resources Technology Satellite) – later renamed Landsat-1. This supported two imaging systems, a RBV (return beam vidicon camera) and a multi-spectral scanner of 80 m ground resolution offering four imagery bands and a continuous digital image swath of 185 km. Despite this early automation of imaging, the advent of regular manned missions and higher image resolution film ensured that camera technology was still being pursued and eventually the Itek Large Format Camera (LFC) flew on a Shuttle mission in 1985, employing high-resolution panchromatic film yielding 8 m ground resolution. Sufficient frames were recorded, mostly for experimental purposes, to establish the value of such resolutions, though many of these scenes were cloud-covered, a continuing problem with imagery taken in the visible wavelengths. The LFC was followed by

Spacelab and the European Metric Camera experiment, but such photograph-ically based systems have largely been replaced by digital imaging systems where the radiometric discrimination can be precisely controlled and recorded in an entirely digital form. There are also clear benefits in recording data at source to optimize the value of the system by selecting precisely those segments of the electromagnetic spectrum required for specific purposes.

Landsat resolution improved considerably in 1982 when the Thematic Mapper instrument was included in the Landsat-4 mission. This is also a scanner but has seven spectral bands with all but one at 29 m resolution. European technology was also advancing fast in the early 1980s – the French and their partners were the first to position a civilian production 10 m digital sensor in space in 1986 with SPOT-1. Unlike Landsat, part of SPOT's design included a mapping capability. Indeed, SPOT-1 incorporated some major technical innovations such as two pointable sensors (HRV: High Resolution Visible) providing a stereo-imaging capability. The only disadvantage of this system is that a stereo pair cannot be acquired by a single pass over a point of interest on earth, consequently changes (in weather, crop maturity, and so on) caused by this temporal delay can adversely affect subsequent informa-tion extraction. SPOT is a 'pushbroom' imaging system: rather than being based on a single pixel scanning the terrain (as in the Landsat scanners), the entire array moves forward with the motion of the spacecraft. Hence geometry of SPOT is significantly superior to that of Landsat and similar systems. SPOT has an array of 6000 imaging sensors in the 10m panchro-matic mode and 3000 imaging sensors in the 20 m multi-spectral mode. In each case, the swath is a continuous 60 km wide path at nadir. This swath increases with off-nadir viewing (up to 27°) but this process also has disad-vantages – for example, the far side of mountains will not be observable where relief is significant.

In contrast to these digitally based developments in the Western world, a variety of photographic imaging systems were also developed and deployed by the former Soviet Union primarily as military initiatives. The KFA-1000 camera has provided 5 m ground resolution colour photography but the metric characteristics of the camera were poor. Progressive improve-ments in camera technology resolution have been achieved: Russia is now marketing photographic imagery and digitally scanned versions of it with 2 m ground resolution, each image covering 40 km by 40 km.

All of the systems summarized thus far have been passive ones; that is, they measure the solar radiation reflected from the earth or longer wave radiation emitted by it. Radar is very different in that such systems are 'active' in transmitting radiation and measuring the extent of the response from the earth or other 'reflectors'. A number of differing radar technolo-gies have been tested. The Space Shuttle has often been employed as a testbed but the most spectacular radar system was an independently launched satellite termed Seasat. Although this failed soon after its launch in 1978, it did provide sufficient stimulus to encourage follow-up systems with ERS-1 and 2 launched by ESA (European Space Agency) in July 1991 and April 1995 respectively. The ERS satellite hosts a cluster of imaging systems which are primarily aimed at observing the oceans, but land-based applications have been successfully demonstrated. Radarsat, a commercial radar satellite, was launched by Canada in late 1995. Radar has many theoretical attractions, particularly for those countries immersed in cloud cover for long periods. Although it affords day or night and all-weather capability, massive processing is necessary to extract good imagery, and there is evidence to show that atmospheric conditions can adversely affect the results of some processes: e.g. the generation of Digital Elevation Models or DEMs (grids of heights describing the land surface). As in other fields of remote sensing, separating what is required (for example, the ground surface, required by engineers) from what can be observed (for example , the vegetation canopy), is sometimes less than simple.

Relevance of past remote sensing to creation of the geographical framework

Given that less than half of the world has been mapped at 1:50,000 scale, that much of what exists is very out-of-date and that there are major discontinuities in mapping across national boundaries, there should be an obvious application for remote sensing which can cover large areas in a consistent and cost-effective way. Recently, some of those involved in the space imaging business have announced that they expect to put NMOs 'out of business'. In reality, the situation is much more complex than this – as we shall see.

Once the Thematic Mapper instrument had been deployed, a series of investigations into its cartographic potential were undertaken, notably in comparisons made with the USGS national map series. These generally concluded that meeting the US national map specifications for 1:50,000 map scale or smaller *was* possible but that there was more potential in map revision applications. The main limitation was seen as the 29 m pixel resolution and hence the difficulty in interpreting and extracting the required topographic detail (Welch et al 1985). Welch's study was based in the regular rural topography of Iowa and the more broken, but still very rural, Georgia. Quite different conclusions were reached elsewhere: for example, in Great Britain, Ordnance Survey concluded that Landsat had no economic role to play in enhancing or updating its 1:50,000 scale mapping. With the advent of SPOT, several mapping tasks were undertaken which benefited from reduced ground control requirements. One of the earliest – and at that time the largest civilian mapping projects to employ stereo space imagery – was the mapping by Ordnance Survey of 25,000 km^2 of North East Yemen at 1:100,000 scale (Murray and Farrow 1988). In an area with a highly suitable terrain of mountains and deserts, significant project savings were recorded (10 percent) against the budget which had been based on using aerial photography. This saving was primarily due to the fewer images and hence smaller volume of image processing overheads in the project (there was a 1:20 SPOT image: aerial image ratio). A similar cartographic contract was undertaken shortly afterwards by the French NMO in north-eastern Africa, around Djibouti, mostly at 1:50,000 scale, again using stereo SPOT imagery. The results confirmed a similar project saving over the use of aerial photography.

The early emphasis was on traditional cartographic mapping but more recently the major growth has been in the field of new products which are often not available from standard mapping. In particular, these have included products for use in GIS, such as orthophotography and DEMs which can exploit the possibilities of automation offered by digital image processing. The owners of SPOT have set up mechanisms to add value to the basic imagery through a firm called SPOT-Image (see Grelot chapter on the relationship between this and the NMO). In addition to SPOT-Image, new commercial companies such as ISTAR in France have emerged either as stand-alone entities or in partnership with mapping organizations. Products are increasingly tailored to meet a specific market or more commonly specific project needs, e.g. telecommunications planning models.

We can conclude that some progress therefore has been made over the quarter century since the launch of Landsat-1. Putting earth observation satellites into space, although expensive, is no longer the preserve of the old super-powers, Russia and the USA. Europe, through the European Space Agency (ESA), China, and others have been joined by India and Japan in leading earth observation technology. Valuable instruments have now been established in orbit, such as India's 6 m panchromatic sensor IRS-1C. The efficacy of satellite imagery is clear, particularly where the resolution of the existing mapping is either inadequate or mapping does not exist already. But in the more developed part of the world and in urban or peri-urban landscapes, the topographic density and complexity demands much better than 10 m resolution. As a commercial prospect, SPOT and similar satellites have helped to develop a market but have never yet been profitable even if all the launch and R&D costs have been written off by the countries concerned.

Simultaneously with these developments in space imaging has been a large growth and 'routinization' of the creation of images of the earth from which all distortions have been removed. These, termed digital orthophotos, have become highly popular especially in the USA, and are being sold by a multiplicity of firms using aerial survey – namely, cameras in aircraft. Juracek (1996) described the state of progress of the national Digital Orthophoto Quad programme in the USA, which has involved creating monochrome imagery of 1 m resolution in conjunction with the states.

Imagery has been acquired for some 80 percent of the conterminous USA (though some states claim they need colour photography) although much of the imagery has yet to be published in a digital form. The aerial photograph is scanned into computer form and rectified, then overlaid with some annotation such as road and place names. Plate 9 shows a typical example.

The next generation of imaging

The release of military technology into the civilian domain after the end of the Cold War has led to the creation of a number of commercial organizations in the imaging field with global out-reach and ambitions (Fritz 1996). Their aims are to create orthophoto-like and other products from space imagery and simultaneously acquire much of the air photography market and generate new business.

The most significant step forward for mapping and geospatial data gathering is the move forward to 3 m, 2 m, 1 m, and, in some cases, 0.8 m digital imaging resolution. Such higher-resolution imagery has a number of implications: it introduces direct competition with existing aerial photography systems for images at scales of c.1:20,000 and smaller, it encourages and supports the adoption of digital imagery, and finally, existing mapping products will be challenged. Plate 10 (a) to 10 (c) show simulations of what has been predicted will be available at 1 m resolution, as compared to 3 m and 10 m resolution; the size of each pixel in the 1 m resolution image has been set to emphasize the huge variation in what may be seen.

The realization of the full potential of these implications is, however, dependent on two equally important matters:

- successful implementation of the technology; and
- its economic success in the market place.

Little can yet be said about the likely economic success of the imagery, but most NMOs will have made their own assessments of the imagery, rather than simply accepting the claims of vendors. The Ordnance Survey assessment, employing simulated imagery, suggests that while it may be possible to *detect* features in the imagery, precise *interpretation* and accurate *locational positioning* are severely limited for the core mapping activities. The limitation of the 1 m pixel compared with a 0.2 m pixel normally used in equivalent aerial photography surveys is the primary reason for this.

In mapping road and other networks, where centre-line geometry is required, positional accuracy requirements can be less demanding and unless the object is obscured by vegetation its location can usually be identified. However, other features vital to the provision of a high-resolution mapping framework, such as buildings, land, and property boundary features (hedges, fences, walls, and so on), public pavements, highway ornament (gantries, signs, and suchlike), cannot be correctly and routinely interpreted with a 1 m pixel at the larger survey scales (e.g. 1:1,250 and 1:2,500).

It has been claimed that 1:2,400 scale mapping is possible from space with a 1 m sensor. Such a mapping scale usually has a positional accuracy requirement in the order of ±0.8–1.0 m (relative to the local survey control network). With aerial photography this normally demands digital images of 0.1–0.2 m resolution to meet that level of positional accuracy. This relationship, of image to map scale, is a key issue (Doyle 1982), and it would be more realistic to assume that mapping scales in the order of 1:5000–1:15,000 will be possible from 1 m space imagery. Even then topographic detail, such as the full depiction of buildings, would not be possible and some generalization would be necessary.

One potential technical barrier to widespread use of this imagery is the very large volumes of file space it requires. By way of example, a detailed Ordnance Survey vector map compiled at 1:2500 scale and, in effect having a resolution of about 0.1 m, typically occupies about 0.25 Mb. Some reduction in this could be obtained by various data compaction techniques. A 1 m resolution satellite image of the same area would occupy in raw, 11 bit encoded form some 1.5 Mb, i.e. approximately six times the storage space. Even after file compaction of the image, it is likely to occupy some two to three times the storage of a standard vector map but is less suitable for further processing. Compression techniques are increasingly successful but some loss of content is inevitable if high compression ratios are employed on aerial or space images. This is because 'photographs' are continuous tone compared with, say, a raster version of a map, which may be represented by a small number of colours. In Britain – a relatively small country – there are some 150,000 large-scale vector map tiles (and 67,000 more detailed ones). Such problems of processing power and storage space have always been overcome in the past so it is wise to accept they will be so in the future, but this probably indicates that acceptance of such imagery will not be instantaneous except for small area projects.

The essence of most remote sensing to date has been that updating is achieved by collecting an entirely new image of the same area. In contrast, updating the framework in many of the more advanced countries has been by editing the database representation of only those features which change in the real world; data collection systems and local intelligence (e.g. through planning systems) have ensured that this is a highly economical way to proceed. Rates of change of the features in the framework database seem to vary somewhat but are rarely greater than 1 or 2 percent per annum – yet detecting these important changes is vital. This implies that simply collecting repeated new images is of little value unless change can be automatically extracted and stored. This is still very much a research matter but some successes are being achieved, both in change detection and in innovative new processes to create new products and services such as urban 3-D modelling (see Haala and Anders 1996), largely by automated means.

National security and sensitivity issues are raised by the general availability of high-resolution images. In practice, the US government controls the availability of imagery through licensing of the commercial firms involved but this is only applicable for US-based data collecting organizations (and other governments may well be less than delighted because access to information about their territories is controlled by the USA). But the proposed 1 to 3 m imagery still lags behind estimates of the technology currently being planned or operated by various military bodies; for example, 0.3 m in the US, 1 m in Israel, and France has recently deployed Helios-1 at around 1–2 m resolution. On the other hand, some military agencies are also proposing to procure imagery from the commercial dealers, which appears to confirm that civilian and military requirements are increasingly overlapping as budgets are universally reduced.

Table 10.2 sets out the different characteristics, especially the spatial and temporal ones, of the main satellite imaging systems launched thus far and those predicted at the time of writing (early 1997). The selection has been made largely on the grounds of their relevance to creating and maintaining an up-to-date geographical framework. Clearly, the value of these systems will vary considerably in different parts of the world. In highly developed European nations, the value has been modest thus far, but in unmapped areas in some parts of Asia and Latin America their value may be much greater.

In addition to these systems operating in the visible wavebands, radar systems – although more complex – also hold significant advantages as described earlier. It seems likely that these too will make a major contribution to the framework but over a longer time perspective and so are not considered further here.

Extracting added value

Images, particularly multi-spectral images and stereo pairs, contain vast stores of information. The raw image can be processed to provide land cover information, determine the type and health of crops, analyse the environment and other specialist applications and needs. Much of this information can be limited in value unless it can be combined with another data set(s), in particular some form of reference or framework data such as land parcel boundary extents (within which a crop is grown), the courses of highways and water networks and their attributes (names, classifications, usage, and so on).

The combination of different data sets is achieved by use of geographical information systems (GIS), described in the next section. It is worth noting here, though, that growth in the capacity of personal computers, allied to the use of networking for information dissemination (see last section), is likely to transform the extraction of added value from imagery and hence multiply its uses and its financial value.

Table 10.2 Imaging sensors and their relevance to NMOs

Satellite	Operational	Stereo capability	Spatial resolution	Image extent (km)	Temporal resolution	Relevance to mapping
Landsat 4-5	1984 on	No	29 m	185 (sq.)	16 day repeat	Limited to small-scale and simple topographic areas
KFA-1000	1974 on	Yes	5–7 m	80 (sq.)	Mission	1:25,000 scale mapping; height accuracy weak
KVR-1000	1984 on	Yes	2 m	40 × 160	Mission	1:10,000 and smaller-scale mapping
SPOT 1-3 (SPOT-3 failed in late 1996)	1986 on	Yes	10 m	60 (sq.)	16 day repeat	Proven capability for image maps and line mapping in favourable terrain at 1:50,000 and smaller
IRS-1C	1995	Yes (cross track)	5.8 m	70 (sq.)	24 day repeat	Possibly 1:25,000 and smaller-scale mapping
CRSS (Space Imaging)	Q4 1997	Yes	1 m	11 (sq.)	1–3 day revisit	Medium scale 1:10,000 and smaller?
Orbview 1	Q? 1997	Yes	1 m	8 (sq.)	< 3 day revisit	Medium scale 1:10,000 and smaller?
Earlybird	1996 (delayed) Q2 1997	Yes	3 m	6 (sq.)	2–3 day revisit	Small scale 1:25,000 and smaller?
Quickbird	Q? 1997	Yes	1 m	30 (sq.)	2–3 day revisit	Medium scale 1:10,000 and smaller?

GEOGRAPHICAL INFORMATION SYSTEMS (GIS)

In the 1970s, handling geographical or geospatial data was something done by researchers. Today it is almost routine and tools for doing it are being included in many widely used computer packages. The revolution which has occurred in these two decades has come about because of the development of relatively low-cost and relatively easy-to-use geographical information systems (GIS). Much has been written on these systems (see, for instance, Longley, Goodchild, Maguire, and Rhind 1997), so only a brief description will be given here.

The term 'GIS' is now used to include almost all software for handling geographical or geospatial data, ranging from simple mapping on a desktop PC, through research tools for analysis of complexes of environmental data sets to the largest systems for managing utility assets worth billions of dollars. It is therefore difficult to define a GIS to universal satisfaction, not least because the range of applications has expanded so dramatically over recent years. In the Introduction (page 4), the following list of questions was cited as being capable of being answered by maps:

- What is at position X on the earth's surface?
- Where can we find features of type Y?
- How do I get from point A to point B? (or what is the most efficient way to travel to a number of different places? or where should I locate my shop in relation to my customers?)
- What geographical pattern (if any) is formed by features of type ...?
- How has the geography changed between X years ago and now?
- How can I hide my forces and their movements from my enemies?
- What will happen if I change the geography? (e.g. by building a new road)

In reality, of course, answering these questions is only possible with good framework and other data plus an effective GIS. There are two particular characteristics of GIS that enable them to provide answers to the type of questions listed. The first is the ability to apply spatial operators to the data. An example of this would be to retrieve all crimes of a given type within a local government area (as compared, say, with a police authority area). Another example is to ask for a map of all the destinations that can be reached by driving for an hour from the Channel Tunnel detraining point. In essence, both of these amount to applying a 'cookie cutter' to a seamless map and scissoring out, then tabulating, all the information of interest. The second characteristic is the ability to link data sets together; this is an essential feature because data are collected by different organizations and tailored to their own particular purposes without regard to other potential uses. As was also indicated in the Introduction to this book, there are several ways of adding value through linking data but the added value may well be much greater than the original value of the data sets considered singly.

The important point is that GIS can perform all these operations because they use geography or space as the only common key between the data sets (the relevant parts of the two sets of information are linked together where they relate to the same space). With this capability, we can add value: from 20 data sets covering the same region, we can produce 190 pairs of data sets and over a million possible combinations in total. Although many of these will be valueless, the range of applications is inevitably much greater than with the original 20 data sets alone. If all this appears simple, it rarely is in practice: the volumes of data involved, the 'fuzziness' of many geographical data, the choice of methods available that can give different results, and the need to do all this economically and to meet (usually tight) deadlines renders the practice of GIS much more complex than the principles. The great advantage, however, is that the same tools can be used – even if they are sometimes combined, Lego-like, in different ways – in all countries and for a variety of applications that range from the micro scale in dealing with individual houses or streets to the global scale.

It follows from this that value adding is potentially a very significant factor in the Geographical Information 'industry. Who carries it out is as yet unclear. In principle, it may be the end-user, the 'raw data' suppliers, or some intermediaries. Where NMOs are expected to generate revenues (see, for instance, chapters by Robertson and Gartner, Sandgren and Rhind in this book), the ability to add value is of great importance and thus requires these organizations to become expert in GIS, in other data sets, and in the theory and practice of data integration, as well as in their own data.

GIS as a business

From the creation of the first true GIS in Canada in the 1960s, through the launch of the first sophisticated commercial system in the early 1980s, up to the present situation where there are hundreds of software packages but only four or five main suppliers (mostly American), this has become a major international business.

A recent American study (Frost and Sullivan 1996) suggested that major changes in the GIS market place included a switch from expensive UNIX workstations to powerful PC computers, a move towards greater interoperability (see chapter by Salgé) and wider use because of the lower price of systems, including the incorporation of selected GIS capabilities in office software. The same study argued that the size of the European market for GIS hardware, software, and services was US$270 million in 1992 and that this had grown to $430 million three years later. Over half of total GIS revenue arises, according to Frost and Sullivan, from sales of GIS software, with the rest coming from services of various kinds (notably consulting, systems integration, and data). Of these 1995 revenues, some $22 million was said to arise from the data acquisition and conversion (DAC) market place.

These figures demonstrate the importance and growth of the GIS market. The same sort of trends are now seen elsewhere in the world: though early growth was concentrated in the United States, most US vendors of software now make more revenue outside of that country than within it. But these figures are also questionable in at least one respect: they vastly under-state the expenditure on data collection. For example, the annual revenues of Ordnance Survey from selling or leasing data and selling paper maps of Britain alone in 1995 was larger by a factor of five than the Frost and Sullivan figures[1] for DAC for all of Europe! Indeed, the annual gross public sector expenditure on creating or maintaining the framework in the European Union alone cannot be less than about $1 billion. There is no good evidence on which to estimate comparable figures world-wide, but the total cannot be less than $3 billion per annum and may well be twice or three times as large. These figures have been largely unchanged for many years; indeed, they may be smaller now than hitherto because of reforms of government which are detailed in the chapters by Robertson and Gartner, O'Donnell and Penton, Jakobsen, and others later in this book. The difference is that much wider use is now being made of the resulting data because of the ready availability of GIS technology.

THE INTERNET

The Internet is probably the most rapidly expanding technology – ever. From its origins as a fault-tolerant network for US and NATO military purposes in the 1960s, the Internet is now one of the foundations of the 'Information Superhighway' – or at least it is an indication of its potential (some commentators consider present technology to be closer to an 'information superfootpath'). In this section of the chapter, we briefly look at the state of Internet today and forecast how it may impinge on Geographic Information provision in the future, especially in relation to the geographic framework.

The Internet comprises a network of computer networks which communicate with one another using a simple set of standards. Packets of digital data are passed between systems in such a way that each message can be handled without any central control. 'Name servers' know where to route data, and, as the name services are multiple, a message is almost guaranteed to get through. This redundancy forms the basis of the fault tolerance for military use; there is no central hub equivalent to a telephone exchange whose destruction would jeopardize the whole network. The Internet itself is simply a means of providing communications; it is the services which exist on that network that provide users with functionality. Equally, there is no reason why the Internet technology cannot exist in a closed form for a particular organization (then called an Intranet).

From its military beginnings, civilian use of the Internet commenced with academic networks. But until the late 1980s, the only services widely used were electronic mail (e-mail) and messaging, remote log-in to distant machines (TELNET), and file transfer (FTP). The real explosion in public interest in the Internet came with the development of the World Wide Web (WWW) by scientists at the European nuclear research facility at CERN in the early 1990s. On top of the network of the Internet, the WWW provides even users with no specialist knowledge access to information sources world-wide very quickly. Two complementary concepts made this possible. First, there was acceptance of remote users being able to contact computers anywhere using the Internet. This concept of free access came about because of the academic beginnings, but none the less represents a radical change in regard to attitudes to computer use in many organizations where such facilities were previously closed to the outside world. In part this was

Plate 1 Maps produced in the range of 1:200,000 to 1:250,000 scale by different National Mapping Organizations

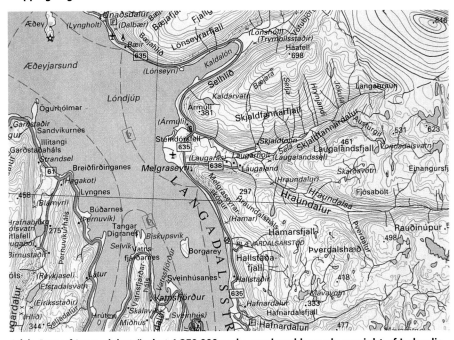

1 (a) Part of Langadalsströnd at 1:250,000 scale, produced by and copyright of Icelandic Geodetic Survey

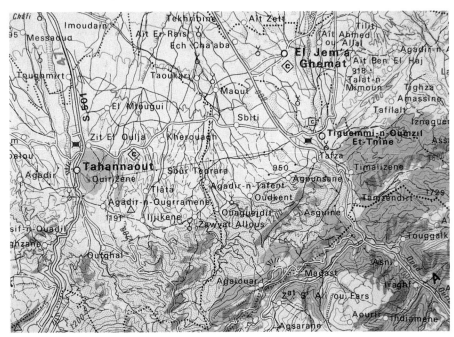

1 (b) Part of Marrakech at 1:250,000 scale, produced by and copyright of Division de la Cartographie, DCFTT

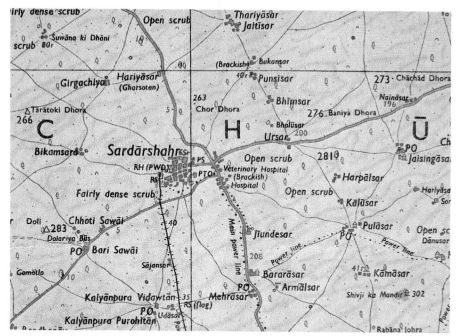

1 (c) Part of Rajasthan at 1:250,000 scale, produced by Surveyor General of India and copyright of the Government of India, 1974

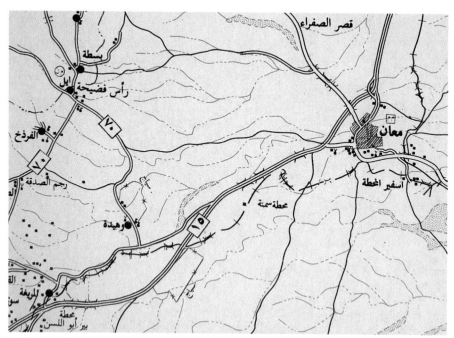

1 (d) Part of Jordan at 1:250,000 scale, produced by the Royal Jordanian Geographic Centre and copyright of the Royal Jordanian Government

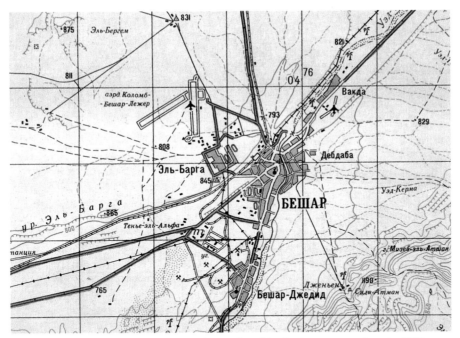

1 (e)   Becher in Algeria at 1:200,000 scale, produced by Soviet cartographers in 1987

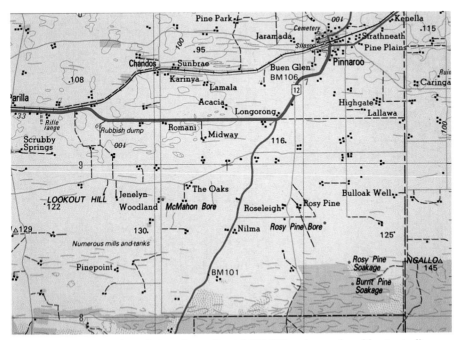

1 (f)   Pinnaroo area of South East Australia at 1:250,000 scale, produced by Australian Survey and Land Information Group (AUSLIG) and copyright of the Commonwealth of Australia 1983

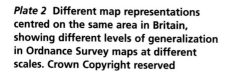

Plate 2 Different map representations centred on the same area in Britain, showing different levels of generalization in Ordnance Survey maps at different scales. Crown Copyright reserved

2 (a) (*Right*) Land-line data plotted at 1:1250 scale, showing house names, property seeds, pavements, road centre lines, etc

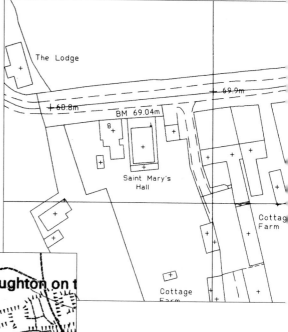

2 (b) (*Left*) Landplan map plotted on customer request from generalized Landline data at 1:10,000 scale

2 (c) (*Right*) Meridian data assembled from different sources and plotted at 1:25,000 scale showing selected features only in a highly generalized fashion

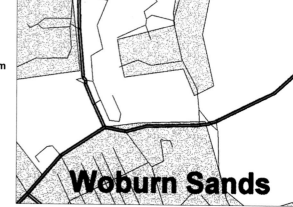

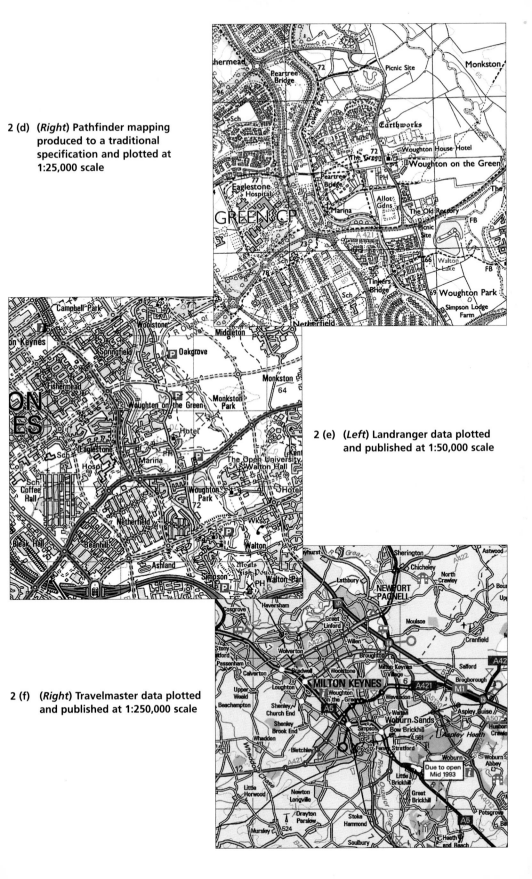

2 (d) (*Right*) Pathfinder mapping produced to a traditional specification and plotted at 1:25,000 scale

2 (e) (*Left*) Landranger data plotted and published at 1:50,000 scale

2 (f) (*Right*) Travelmaster data plotted and published at 1:250,000 scale

Plate 3 Geodetic-quality Global
Positioning System receiver as of 1996

Plate 4 Typical monumented survey
control point in Malawi before the
advent of the Global Positioning System
(courtesy Ordnance Survey)

Plate 5 **A typical Global Positioning System permanent receiving station** (courtesy Japanese Geographical Survey Institute)

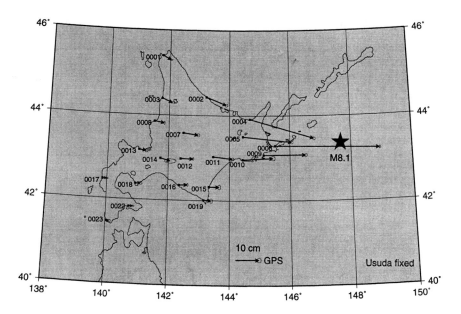

Plate 6 The horizontal components of the displacement vectors after the 1994 Hokkaido-Toho-Oki earthquake, as monitored by the GRAPES system of the Japanese Geographical Survey Institute

(courtesy Japanese Geographical Survey Institute)

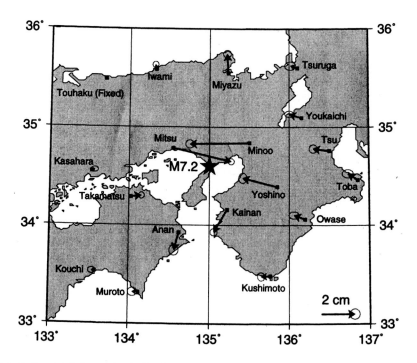

Plate 7 Crustal deformation following the 1995 Hyogo-ken Nanbu earthquake in the densely-populated Kobe area, as immediately detected by GRAPES

(courtesy Japanese Geographical Survey Institute)

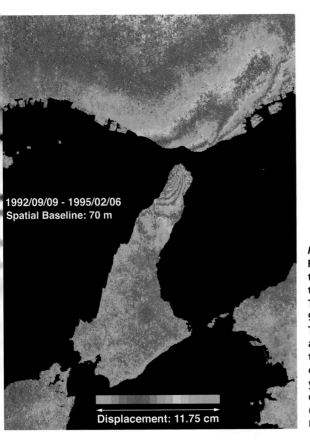

1992/09/09 - 1995/02/06
Spatial Baseline: 70 m

Displacement: 11.75 cm

Plate 8 The result of Synthetic Aperture Radar (SAR) interferometry which reveals the crustal deformation associated with the 1995 Hyogo-ken Nanbu earthquake. The SAR data used were acquired on 9 September 1992 and 6 February 1995. The fringes in the figure indicate the amount of displacement of each spot in the direction towards the satellite. A full cycle of colour change (blue-purple-yellow-green-blue) corresponds to a displacement of 11.8 cm
(courtesy Japanese Geographical Survey Institute)

Plate 9 1 km square extract of a USGS Digital Orthophoto Quadrangle image made up of 1 m pixel resolution data for DeKalb County, Georgia
(courtesy US Geological Survey 1995)

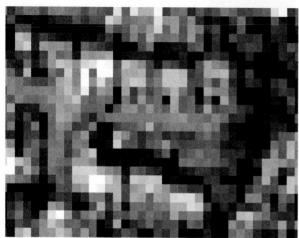

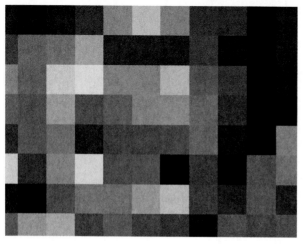

Plate 10 Simulations of high (1 metre) resolution imagery (*10a: top*) with other of the same area shown at 3 metres (*10b: centre*) and 10 metres (*10c: left*) resolution. The views are all shown at a large scale to demonstrate the differences

Plate 11 Sample Census collector map produced under the Australian PSMA/ICSM initiative to create a 'first pass framework' showing combination of cadastral and topographic data

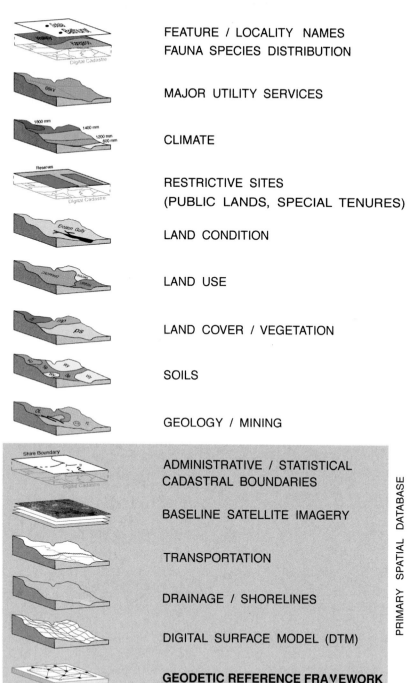

FEATURE / LOCALITY NAMES
FAUNA SPECIES DISTRIBUTION

MAJOR UTILITY SERVICES

CLIMATE

RESTRICTIVE SITES
(PUBLIC LANDS, SPECIAL TENURES)

LAND CONDITION

LAND USE

LAND COVER / VEGETATION

SOILS

GEOLOGY / MINING

ADMINISTRATIVE / STATISTICAL
CADASTRAL BOUNDARIES

BASELINE SATELLITE IMAGERY

TRANSPORTATION

DRAINAGE / SHORELINES

DIGITAL SURFACE MODEL (DTM)

GEODETIC REFERENCE FRAMEWORK

PRIMARY SPATIAL DATABASE

Plate 12 New South Wales Natural Resources Inventory and the Primary Spatial
Database

made possible by the sharp reduction in cost of computer hardware at the time power increased multifold. Secondly, there came about recognition of the power of hypermedia in which the traditional sequential reading of text, viewing of a video, or listening to sounds could be indexed and cross-referenced to add a new dimension to information sources. In the hypermedia context, simple text files can reference other text, pictures, video, or sounds which can in turn reference other sources and so on. It is a simple concept (and simple to implement), already used, for example on CD-ROM information sources. The power of the WWW comes from linking hypermedia to world-wide information banks. Data sources can be on any computer connected to Internet, anywhere. This is a striking example of how to add value by bringing data sets together.

Figure 10.1 shows the explosive growth of the use of the WWW site of the US NMO, the US Geological Survey's National Mapping Division (USGS NMD). Its use has gone up about fivefold in two years judged by the number of accesses and about fourfold judged by the volume of data transferred to users. All this reflects the fact that the new technologies make the process of networking, long a 'black art' of computer management, as simple as ordering a pizza – with the result that for a thousand pounds (or dollars) for a personal computer and a few pounds per month anyone with a telephone connection in a majority of countries now has access to vast resources of information. Figure 10.2 shows that this is not restricted to the United States: the number of countries from which accesses over the Internet of the USGS NMD WWW server has doubled in the same two-year period. Equally, within organizations there is increasing realization of the power of closed Internet-like communications facilities capable of transmitting organizational data in an Intranet.

However, this power and flexibility are in their early stages. Computers are still not powerful enough and there are too many bottlenecks caused by lack of communications bandwidth in the uncontrolled connections between networks. Because of its nature, Internet growth cannot be planned; it happens. Also, because the owners of the various nodes in the networks pay for their own systems (normally by renting out a service to other end-users in some way), there can be no planned overall funding. But the growth of major service providers and new technologies means that funding is now being addressed in very practical ways. Communications are also improving, and by 2000 world-wide communications as well as local (often the main constraint is in the final connection to the user from the telephone exchange) should be much improved; whether the long waits often experienced to obtain information across the Internet will be shorter will depend on whether the communications improve faster than the growth of demand. There are many complementary technologies, such as 'video on demand', cable television, high-capacity twisted wire connections, all contributing to provide the infrastructure – and the demand and revenues – which will make the true information superhighway happen.

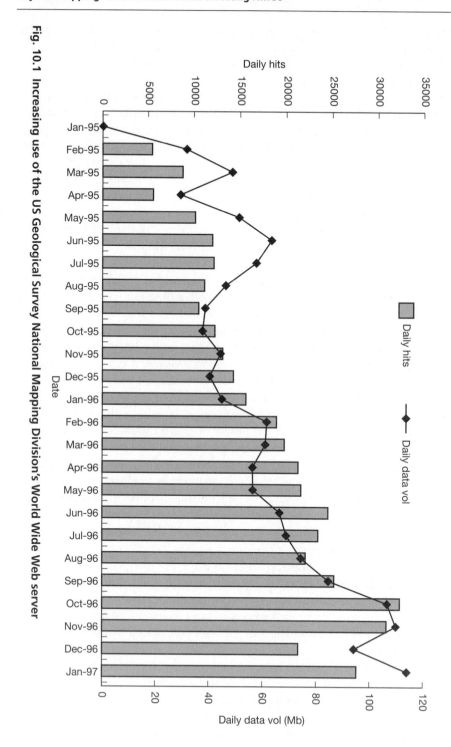

Fig. 10.1 Increasing use of the US Geological Survey National Mapping Division's World Wide Web server

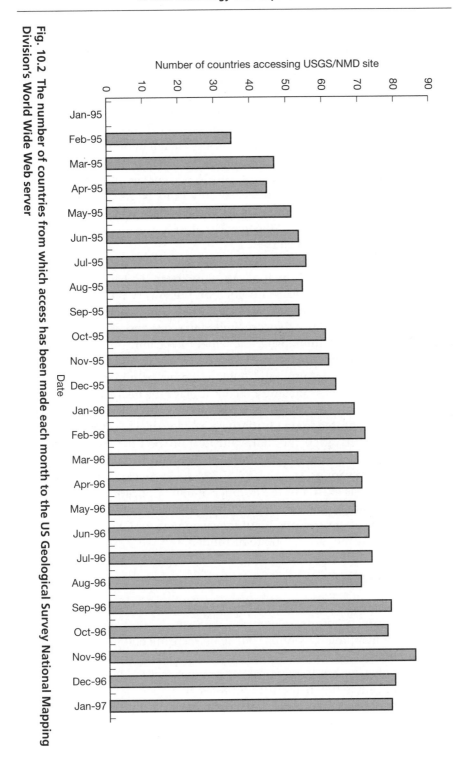

Fig. 10.2 The number of countries from which access has been made each month to the US Geological Survey National Mapping Division's World Wide Web server

To some degree, the Internet has not yet become core to the GIS community except in the USA: it has been claimed that there is little evidence yet of realizing full exploitation[2] other than by academics. However, the vision of GIS as an integrating technology probably can only be realized if the Internet does prove to be successful. Figure 10.3 shows that this wider use of the Internet seems to have occurred in the USA, at least so far as the NMO is concerned: commercial users (including individuals accessing the server via on-line services like Compuserve) make up to 60 percent of all accesses whose sources are identifiable of the USGS/NMD WWW server. The US government uses between 10 and 20 percent, about half of which is internal use within USGS; military use is only 1 or 2 percent – similar to that of not-for-profit organizations, whilst the educational community as a whole makes between 20 and 30 percent of all accesses, all measured on the basis of volume of data transferred.

The types of Geographic Information accessible over the Web extend far beyond that made available by the NMOs. By the mid-1990s, the first real if simple applications for GIS technology on the WWW had emerged, but these are based upon unsophisticated, often crude cartography and – because of the technology – they are limited in scope and elegance of result. None the less, it is an immense achievement to be able, for free and from anywhere in the world, to give any address in the USA and be able to determine the nearest VISA Automatic Teller Machine[3] or, given an Australian address, to find out near instantly the location of the nearest plumber. [4] In both cases, maps can be created on-screen. But we are still a long way from a vision of integrated data. Initiatives are localized, often related to publicity, which is often the main purpose of the relevant service. We cannot as yet determine the locations of ATMs in Britain, and a native Japanese speaker cannot use the USA VISA service in his own language or script. Many ideas exist, but the number of real applications is small and the level of service is still low. In part this is because of the technology, and in part because of uncertainty about the customers for GIS services on the Internet and how the services are to be funded.

Internet problems

Equally, one can already download from some sites, such as that of the US Geological Survey, [5] digital geographic data which allow the user to tailor his/her own mapping if required. But again there are both unresolved technical and marketing issues. Digital map data are large in volume but the average home user has to rely on a service that would allow transfer of a typical 1 megabyte file in about 15 minutes on a good day (if done before the majority of users in the USA wake up; more typically, transferring 1 MB might take 30 minutes or more). Although the data from organizations such as USGS may be free, there is a break-even point where a user might prefer to order a CD-ROM to arrive by post the following day. In practice, it would

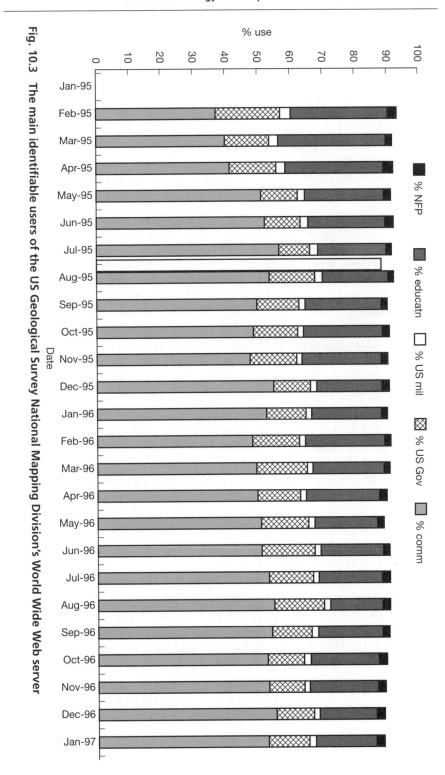

Fig. 10.3 The main identifiable users of the US Geological Survey National Mapping Division's World Wide Web server

take several weeks to transfer the whole contents of a CD-ROM (600 MB) over a telephone line This effectively rules out use of the Internet for mass market data supply at present to the home or small office. But sophisticated services – those already available to some organizations – can transfer megabytes in seconds. These show how GIS and the Internet can work together. As already mentioned, by the end of the century the bandwidth problem should have disappeared and transmission speeds over present internal networks (>20 megabits/second) will be available to all telephone users. If customers are going to take such on-line access for granted (and the evidence is that this is already happening in some communities), NMOs have to plan to provide much, if not all, of their data on-line in some form or other in the next few years.

But there are other problems. Simply locating geographical data is difficult. This is partly due to the nature of the search engines currently available. Whilst it is possible to use WWW searching software (such as Alta Vista, Excite or Yahoo!) to identify text strings or key words with remarkable speed, Geographical Information requires more complex, 'fuzzy' searches other than where place names are used. It is at present not even easy to identify the source of any of data required in other than a few countries. Metadata services that contain data about data (e.g. the SINES service run by OS on behalf of the Department of the Environment in the UK or GDDD run by MEGRIN on behalf of the European National Mapping Agencies) are relatively rare outside the USA and are in a very simple form at present. At best they can give a pointer to where the data required might be held and whether they are publicly available. Fortunately, the more fundamental problems of dealing intelligently with Geographical Information in an electronic, on-line library are now being addressed through systems such as KINDS (Knowledge based Information about National Data Sets) based on the MIDAS service at the University of Manchester, the Alexandria Digital Library Project of the US National Center for Geographic Information and Analysis, or the ESMI (European Spatial Metadata Infrastructure) project being funded by the European Union INFO 2000 programme.

At the time of writing (early 1997), there are few services for ordering or delivering data are available outside the USA because of the lack of suitable ordering, payment, and delivery systems (though there are many predictions that the situation will change rapidly). The issues related to data copyright, ownership, liability and so on are extremely complicated and are made more so by the nature of the Internet: by its very nature, the Internet is designed to pass information easily. Ensuring that data are only used by those who have paid for them (the excludability criterion), quite apart from the issues of secure payment on the Internet, presents substantial intellectual, technical, and legal challenges – especially when international trading is taking place.

Looking ahead

Looking beyond the model of data delivery, the whole architecture of GIS is being changed by the technological capabilities of the Internet. Instead of monolithic, stand-alone GIS systems (operating alongside somewhat more integrated databases, spreadsheets, word processors, and so on) there is an increasing trend towards smaller client GIS that will undertake more limited but more targeted tasks for users. Desktop GIS have existed for some years but these may well be superseded by Internet 'browser' packages which will function as a primitive word processor and document publisher as well as a GIS (which may include database access). Such browsers are becoming more powerful almost daily, often fuelled by new elements that are themselves loaded by means of the Internet. New languages such as JAVA allow data and programmes to manipulate the data to be combined.

Enthusiasts for the Internet forecast an explosion of use of GIS by end-users who have no need to learn the 'tricks' of GIS, such as topological modelling and symbol placement on maps; those can now be concealed. To that extent, the use of Geographical Information and maps is being de-skilled by use of the new GIS and the Internet. And this is being done at ever-decreasing cost: the marginal cost of adding users to Intranet systems can be a few tens of pounds compared to the seat licence costs of traditional GIS.

The future, therefore, is one in which data become more and more commodities, but will not be sold or transferred in bulk. If present predictions come to fruition, data will be accessed as required by end-users running a spectrum of types of GIS from simple to complex and who (in many countries) will pay for the data as they use them. These users will use intelligent systems to locate, using terminology familiar to them (rather than that imposed by standard database descriptions), data appropriate to their needs. They need not store and have to manage the data themselves. Just as important, they will be able to use the latest version of the data (or the latest edition of a historical version). The implications for NMOs acting as custodians or owners of the geographical framework are clear. They must achieve the flexibility to provide data on the Internet to satisfy customer needs. In some cases, this will reduce costs as delivery mechanisms are or will be in place. However, they will find that, instead of having local quasi-monopolies, they may have to compete with international organizations for customers. Some data, particularly at small scales or low resolution, will be created beyond national boundaries and jurisdictions. So NMOs will have to compete on quality and service. With the ease of overlaying or integrating data, any limitations of accuracy, timeliness, or efficiency will be apparent to all. At the same time, NMOs will discover that the market is not just local; world-wide customers will exist. That too will bring both problems and opportunities.

IMPLICATIONS FOR NATIONAL MAPPING AGENCIES

The implications for national mapping agencies of GPS, high-resolution space imagery, new GIS, and the Internet are apparent in many forms. There is a change in emphasis from the traditional geodesy and map-making to data provision and exploitation. We have already seen the emergence of a parallel industry based around 'GIS solutions' providing data or systems tailored to meet clients' requirements. The NMOs can no longer claim to be the sole experts in geographical positioning when the public are able to locate themselves to a precision equivalent to precise geodesy of a few years ago. We see the redundancy of traditional networks of triangulation pillars that were created at enormous cost and effort: constant monitoring of foreign satellite systems provides the national geodetic frameworks. We see the provision of imagery that might replace or supplement mapping in near-real time. We already see maps being created to specifications of individual users by GIS, possibly drawing data from across the world.

In these circumstances, there has to be a change in the role and thinking of NMOs. To continue to play a valuable role, they need to mutate from being the experts in high-quality cartography and geodesy to being data integrators and exploiters, certification agencies, reconciliation authorities, and the like. As is argued elsewhere in this book, the traditional work of data capturing and cartography may increasingly be carried out by contractors or close to the customer. Competition, particularly in smaller, derived scale mapping, will increase as new sensors or competitive mapping becomes more commonplace. Products themselves will change, reflecting new forms of data capture and new technologies such as hypermedia to present the information.

Technology will drive much of this change – but will not control all developments. Existing use of data by customers, the necessary financial investments and national legislation will all play key roles in ensuring what use society is able to make of the new tools. These factors, plus leadership of the NMOs and other organizations, will decide whether the framework for the world is completed, maintained, and evolves into new but valuable forms as new technologies now permit.

NOTES

1. The only National Mapping Agency cited in the Frost and Sullivan 1996 European report is the Swedish one.
2. For a technical description of existing GIS services, see *Developing Geographic Services on the World Wide Web*, by Anthony P. Steinke and Paul Bristow, Charles Sturt University, P O Box 789, Albury, NSW 2640, Australia asteinke@csu.edu.au, http://life.cse.edu.au/~asteinke pbristow@csu/edu/au, http://www.csu.edu.au/phonebook/pbristow.html
3. http://www.visa.com

4. http://www.whitepages.co.au
5. http://www.usgs.gov

REFERENCES

Beutler G, Mueller II, Neilan R 1996 The International GPS Service for Geodynamics (IGS): The story. In Beutler G, Hein GW, Melbourne WG, Seeber G (eds) *GPS trends in precise terrestrial, airborne, and spaceborne applications*. Berlin, International Union of Geodesy and Geophysics. Springer: 3–13

Calvert CE 1988 GPS and the Channel Tunnel. *Survey Review* 30: 3–13

Cannon ME, Lachapelle G 1996 Kinematic GPS trends – equipment, methodologies and applications. In Beutler G, Hein GW, Melbourne WG, Seeber G (eds) *GPS trends in precise terrestrial, airborne, and spaceborne applications*. Berlin, International Union of Geodesy and Geophysics, Springer: 161–9

Chisholm J 1996, Cars of convenience: instant-rent-a-car. *GPS World* 7 (4): 46–54

Doyle FJ 1982 Satellite systems for cartograph. *International Archives of Photogrammetry and Remote Sensing* 24 (1): 180–5

Doyle FJ 1996 Thirty years of mapping from space. *International Archives of Photogrammetry and Remote Sensing* XXXI-B4: 222–30

Fritz LW (1996) Commercial earth observation satellites. *International Archives of Photogrammetry and Remote Sensing* XXXI-B4: 273–82

Frost and Sullivan 1996 *European Geographical Information Systems market*. Mountain View, CA, Frost and Sullivan

Haala N, Anders K-H 1996 Fusion of 2D GIS and image data for 3D building reconstruction. *International Archives of Photogrammetry and Remote Sensing* XXXI-B3: 285–90

Hedling G, Jonsson B 1996 New developments in the SWEPOS Network Paper presented at Institute of Navigation ION 96 Conference, 18–20 September 1996

Juracek KE 1996 US Geological Survey's role in state GIS. *Geo Information Systems* 6 (7): 36–40

Longley P, Goodchild MF, Maguire DJ, Rhind DW (eds) 1997 *Geographical information systems: principles, techniques, management and applications*. Cambridge, GeoInformation International

Mitchell S, Jackson W, Cubbedge S, Higbee T 1996 Navigation solution accuracy from a spaceborne GPS receiver. *GPS World* 7 (6): 42–50

Murray KJ, Farrow JE 1988 Experiences producing small scale line mapping from SPOT imagery. *International archives of photogrammetry and remote sensing* 27 (Part B11), Commission IV: 407–21

Rossbach U, Habrich H, Zarraoa N 1996 *Transformation Parameters between PZ-90 and WGS 84*. Paper presented at Institute of Navigation ION96, 18–20 September 1996

Seeber G 1994, *Satellite geodesy*. Berlin and New York, de Gruyter

Seeber G, Boeder V, Goldan H-J, Schmitz M, Wuebbena G 1996 Precise GPS positioning in marine and airborne applications. In Beutler G, Hein GW, Melbourne WG, Seeber G (eds) *GPS trends in precise terrestrial, airborne, and spaceborne applications*. Berlin, International Union of Geodesy and Geophysics, Springer: 202–11

Shreenan R, Becker R 1996 New products. *Geomatica* 50 (3): 324–5

Welch R, Jordan TR, Ehlers M 1985 Comparative evaluations of the geodetic accuracy and cartographic potential of Landsat-4 and Landsat-5 Thematic Image Data. *Photogrammetric Engineering and Remote Sensing* 51 (11): 1799–812

CHAPTER 11

International standards and the national mapping organizations

François Salgé

SUMMARY

This chapter describes the need for standardization of Geographic Information if wider and safer use is to be made of it. It summarizes the different approaches of the European standards body and the International Organization for Standards (ISO) which are both actively involved in this area and it sets out how they are collaborating. Throughout, examples are given based on European experience, notably involving the role of the European Commission (the public service of the European Union) but there are parallels in other parts of the world. Finally, a vision of the future situation is anticipated, based on the spread of National Spatial Data Infrastructures (NSDIs) and regional and global versions of them, plus the European Commission's concepts on a European policy framework for a geographic infrastructure (see Chapter 14). From all this, the likely and potential roles of national mapping organizations (NMOs) are deduced.

THE NEED FOR GEOGRAPHIC INFORMATION STANDARDS

The ability to use different software systems in combination and to populate them with data from many different sources is crucial if we are to be efficient and effective. In technical terms, this aim is achieved through interoperability of Geographic Information Systems (GIS) and re-usability of Geographic Information (GI) in different application sectors. The GIS market is now international and becoming global. To ensure such interoperability and re-usability across culturally diverse areas, particularly with the increasing requirement of combining GI from various sources and merging them from various countries, requires standardization in this area in order to be highly effective.

The aim of standardization in the field of GI is to define a family of standards which enables the definition, description, structure, query, encoding, and the transfer of GI and related information. The basic purpose is also to enable GI to be 'delivered' to different users, applications, and systems.

As a result of history and political decisions taken since the beginning of this century, GI in paper form (maps) varies between countries in terms of content, scale, projection, and symbology. Converting the analogue information resource into digital form has been a major concern for all levels of government during the last two decades. The totality of this creation and transformation process has resulted in heterogeneous and incompatible data sets and has led to some duplication of effort as the same information may be digitized many times.

The use of GI in digital form is increasing in all levels of local governments and utilities. The private sector also requires GI and related systems. Future information systems will include GI and GIS: that trend is evident in many economic sectors such as environment, route planning and road management, regional and urban planning, defence and security, statistical analysis, and fire and other emergency rescue services. Personal computer software vendors exemplify the importance of GI in providing GIS functionality even in their spreadsheet or word processor packages.

A European example of needs

Supra-national institutions are also showing increasing interest in GI and GIS. This can be exemplified by the actions of the European Commission to meet their internal requirements, to meet their external requirements, and as part of their role of stimulating the market. Internal requirements for GI and GIS arise from the need to formulate and monitor community decisions. The GIS-CO project (or GIS for the Commission) is run by EUROSTAT, the Commission's statistical agency. The project seeks to harmonize the approach of the potentially large numbers of GI users within the Commission. Clearly, the use of common standards would greatly enhance the efficiency of internal operations; it would also ease the provision of information to the European Union from GI providers through use of well-defined exchange formats and harmonized specifications for data content.

Other externally orientated considerations also exist within the Commission, where sectoral directorates (such as agriculture) are aware of the benefit that their economic sector can gain from using GI and GIS. Though some of the 24 directorates are not yet fully aware of the benefits of GIS, it is likely that the situation will change soon – not least because their equivalent ministerial departments in the member states already stimulate and co-ordinate the use of GI. Current users include Directorate General (DG) VI for the monitoring of the common agricultural policy (CAP), DG VII for the European infrastructure transport network and policy, DG XI and the European Environmental Agency (EEA) for the European environment policy, or DG XVI in which regional policy will be improved by using GIS in every local government. Last but not least, Commission-supported projects in the automotive industry have demonstrated the importance of geographic data file standards being available for Road Transport and Traffic Telematic (RTTT) purposes.

In addition to its own use of GI, the Commission has a remit to stimulate the information market and relevant technologies, including the area of Geographical Information. The IMPACT II projects of DG XIII, followed by the INFO 2000 programme and the current discussion on GI 2000 among other directorates, show the importance of Commission stimulation of the information market through appropriate Community funding.

The European umbrella organization for GI (EUROGI), which brings together the national and European associations interested in GI, has clearly identified the standardization issue as strategic for all its members and others at both European and international level. EUROGI's role will obviously not be to design standards but rather to focus on strategic issues; e.g. to identify areas where European standards are needed in the short, medium, and long terms and subsequently to analyse and prioritize the requirements for standards.

Participants in standardization activities

Standardization in the field of Geographic Information arises from four main technological streams (see Figure 11.1). Three of these belong to the general purpose Information and Communication Technology (ICT) industry. The Computer Aided Design stream (CAD/CAM) provides computer graphics tools mainly useful for the geometrical aspects of GI such as STEP (an international standard for the computerized representation and exchange of product data). The Information System (IS) stream started the study of specific extensions to SQL (the Standard Query Language) in order to handle GI from an information system perspective. The electronic data interchange (EDI) stream recognized the requirement to exchange GI for administrative purposes and thus has studied possible GI 'messages' within the EDIFACT context. The fourth stream comes from practices in the GI sector itself which had to develop its own usage of computers over a long period: the unique features of GI information had in the past defied the capabilities of general-purpose systems.

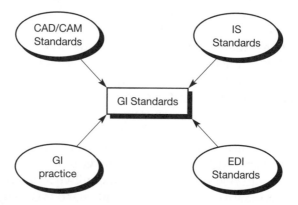

Fig. 11.1 Streams of standardization

As far as standards are concerned, GI actors first grouped themselves either as nationals or as professionals (Figure 11.2). On the one hand, nationals gave birth to national *de jure* standards such as NTF in the UK, EDIGéO in France, SDTS in the USA, and SAIF in Canada. On the other hand, professionals organized in international groups such as DGIWG for the Ministry of Defence of the NATO countries or the International Hydrographic Organization (IHO) created application-orientated international *de facto* standards such as DIGEST or S57. The automotive industry also developed GDF as their own European standard.

For present purposes, the two key international standards organizations are CEN (the European standards organization, Comité Européen de Normalisation) and ISO (the International Organization for Standards). Each has set up its own technical committee (TC) on GI and geomatics, CEN/TC 287 and ISO/TC 211 respectively. When these committees were created, the national standardization bodies, backed by their national GI community, became involved. The objectives of both technical committees are the creation of generic standards which can be used by any application domain, allowing compatibility between domains.

Similarly, in the Road Transport and Traffic Telematic area, CEN and ISO set up technical committees (CEN/TC 278 and ISO/TC 204 respectively) which each defined a work item for the definition of an exchange standard for GI linked to the road network. This standard is bound to be an application-orientated profile of the GI generic standards.

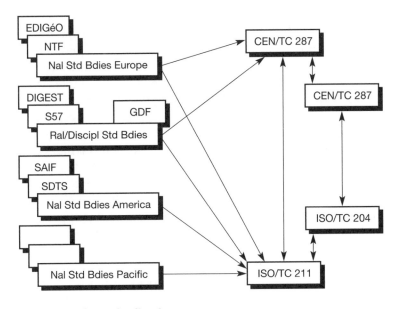

Fig. 11.2 Actors of standardization

CEN AND ISO STANDARDIZATION EFFORTS

When both European and global standardization committees work in over-lapping fields, problems of co-operation, harmonization, and consistency may occur. Given the creation of CEN/TC 287 in October 1991 and ISO/TC 211 in November 1994, it is important that the standardization efforts in the field of GI and geomatics are synchronized.

Although there seems to be unanimous agreement that global standardization solutions should be sought whenever possible, it is clear that both national and regional requirements may differ from global ones. Furthermore, where regional (e.g. European) work has already started and is well advanced before similar global work is undertaken, it cannot be expected that regional work will just cease and simply be subsumed within the global body.

The objectives of ISO/TC 211 and CEN/TC 287 co-operation can be stated as follows:

- to establish globally recognized standards in the field of GI/geomatics;
- to avoid duplication of work and seek an optimal utilization of resources;
- to establish consistency between European and international standards; and
- to establish uniqueness inside the set of international and European standards where requirements are not identical.

CEN and ISO approaches

Many authors have described two concepts for standardization: the data-centric approach and the process-centric approach. In the data-centric approach, the standards can be expected to achieve data portability within an Open Systems scenario. The concept is epitomized by the work of CEN/TC 287. This approach is addressing today's (and yesterday's) most urgent needs. It is argued that data management cannot be distributed within this level of standardization. In this approach, conceptual models, data quality, metadata, transfer, query, and update are key items for standardization. In contrast, the general information market is now considering a new approach to standardization often called process-centric, which reflects the increased interest in information highways. The concept utilizes open operability standards which support distributed data management ideas. The ISO/TC 211 committee is focusing on this approach.

Even if the views on open systems for GI are discounted and appear to be too futurist, the process-centric concept must be the goal which is sought by Europe and the world in the longer term. Nevertheless, this conclusion is not yet widely accepted around the world. Initiatives such as the European GI infrastructure proposals or global GI infrastructure tend to concentrate on the basic failings which render information inaccessible; these can be satisfied by the CEN/TC 287 standards.

There are also situations where the process-centric approach fails to allow complete understanding of the information shared by applications. In the field of GI/geomatics, for example, there is a set of standards between the application and the services allowing for interoperability: spatial analysis and even cartography need to 'understand' the information received through the services. The data-centric approach provides the basis for that understanding. It is, therefore, logical and efficient to consider the data-centric approach as a first step of the process-centric approach, instead of regarding each as representing two opposing approaches. Finally, it is likely that there will be support for an interim data-centric solution since this represents an evolution from the current data transfer and product standards. There should be a strong support for this evolutionary approach, not just in Europe but also in the international groups currently liaising with CEN and ISO technical committees.

Processes of standard creation

The steps involved in formal standardization, together with the terminology in use within ISO and CEN, need to be taken into account (see Figure 11.3). Both organizations follow similar routes when creating standards.

A work programme (WP) is initially defined and the task of writing the first version of the standard as a working group draft (WGD) is assigned to working parties. When the draft is mature enough, the working group transfers the document to the technical committee (TC) which may consider it as a committee draft (CD). After the review process at the TC level, it may eventually be decided to consider the latest version as the official draft standard. This is called a Draft International Standard (DIS) in ISO and prEN (pre-European standard) in CEN. An enquiry is then conducted among the members of ISO and CEN in order to collate the comments, leading to the final draft (FDIS in ISO). This is the subject of a formal vote which, if passed, results in the final standard (IS in ISO or EN in CEN).

CEN and ISO convergence

In circumstances where regional standards (in this case, European) or discipline-orientated standards (in this case from DGIWG or IHO) appear before global standards, the method used to obtain the convergence of CEN and ISO work is to consider the development of standards as phased in urgent areas of application. This allows more local experience to be included in the global developments. CEN/TC 287 started work in 1992 and eight of the work items had resulted in draft prENs by the end of 1996. Assuming the standards are accepted by the members, it is likely that they will be adopted by the end of 1997. The ISO work was starting at a time where CEN work is, from a technical point of view, close to completion. In these circumstances, it has been considered good industrial practice to allow the

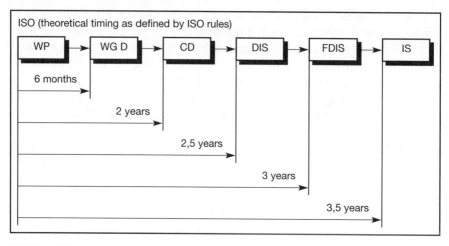

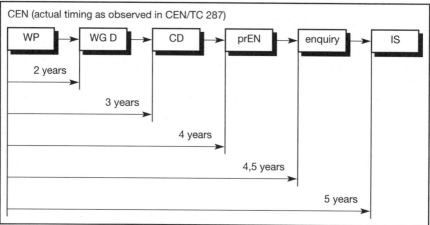

Fig. 11.3 Standard processes for creating standards

CEN work to complete its formal process, while allowing ISO technical comments to be taken into account by CEN and similarly to allow the CEN results to form the basis of the ISO work. This will facilitate mutual influence and trace out a suitable route towards one final set of standards in the longer term.

The process shown in Figure 11.4 is simplified compared to reality, since all practical and formal implications are not necessarily covered. As shown, it does not ensure identical standards in the short term. This, however, is not essential as the difference will appear as a revision and not as a conflicting international standard. It respects the CEN timetable. Furthermore, at the express wish of both committees, the resources invested in CEN will not be wasted whilst still maintaining full global participation. Last but not least, experience of Geographic Information/geomatics standards within a multi-national context will be gained.

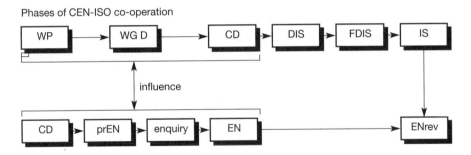

Fig. 11.4 **Phases of CEN-ISO co-operation**

A two-stage solution for international standardization is therefore envisaged:

- the first stage would be data-centric and based on the CEN work;
- the second stage would be process-centric and based on the work carried out by ISO/TC 211.

Given the European Commission's support for the former and the emphasis on the latter on the part of the GIS vendors, the solution ensures that resource implications are minimized and the market would be provided with standards at an early date. However, for this strategy to work, the CEN standards have to be adequate for interim international needs and must have a route to evolve into the second-stage standards. Without such a migration path, the market will not be convinced that they are worth implementing. This hypothesis suggests the need for early evaluation of the CEN work by those involved in process-centric standards, i.e. not only by ISO/TC 211 but also by vendors.

Given the two-stage approach, the transition should be clearly identified in a single Reference Model (RM),[1] the present CEN RM being its data-centric part. Clearly, this comprehensive model should be an ISO activity but should clearly integrate the data-centric and process-centric approaches. According to analyses of the two work programmes, the procedure described above is relevant for the following work items:

- the reference model
- spatial modelling/spatial schema
- quality
- metadata
- data encoding/transfer
- geodetic reference systems
- geographic identifiers (e.g. use of postal addresses or postcodes and zipcodes)
- query and update/services and spatial operators.

But there is much more to agreeing useful standards than following sets of rules. The proposed strategy will be efficient only if a co-operative spirit is accepted by all the partners in the standardization process. One important advantage of the strategy is to ensure (and show) that players in the field of GI are working altogether in the same direction, allowing global solutions to emerge. This will enable the widest possible diffusion of technologies based on GI in the general IT environment.

VISIONS OF THE FUTURE

For many years there has been increasing talk about the information society, often in terms of a second industrial revolution. This talk has received added impetus from US Vice-President Al Gore, the G7 Group, the European Union White Paper by the then President of the EC (Jacques Delors) on 'Croissance, Compétitivité et Emploi', and a major report by EU Commissioner Bangemann and by the European Commission itself. These reports describe and foster the creation of what is widely recognized as the Global Information Society or GIS.[2] GIS is not just the latest buzzword: it is a focal point within society for exploiting new developments in the ICT industries and is the subject of much political support.

A distinction is made between the two terms 'GIS' and the Global Information Infrastructure or 'GII'. An article in the October 1995 issue of the ISO bulletin gave the definition that the GII 'provides the vital services and capabilities required for the information society to prosper'. Another definition often used is that the GII is the enabler for achieving the objective of the Global Information Society.

The likely consequences of all this on our Geographic Information economic sector is as yet unclear. Recognizing that GI is an important part of the information society, some ministers in Europe have urged the European Commission to take a political initiative to study the geographic component of the Global Information Society and the related concept of GeoII. They also suggested that the EU should provide a stronger political impetus to GI at the European level. Directorate General XIII, with the help of the professionals of the GI economic sector including European bodies such as EUROGI and MEGRIN, undertook to justify an EU involvement in GI through a document now known as GI 2000 'Towards a European Policy Framework for GI'; the latest version of this is included in the book as Chapter 14.

As shown in chapters elsewhere in this book by Tosta, Robertson, and Gartner and others, plus the GI 2000 document described above, the NSDI initiatives in the USA, Japan, and other countries have led to action plans to encompass various areas such as:

- stimulating the creation of base data;
- stimulating the creation of metadata services;

- lowering legal barriers and reducing potential risks;
- stimulating public/private sector synergies; and
- facilitating co-ordination at national, regional, and global levels.

At the outset of this chapter, the aim of standardization in the field of GI was defined as being to create a family of standards which enables the definition, description, structure, query, encoding, and the transfer of Geographic Information and related information. The basic purpose is also to enable GI to be 'delivered' to different users, applications, and systems. This must now be reconsidered in the light of the move towards an information society and the technical changes now occurring.

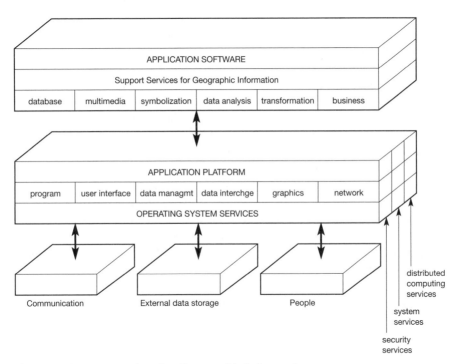

Fig. 11.5 Support services for Geographic Information

The vision of the future of GI is now embedded in a 'virtual GIS', in which a user in his or her own computer will have access to any accessible GI wherever it is in the world and to any spatial analysis function remotely accessible on the network, in order to accomplish their duties. This is best exemplified by the concept of an 'open system' that the OpenGIS consortium (OGC) is currently developing (see Figure 11.5).

The 'virtual GIS' concept will ideally and eventually allow any user to become free of any constraints linked to the computer environment with which he or she is working. The information system will be built gradually, component by component, with the aim of performing a given task with the most appropriate tool.

What is the role of the National Mapping Organizations?

NMOs have worked in the field of GI standards for many years. They often take a leading role since many of their experts are project leaders for different components of the standards process. Many NMOs have, at an earlier time, played key roles in defining national standards.

The very nature of their activities and the widespread use of their data ensures that NMOs are experts in the specifics of GI. NMOs are, none the less, only part of the data-providing community as they deal largely with map or framework data; they are necessary but not sufficient members of the GI community. It is now widely agreed that GI is not limited to map data and encompasses *any* information which can be related to the earth, either directly through co-ordinates or indirectly through reference to geographic identifiers (e.g. postcodes or zip codes). NMOs rely upon feedback from skilled GI users on the nature and shortcomings of their data as experienced through real applications which involve spatial analysis. They also need the expertise and resources of GIS vendors who bring in their knowledge of software development and computer systems.

It is self-evident from all this that NMOs cannot mandate standards for GI. Their role is to facilitate generic standards to emerge but also to foster their effective adoption. The latter can be achieved through designing data products which meet the generic standards, acquiring computer systems meeting international standards, and assisting GI users to define application standards and to implement them.

There is also one other area of standardization in which the role of NMOs is fundamental: the provision of strategic data to the user community (see Figure 11.6). The GI2000 programme recognizes that the creation of base data requires some stimulation. It has been argued that the development of a European marketplace for GI is hampered by the lack of Community-wide base data needed by certain applications. Development of such consistent multi-national base data will require stronger co-operation between Member State agencies such as NMOs, National Statistical Institutes, Census bureaux, environmental agencies, river and coastal authorities, and road and traffic organizations, as well as by private industry. National GI Infrastructure (NGII) concepts are currently developed, under different acronyms, in some countries including the USA, the United Kingdom, the Netherlands, and Japan, some of which are described in other chapters of this book. In each case thus far, the NMOs are key actors.

Though much of the standards work described in this chapter has been carried out in Europe, there is no reason to believe that lessons from the European arena cannot apply world-wide. Given appropriate leadership, therefore, it seems clear that *all* NMOs can make a major contribution to the development of such NGII and in co-ordinating these infrastructures at a regional (e.g. the European or Asian) level and at a global level. The deployment of NMO skills can thus make a major contribution in raising awareness of GI concerns in the Global Information Society. They can ensure that such a society works for the benefit of citizens, rather than simply becoming a technically imposed solution.

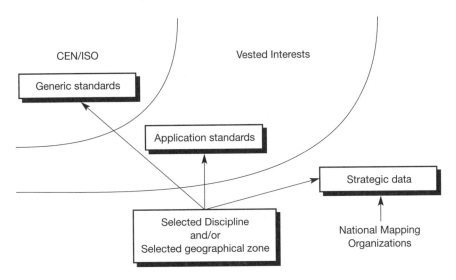

Fig. 11.6 Standards and application CEN-ISO

DISCLAIMER

The views expressed in this paper are those of the author and not necessarily those of the organizations with which he is associated.

NOTES

1. A reference model is a description of the area of standardization. It is framework defining the important concepts, views, layers, and components involved and their relationships. Its role is to explain and give a unified generic vision, key ideas, and scope of what is considered of mutual interest. In the standards arena, a reference model is often used as a broad map on which more specific standards or as-yet-undefined standards can be positioned and compared. Reference models may be descriptive or prescriptive and may serve different purposes, from a very abstract view of the problem area to a rather exact specification of different components and their relationships.

2. GI professionals need to understand this meaning of GIS as the Global Information Society instead of Geographic Information System!

REFERENCES

Brand M, Burrough P, Salgé F, Schüller K 1993 *Report of the committee for investigating the feasibility of creating a European Umbrella Organization for Geographic Information – Phase II. Proposals for setting up EUROGI.* Instigated by the Commission of the European Communities DG XIII-E2 (Information Technology) Luxembourg

EUROSTAT 1994 *GISCO: Le système d'informations géographiques de la Commission Européenne, la dimension spatiale du système statistique Européen.* Luxembourg

Masser I, Arnaud AM, Salgé F, Scholten H 1993 GISDATA Research Programme – *GISDATA Newsletter numbers 1 to 4.* Strasbourg, European Science Foundation

Salgé F 1993 Topographic infrastructure for Europe: a cultural revolution? *Proceedings GIS-LIS Conference.* Budapest, Hungary, May 1993

Salgé F 1994 Geographic Information: the challenge for Europe. In Shand PJ and Ireland PJ (eds) *The 1994 European GIS yearbook.* London, Blenheim

Salgé F 1996 *From an understanding of the European GI economic activity to the reality of a European dataset.* Paper given to GISDATA specialist meeting. Buoux, 8–11 May 1996

Salgé F 1996 Spatial Data Handling keynote address: Twelve years' impact of Spatial Data Handling research on the GIS Community. *Proceedings Spatial Data Handling Conference* (SDH96). Delft, 13–15 August 1996

National spatial data infrastructures and the roles of national mapping organizations

Nancy Tosta

SUMMARY

Geospatial data technologies are changing the means of doing business of many national mapping organizations (NMOs). The spread of geographic information systems (GIS) and other tools and the degree of co-ordination and data-sharing among users of the technology vary considerably within and across nations world-wide. Responsibilities, authorities, and approaches to map and geospatial database development and co-ordination vary greatly among these NMOs. Some of these differences are based on political or institutional factors, a few may be a function of technology, while others are due to geography and human behaviour. Despite these national differences, the effects of new technology and other factors are ensuring that the roles of – as well as the techniques used by – NMOs are changing.

Nowhere is this more obvious than in the United States. In the early 1990s, the US mapping community began discussions about development of a National Spatial Data Infrastructure (NSDI) to promote geospatial data-sharing. The NSDI involves all levels of government as well as the private and academic sectors. It has contributed to a changing role for the National Mapping Division (NMD) of the US Geological Survey. Actual data production activities by the NMD are likely to decline in the future, whilst its co-ordination efforts increase. Over the last two years, NSDI-like initiatives have begun in many other nations and these are likely to have significant implications for NMOs world-wide.

INTRODUCTION

Over the last two decades computer technology, and specifically GIS technology, has changed the way that most government agencies and private sector organizations conduct business. Dependencies on computers and growing requirements to analyse complex environmental, social, and economic situations are creating increasing demands for digital data. Geospatial data collection and management tools that allow the integration and analysis of information common to specific locations have become ubiquitous in many organizations. These tools include geographic information systems (GIS), global positioning systems (GPS), map digitizing and scanning equipment, and image processing systems. These tools have provided the many government and private sector organizations that utilize them with the ability to produce and manage their own geospatial information. These spreading capabilities and increased appetites for digital data are rapidly changing the environment within which NMOs conduct business and ultimately are likely to change their data management practices.

In the USA, the spread of GIS technologies is not limited to federal government agencies. A glance at the growing number of state, regional, national, and even international GIS conferences indicates a proliferation of organizations that collect and manage geospatial information to meet their needs. Numerous state government agencies in all 50 states in the USA, along with an uncounted number of the more than 3100 counties and tens of thousands cities, towns, and other municipalities, are now using GIS tools. In many cases they have simply automated the procedures they previously undertook manually, such as tax assessment, utility inventories, natural resource management, or permit tracking. In other situations they are using the GIS for analytical purposes such as understanding the spread of infectious diseases, predicting flood peaks, or assessing environmental effects of pollutants.

Regardless of the applications which they develop and use, nearly all organizations have spent time digitizing maps or images to create the fundamental geospatial data they require to conduct their business, most usually including roads, administrative boundaries, ownership (e.g. cadastre), and water features. This fact, taken with the reality that many organizations require more digital geospatial data than they have the resources to develop and maintain, has been the primary impetus behind development of the concept of an NSDI in the USA.

The NSDI is conceived to be an umbrella of policies, standards, and procedures that will encourage data-sharing within and among organizations. The goals are to foster more efficient production, management, and use of geospatial data, while minimizing investments which lead to duplication of data sets. Given the relatively open policies for access to information in the US as opposed to most other countries of the world, where data are usually copyrighted, licensed, and priced at higher levels, the situation of proliferating data sets may be more acute in the USA than elsewhere. However, government and private sector agencies in many other nations are facing the same vexing reality that their needs for accurate digital geospatial data exceed their capacity to create and maintain the data. Efficiency in the use of public resources is a goal in most nations, which probably partly explains the rapid global spread of the concept of NSDI. Australia, Canada, Japan, the Netherlands, Malaysia, and Portugal are examples of some of the nations currently known to have activities under way to develop NSDIs.

Within the European Community, discussions have begun to develop a 'Global Information Infrastructure' within the context of the GI2000 programme. Reasons other than economic imperatives for the interest in NSDI in many nations may be more difficult to explain, but could partly be a function of the true value of GIS as an integrating tool. When organizations and nations begin to think geographically rather than institutionally, the need to integrate information across traditional divisions, whether they be jurisdictional or discipline-based, becomes obvious. Broad thinking, co-operation, and trust are fundamental building blocks of the NSDI.

One other technological development affecting attitudes about data-sharing is the rapid growth of the Internet. With an estimated 50 million users globally, the Internet is an example of the growing electronic web that is changing how organizations think about both providing and accessing information. In the USA, nearly all federal agencies and an increasing number of state and local governments are using the Internet and the World Wide Web (WWW) to describe the work they conduct. Private sector businesses are including WWW Home Page addresses in all forms of advertising and, although many have yet to realize any direct financial benefit from the use of the Internet, lack of Web presence is increasingly seen as a handicap. The ability to communicate anytime, anywhere, in a multitude of formats, with access to massive volumes of previously unknown information, coupled with tools such as GIS for integration, is dramatically changing everything that organizations think about information ownership, integration, and provision. These changes have contributed to the evolution of the NSDI, primarily in the USA, but increasingly they are becoming manifest internationally.

BACKGROUND TO THE US NATIONAL SPATIAL DATA INFRASTRUCTURE AND THE ROLE OF THE NMD

For more than a century, the National Mapping Division (NMD) of the US Geological Survey in the Department of the Interior has been the primary producer of a standard set of maps that define the geography of the USA. The NMD has also traditionally been the implementor and, to a major extent, the setter of civilian map standards for the nation, adopting a National Map Accuracy Standard that applied to all of the map sheets it produces (US Bureau of the Budget 1947). The NMD has concentrated on map production in the federal lands but the entire nation has been mapped on paper at some time in the last 40 to 50 years at a scale of 1:24,000. Currently, not all of these data are digital, particularly at the 1:24,000 scale, although several themes of data, including roads, hydrography, and administrative boundaries, do exist for the nation in digital form based on 1:100,000 scale mapping. The role of the NMD in digital data production and standards is changing as more organizations assume responsibilities for producing their own digital geospatial data.

In the US federal government, the President's Office of Management and Budget (OMB) is responsible for establishing overall federal policies, among which are those that relate to collecting, managing, co-ordinating, and disseminating information. The OMB issues 'Circulars' defining federal agency activities and responsibilities. For many years, the process of identifying and co-ordinating national requirements for topographic map products created by the NMD, as well as geodetic control and cartographic representations of international boundaries developed by other agencies, was defined by OMB Circular A-16 and accompanying exhibits. The Circular established a process of solicitation of federal agencies and state governments to identify priority mapping needs for traditional NMD products. In 1990, the OMB revised this Circular based on an awareness that many federal agencies had requirements for and were themselves producing geospatial data, that geospatial data tools such as GIS were being procured by an increasing number of federal agencies, and that duplication of data collection efforts might be a problem. A revised circular A-16, entitled 'Co-ordination of Surveying, Mapping, and Related Spatial Data Activities', was issued in October 1990 (Office of Management and Budget 1990).

The revised Circular A-16 defines responsibilities for specific federal agencies related to co-ordinating requirements and developing standards for the collection of numerous themes of geospatial data including, for example, soils, transportation, geology, vegetation, and cadastral data. In general, the lead agencies identified in the Circular are those with primary responsibilities for using or collecting the noted theme of data. The base cartographic category, assigned to the NMD, relates to several other themes of data, including transportation (assigned to the Department of Transportation) and cadastral (assigned to the Bureau of Land Management within the Department of the Interior), which has led to an increased need for co-ordination. As indicated by the transportation and cadastral examples, other agencies have been assigned responsibilities in certain situations that were traditionally assumed to fall under the purview of the NMD.

In addition to designating lead federal agencies, the Circular created the Federal Geographic Data Committee (FGDC) as an inter-agency committee of federal agencies that collect, manage, or make use of geospatial data. The goals of the FGDC are to promote the development of distributed database systems, encourage development and implementation of standards, promote technology development, promote co-ordination mechanisms, publish reports, and perform special studies. The NMD provides staffing and resources to support the operations of the FGDC. From late 1993 up to the writing of this chapter (late 1996), the Secretary of the Interior personally chaired the FGDC. This has given the committee more political visibility than it enjoyed previously. Circular A-16 identified as a goal of the efforts of the federal agencies and the FGDC the 'eventual development of a national digital spatial information resource, with the involvement of Federal, State, and local governments, and the private sector' (Office of Management and Budget 1990).

Related to the discussions in this chapter is another policy of the US federal government, reaffirmed by OMB in Circular A-130 in June 1993. This Circular, entitled 'Management of Federal Information Resources', specifies that it is the policy of the US government to make data and information produced at government expense available for the cost of disseminating that information and no higher. There are some exceptions to this policy where laws or statutes have otherwise been established and in cases of protection of privacy and national security concerns. But for the most part, geospatial data produced by federal agencies is covered by this policy. In another policy relevant to map and data products, the federal government (with a few exceptions) is not allowed to hold copyrights on any of the data it produces. These two policies are factors that contribute to the different nature of mapping roles and responsibilities in the USA as compared to other countries of the world. The NMD does not copyright map data it distributes, nor does it charge for the cost of creating the information. Users of the data sets are free to re-use, repackage, or sell the data in any form they see fit.

Also during the early 1990s and shortly after the issuance of the revised Circular A-16, the Mapping Science Committee (MSC) of the National Research Council, primarily funded at that time by the NMD, began investigating the research responsibilities and the future of the NMD. The MSC coined the phrase 'National Spatial Data Infrastructure' (NSDI) and identified it as the comprehensive and co-ordinated environment for the production, management, dissemination, and use of geospatial data. The NSDI was conceived to be the totality of the policies, technology, institutions, data, and individuals that were producing and using geospatial data within the United States. The MSC published a document in 1993 entitled 'Toward a Co-ordinated Spatial Data Infrastructure for the Nation' that outlined a number of actions and responsibilities for various agencies and for the FGDC which related to the NSDI (MSC 1993).

The FGDC adopted the phrase 'NSDI' to describe the goal of a 'national digital spatial information resource' as outlined in Circular A-16, and shared the concept of the NSDI with the Clinton administration's teams which were exploring means to 're-invent' the federal government in early 1993. The NSDI was recognized as an idea and a means to foster better intergovernmental relations, to empower state and local governments in the development of geospatial data sets, and to improve the performance of the federal government. In September 1993, the NSDI was listed as one of the National Performance Review (NPR) initiatives to re-invent federal government. Vice-President Gore stated that, 'In partnership with State and local governments and private companies we will create a National Spatial Data Infrastructure' (Gore 1993). Many of the initiatives in the NPR focused on establishing accountability and control at lower levels in organizations, as well as at lower levels within the federal-state-local government infrastructure.

One of the primary means of implementing the initiatives of the National Performance Review was through Presidential Executive Orders. The Clinton administration began work on an Executive Order related to the NSDI in late 1993. In April of 1994, Executive Order No. 12906: 'Co-ordinating Geographic Data Acquisition and Access: The National Spatial Data Infrastructure', was signed by President Clinton, directing that federal agencies carry out certain tasks to implement the NSDI. These tasks were similar to those that had been outlined by the FGDC in its Strategic Plan a month earlier. The Executive Order created an environment within which new partnerships were not only encouraged, but required. In the USA, Presidential Executive Orders are only applicable to federal agencies but, in this case, these agencies were directed to find partners (specifically among other levels of government). State and local governments will often voluntarily co-operate with federal agencies if this makes it likely to result in funding or improve their access to data. Additionally, the Executive Order had significant effects in increasing the level of awareness about the value, use, and management of geospatial data among federal agencies specifically but, perhaps more importantly, it raised the political visibility of geospatial data collection, management, and use nationally and internationally. The fact that the President of the United States had issued a policy document defining the importance of co-ordinating geospatial data did more to spread awareness about the NSDI than any other single action of agencies or individuals involved in the geospatial data field.

THE OTHER US PLAYERS IN THE GEOSPATIAL DATA ENVIRONMENT

In some cases, data management activities of one level of government have initially been developed based on geographic data collected at the next higher level of government. This is especially true with the states in the United States relying on 1:100,000 or 1:24,000 scale mapping completed by the NMD. This is less true in US local government agencies, which do not usually find mapping scales of 1:24,000 useful to meet their needs and where other large-scale public domain data sets are not readily available. It is also less likely to be true in situations where the use of geospatial data may be more tightly licensed and constrained as in the practices of some local governments in the USA and throughout many other nations.

In the case of states, the use of NMD data is not always carried out through co-operative or data-sharing agreements, but simply on the basis of NMD data being available in the public domain. The NMD may or may   not be aware that an organization is making use of its information. The proliferation of GIS tools in numerous organizations may contribute to multiple agencies within a single geographic area manipulating the same data independently. Once integrated into an organization's operation, these data are updated and subsequently maintained, often with little interaction with NMD or with other agencies. To some extent this has resulted in a proliferation of redundant data sets, varying in degrees of accuracy and currency.

Many agencies also make use of the TIGER (Topologically Integrated Geographic Encoding and Referencing) digital database of the US Census Bureau because it provides access to socio-economic and demographic information as well as roads, addresses, and other cultural features. The base for the TIGER data set was primarily built by NMD in support of the 1990 Census from NMD 1:100,000 scale map sheets of hydrography, boundary, and transportation data. The Census Bureau subsequently added census-required coding to some of the files, and replaced much of the 1:100,000 data in major urban areas because time constraints made it easier to use their already richly coded data. However, these data were not as spatially accurate as the NMD 1:100,000 scale digital files, resulting in a national data set of varying spatial accuracy. This was not of special concern to the Census Bureau because spatial accuracy is not as critical for their particular application as are completeness, currency, and the relative relationships of features. The Bureau worked with state and local jurisdictions to try to ensure currency in their files prior to the 1990 Census.

The lack of spatial accuracy is, however, very frustrating to many local jurisdictions who try to build their GIS on TIGER or try to integrate TIGER with other data collected locally, usually at higher resolutions. Many local agencies have argued that the Census Bureau should rely on local data for conducting the Census. Requirements for coding consistency across the nation and the magnitude of the task of dealing with thousands of local jurisdictions, many with differing data formats, have prevented this from occurring at any significant scale. This situation is a continuous source of contention in the US geospatial data community. The NSDI Executive Order required that a plan be developed to help resolve this issue and this will be described more extensively in the next section.

Many organizations appear to be on the second or even third round of creating digital geospatial data for their geography, developing higher-resolution data sets in each subsequent round. As systems are re-engineered, states often move from generating entire databases at 1:100,000 scale to using 1:24,000 or larger scales over specific areas of interest. Local jurisdictions may evolve from 1:10,000 scale overviews to automation of parcel records at 1:1000 and larger scales.

The geographic size of a jurisdiction, types of issues, and levels of funding influence the scale of data collected. Many organizations, particularly federal agencies, but states as well, have developed programmes creating standard scale maps, as for example the NMD's programme of 1:250,000, 1:100,000, and 1:24,000 scale data for the nation. Another example is the US Fish and

Wildlife Service that develops National Wetland Inventory maps at 1:24,000 scale for the nation. This approach has favoured the developers of data who can standardize procedures, classifications, and equipment, but not necessarily the users of data who may have unique needs. The shift from paper map production, requiring specialized equipment and large printing presses, to desktop management of digital data has changed the demand for geospatial data. In many places, geospatial data that are slightly different from the standard product will be re-collected or re-created because the 'standard scale' or the 'standard classification' did not meet the particular needs of the users. The 'doing the same thing everywhere' approach, particularly over states as large and diverse as California or Texas, is being rethought. In many situations, larger scales of data are desired by organizations for management purposes in certain limited areas (e.g. downtown urban centres), but the cost of their collection universally is prohibitive. Recognizing this, the FGDC Framework discussions are examining alternative approaches to database development whereby data at different resolutions (potentially collected by a number of different organizations) may be integrated through the use of a minimal set of common standards.

THE NATIONAL SPATIAL DATA INFRASTRUCTURE AGENDA

The NSDI is defined in the Presidential Executive Order as 'the technology, policies, standards, and human resources necessary to acquire, process, store, distribute, and improve utilisation of geospatial data' (Clinton 1994). The Executive Order and the FGDC identified three primary areas to promote development of the NSDI. The first activity area is the development of standards; the second, improvement of access to and sharing of data by developing the National Geospatial Data Clearinghouse; and the third is the development of the National Digital Geospatial Data Framework. All of these efforts are to be carried out through partnerships among federal, state, and local agencies, the private and academic sectors, and non-profit organizations.

Standards

One component of the FGDC is a series of sub-committees based on different themes of geospatial data (e.g. soils, transportation, cadastral), each chaired by a different federal agency as designated by the OMB in Circular A-16. Figure 12.1 illustrates the structure of the committees and responsibilities. Several working groups have been formed to address issues on which there is a desire among agencies to co-ordinate and which cross sub-committee interests (e.g. Clearinghouse, Standards, Natural Resource Inventories). Many of these groups are developing standards for data collection and content, classifications, data presentation, and data

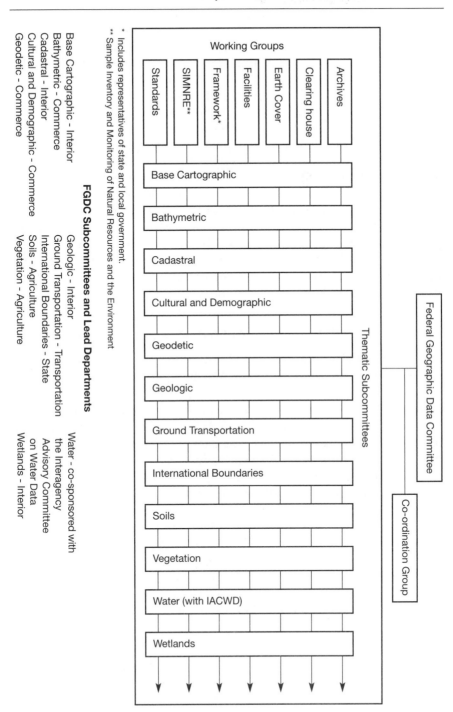

Figure 12.1 The Federal Geographic Data Committee structure of sub-committees and their responsibilities

management to facilitate data-sharing. For example, the Standards Working Group developed the metadata standard, which was formally adopted by the FGDC on 8 June 1994 and mandated in the NSDI Executive Order for use by all federal agencies on new geospatial data collected after January 1995. Cadastral and Wetlands standards are close to adoption at the time of writing, while those for vegetation, soils, elevation, orthoimagery, and others are working their way through the process. All of the FGDC-developed standards undergo an extensive public review process that includes nationally advertised comment and testing phases, and solicitation of comments from state and local government agencies, private sector firms, and professional societies. It is expected that the standards developed will be useful to geospatial data producers, users, and managers in all of these organizations. The NSDI Executive Order mandated that federal agencies use all FGDC-adopted standards. As stated previously, this standards process, distributing responsibility for development of geospatial data standards among agencies, shifts some of the responsibilities traditionally held by the NMD.

National Geospatial Data Clearinghouse

The second activity area is intended to facilitate access to data, with the goal of minimizing duplication and assisting partnerships for data production where common needs exist. This is being done by helping to 'advertise' the availability of data through development of a National Geospatial Data Clearinghouse. The strategy is that agencies producing data will describe the existence of the data with metadata, and will serve those metadata on the Internet in such a way that they can be accessed by commonly used Internet search and query tools. The FGDC-adopted metadata standard describes the content and characteristics of geospatial data sets. The NSDI Executive Order, besides requiring that federal agencies describe their data using the metadata standard, also stipulated that agencies make these metadata accessible electronically. Nearly all federal agencies, as well as most states and numerous local jurisdictions, have become active users of the Internet for disseminating geospatial data. This model does not necessarily assume that data will be distributed for free. Many of the agencies that are serving data on the net have discovered that thousands of files are being accessed monthly, where previous manual distribution approaches were limited to tens or, in some cases, hundreds of files. Some of these data sets require the payment of a fee, others are free. The Clearinghouse can also be used to help find partners for database development by advertising interest in or needs for data.

Digital geospatial data framework

The third activity area is the conceptualization and development of a digital geospatial framework data set that will form the foundation for the collection of other data to minimize (it is hoped) data redundancy and to facilitate the integration and use of geospatial data. This data set is envisaged as consisting of the most commonly required data for most geospatial applications, including digital orthoimagery, geodetic control, elevation, transportation, hydrology, administrative boundaries, and cadastral or ownership information. The Executive Order directed the FGDC to develop a plan for completing initial implementation of the framework by the year 2000, considering the requirements for developing a database useful for the decennial census by 1998. During 1994, a vision and conceptual plan were developed by the FGDC Framework Working Group (consisting of representatives of state, local, and regional government as well as federal agencies) and was published as a Framework Report (FGDC 1995).

Organizations from different levels of government and occasionally the private sector are increasingly forming consortia in their geographic areas to build and maintain digital geospatial data sets that meet a diversity of needs. Examples include various cities in the USA where regional efforts have developed among major cities and surrounding jurisdictions (e.g. Dallas, Texas), between city and county governments (e.g. San Diego, California), and between state and federal agencies (e.g. in Utah). The characteristics of these partnerships vary depending on the level of technology development within the partner jurisdictions, on institutional relations, on the funding, and on the problems being addressed. Participants in many of these consortia were invited to workshops sponsored by the FGDC in 1995 and 1996 to examine the framework concept as articulated in the Framework Report. The goal of these workshops was to distil the experience and knowledge about co-ordination and data-sharing to contribute to a guidebook and procedures for the many other jurisdictions nation-wide that are considering similar working relationships. This goal recognizes that investments in geospatial data development at the local level are significant and often result in higher-resolution data than can easily be collected by states or the NMD and that data are often most effectively and efficiently maintained at their site of use. The expected outcome of these actions is development of a multitude of data sets at the local or regional level that comply with minimal standards and that can be integrated, aggregated, or generalized to build data sets over increasingly larger geographic areas up to and including the nation. A major goal of the FGDC in the evolution of the NSDI is to encourage this increasing number of distributed data partnerships to generate their detailed digital geospatial data under the umbrella of national standards so as to make it possible to link disparate data sets more easily. Framework standards are under discussion by the representatives of the various consortia and the FGDC sub-committees.

NEW ROLES FOR THE NMD AND OTHER NMOs

In 1994, the Mapping Science Committee of the National Research Council published a document entitled 'Promoting the National Spatial Data Infrastructure through partnerships'. This report offered several suggestions to federal and state government agencies and to the FGDC to help develop the NSDI through partnerships. It also noted a challenge to the NMD regarding its role in the NSDI. To quote the MSC:

> Organisations that build and maintain spatial data have a vested interest in the quality of the data when the success of critical missions depends on the accuracy and availability of the data. This suggests that data stewardship roles may be served best by organisations that collect data for the purpose of meeting specific operational missions. These spatial data stewards have commitments to their own organisations as well as obligations to meet the needs of partners throughout all levels of government. The mission of spatial data stewards could be expanded to meet data needs of multiple organisations as well as their own business needs. Currently, a major mission of the US Geological Survey is one of data collection. The stewardship concept introduced here is different from the data steward role of the USGS in that business needs other than a data collection mission also drive the development and maintenance of data.
>
> *(MSC 1994)*

The MSC statement neatly summarizes several issues encountered in FGDC discussions about partnerships. Increasingly, distributed technological capabilities for producing and manipulating digital geospatial data have led to more agencies assuming responsibility for developing their own existing data, sometimes by adding value to it. Such added value often necessitates partnering with other bodies – to share the work burden, to acquire new skills, or to link data together. Consequently, agencies that produce geospatial data need to develop the ability to partner with a variety of organizations (probably including some in the private as well as the public sectors), in each case potentially adopting a different role. State and local government representatives have often expressed the concern that federal agencies tend to treat them as contractors rather than as partners, requiring that federal standards be met with little concern for state or local needs. Understanding mutual requirements over different geographies, without demanding data simply for data's sake, is essential to the process of building effective partnerships.

Many data-sharing efforts in the USA are now developing around 'places' or 'communities'. There appears to be a trend emerging in organizational thinking from the traditional jurisdiction or institutional model that considers federal, state, and local levels of government as units of responsibility towards a more geographically driven mode that recognizes global, regional, and neighbourhood units of resolution. Several federal agencies are shifting their management programmes to regions, water-sheds, ecosystems, or communities that are more geographically relevant. For example, the Environmental Protection Agency has created a 'Community Based Environmental Protection' initiative and the Natural Resources Conservation Service is organizing most field office assign-ments around watersheds. Federal agencies acknowledge that their role in many of these geographic settings may be minimal, unless they are major land managers. This thinking is in keeping with policies of the Clinton administration to devolve federal government responsibilities.

In many cases, issues such as economic development, transportation planning, growth management, or community health are forcing the need to think geographically. Most of these geographically relevant activities require geospatial data. But because they are issues that are not necessarily within the purview of a specific government entity, they may be more likely to result in co-operative data efforts among various government agencies and other sectors within the geography. The Mississippi River flood in 1993 prompted numerous agencies to unite to develop a multi-state GIS database that allowed analysis of recovery and mitigation options. The NMD, in this case, was the co-ordinator for the project and a contributor of significant funding. But NMD's role in other efforts may be less clear.

A primary future role of the National Mapping Division of the USGS may be in promoting standards to help integrate locally collected 'large-scale' data from which 'smaller-scale' maps of portions or the whole of the nation can be created. In some cases, NMD may actually perform this inte-gration. In addition, where no local data collection efforts exist, NMD may continue to have responsibility for producing original, detailed data: this may well be true over federal lands. Finally, the NMD is likely to continue to have a role in producing very small-scale maps of the nation derived from satellite imagery.

CONCLUSIONS

Although the climate of geospatial data production and use in the USA may be defined by a unique combination of variables, many of which do not occur together in other parts of the world, times are likely to change for NMOs everywhere. The concepts of an NSDI have spread throughout many nations, if only because GIS technology has become pervasive. Within the USA, widespread availability of geospatial data technology tools, the development of the National Information Infrastructure, the rela-tively 'free' availability of digital geospatial data, the 're-invention' of government to define responsibilities at lower levels, the political support for national co-ordination efforts, and a growing concern about the costs of government are creating a climate of change. New ways of doing business in this environment are being defined through the concepts of the NSDI and a variety of partnerships. As a consequence, traditional NMO activities in the USA may give way to greater responsibilities for co-ordination and standards, more facilitation services and research, and less 'hands-on' geospatial data production. It seems inevitable that some parallel developments will occur elsewhere and strongly influence the role and activities of NMOs in many other countries.

REFERENCES

Clinton WJ 1994 Executive Order 12906. *Co-ordinating geographic data acquisition and access: the National Spatial Data Infrastructure.* Washington, DC, April 11

FGDC 1995 *Development of a national digital geospatial data framework.* Washington, DC, Federal Geographic Data Committee

Gore A 1993 *From red tape to results: creating a government that works better and costs less.* Report of the National Performance Review. Washington, DC, US Government Printing Office

MSC, National Research Council 1993 *Toward a coordinated spatial data infrastructure for the nation.* Washington, DC, National Academy Press

MSC, National Research Council 1994 *Promoting the National Spatial Data Infrastructure through partnerships.* Washington, DC, National Academy Press

Office of Management and Budget 1993 *Circular A-130: management of federal information resources.* Washington, DC, 25 June

Office of Management and Budget 1990 *Circular A-16: Coordination of surveying, mapping, and related spatial data activities.* Washington, DC, 19 October

US Bureau of the Budget 1947 *National map accuracy standards.* Washington, DC, US Government Printing Office

CHAPTER 13

The Australian National Spatial Data Infrastructure

Desmond J Mooney and Donald M Grant

SUMMARY

This chapter discusses the development of National Spatial Data Infrastructures (NSDIs), drawing on the pragmatic experience gained during the building of a 'first pass' national data infrastructure for Australia. Issues that have emerged from this initiative, including standards, pricing, national co-ordination, the pressures from competing infrastructures, and infrastructure responsibility, are discussed. The benefits of the provision and use of this framework are documented, and the chapter concludes with comments on the issues that will affect the NSDIs of the future.

INTRODUCTION

For many nations, the spatial information industry of the 1980s was dominated by the capture of the fundamental data layers of cadastre and topography in state- or jurisdiction-wide coverages. These layers were then related to some rudimentary textual data concerning ownership and land valuation. For these nations, the current challenge is to build these often disparate data sets and the emerging utility and environmental layers into an integrated, homogeneous NSDI.

The urgency for building NSDIs cannot be over-stated. In many nations there is already evidence of duplication and fragmentation of the fundamental data sets that were captured in the 1980s at great expense. Hybrid, look-alike data sets purporting to provide an NSDI are also beginning to emerge. Many people in the spatial information industry and society generally may not be concerned at this trend and may even believe that it fits neatly with the economic and market theory adopted by their respective governments. In Australia, for example, sound arguments based on government policy concerning contestability of markets and competitiveness could be produced to support the development of competing national spatial data sets. However, a strong case can also be mounted that points to enormous long-term benefits arising from the development of a single integrated homogeneous national spatial data set. This may not exactly align with economic theory based on perfect market conditions but, equally, we do not live in a perfect market.

In the last decade there have been continuing arguments regarding definitions and the meanings of words associated with the land and Geographic Information industry. Geographic Information Systems (GIS), land information systems, spatial information systems – what do they mean? Which ones are sub-sets of the other? Are GIS a sub-set of land information systems or vice versa? In time, common sense prevailed and most realized that these debates are of little consequence. The collection of data related to our world, provided that it is held in a meaningful format and which can easily be combined with other data sources to assist in decision-making, has become more important than these circular academic debates.

That said, one recent definition of a NSDI is useful to consider. The definition that follows arose from an Executive Order from the President of the USA, Bill Clinton, in April 1994 (see also Tosta in this book):

> 'National spatial data infrastructure means the technology, policies, standards and human resources necessary to acquire, process, store, distribute and improve utilisation of geospatial data.
>
> Geospatial data means information that identifies the geographic location and characteristics of natural or constructed features and boundaries on earth. This information may be derived from, among other things, remote sensing, mapping and surveying technologies. Statistical data may be included in this definition at the discretion of the collecting agency.
>
> *(Clinton 1994)*

The above, rather all-encompassing statement, adequately defines what is meant by a NSDI in this chapter.

THE AUSTRALIAN EXPERIENCE

Australian government organizations with a surveying and mapping function traditionally focused upon particular activities within single projects. They collected data, consumed, and then discarded it. However, with demands for public sector cost-cutting and greater accountability, the states and territories have sought increased co-ordination of land information. In the mid-1980s and early 1990s, capture of the cadastral pattern in digital form became a key mandate of survey and mapping organizations throughout Australia. It was thought that this pattern would be the key building block on which all other spatial data were to be overlaid. An additional incentive to this approach was the belief that this data layer would provide a valuable source of revenue for the owner of the data by licensing others to use it. This phase of development has lead to the integration of core data sets, usually based on the cadastre, providing a state-wide and comprehensive data source of high integrity.

A study of the benefits of the existing land and geographic data infrastructure commissioned by the Australian New Zealand Land Information Council (ANZLIC) in 1994 revealed that, for every Australian dollar invested in producing land and geographic data, 4 dollars of benefit was generated within the economy (PW 1995). In New South Wales, another study revealed that, for every dollar invested in the capture of the cadastral data, 9 dollars in benefits would be provided (PWU 1990). Similar cost benefits were predicted in the other states and territories of Australia.

Over the years, such predictions of the benefits have, to a large extent, proved to be conservative. For example, over the period 1989-94 the benefit of land and geographic data usage to the Australian economy was calculated to be in the order of A\$4.5 billion. While the use of the established infrastructure for supplying data over the same period had saved users over A\$5 billion, much of that saved has been re-invested to generate additional economic activity (PW 1995). In 1991, an investment of A\$30 million by the government of New South Wales to complete the survey network and accelerate the digital capture of the cadastre has surpassed expectations. In July 1996, 18 months after the completion of that capture, revenues of about A\$20 million had been realized and additional benefits, arising from avoided costs, in the order of A\$35 million were calculated. The New South Wales figures represent only five years of a fifteen-year cost/benefit period and returns already exceed predictions.

In Australia, the benefits of the provision of fundamental data sets have been distributed across a broad spectrum of economic activities ranging from the operation of electricity, gas, and water utilities to the development of projects involving agriculture, mining, and environmental management. These benefits, although difficult to quantify in monetary terms, have been identified as (PW 1995):

- improved business and strategic planning;
- increased productivity;
- the development of new business opportunities;
- improved scheduling and co-ordination of investment projects; and
- improvements in the utilization, pricing, maintenance, and disposal of fixed assets.

Around 1992 it became clear that many of the users of these early databases required more than just the cadastre. Many needed the information contained in the traditional topographic layers held by the various public sector mapping agencies. The main impetus for this came from the need for organizations to have an 'as-built' representation of the landscape coupled with the shape of the surface. The change from the earlier use of the cadastre as an administrative tool showing legal ownership, restrictions and land values, to the use of the cadastre as a framework for a more comprehensive depiction of our landscape, was a reflection of the growing sophistication of the client base. What began as two distinct data sets – namely, the cadastre and the topographic data sets – has merged to become part of a more meaningful digital representation of the earth and its associated attributes.

Data collection was necessarily focused on the states and territories as the owners of existing land management processes, but each jurisdiction had its 'own ways of doing things'. Data items were collected to different accuracies and updated at different intervals in response to immediate user requirements, available budgetary support, and prevailing technologies. As a result, broad disparities in data quality are a feature of Australia's land and Geographic Information infrastructure. Whilst these developments marked the beginning of a spatial data infrastructure, it was far from a national infrastructure. In contrast to the data collection agencies, the spatial information industry was not limited by jurisdictional boundaries. As a result, the collection agencies began to hear cries for a homogeneous national spatial data coverage from the market place.

The first pass

Although the benefits of investing in a national data infrastructure were well recognized by the many co-ordinating and policy bodies associated with the spatial information industry in Australia, it was not until a significant national project arose that any real impetus was given to the building of such an infrastructure. The first project of national significance involved the provision of a digital mapping base for the Australian Bureau of Statistics (ABS) 1996 Census of Population and Housing. The Intergovernmental Committee of Surveying and Mapping (ICSM), comprising the heads of the state, territory, and federal government mapping organizations, had for many years promulgated the building of a national cadastral database (NCDB) and a national topographic database (NTDB). To satisfy the requirements of the ABS, elements from both these databases would be needed.

As mentioned in the previous section, although each jurisdiction had realized the need to bring its own data sets together, little progress had been made to integrate the individual jurisdictions' data sets to build a national data infrastructure. Despite many years of debate regarding the content and standards of these national data sets, without the demands of a 'real job' there was no urgency to finalize these issues.

Under the banner of the Public Sector Mapping Agencies (PSMA), the members of the ICSM seized the opportunity to respond to the ABS project as a means to accelerate the building of a national data infrastructure. It was seen that successful completion of the project would result in a 'first pass' seamless digital map database of Australia. Although the database would be tailored to specific ABS requirements, all members of the PSMA would benefit by the critical process of data evaluation that precedes the data integration. Errors and deficiencies in each jurisdiction's topographic and cadastral data would be identified during the quality assurance process and passed back to the custodial agency. For some states this would be the first time that their digital map data had undergone this level of scrutiny. The PSMA data would also be capable of being updated and upgraded for successive censuses and for other clients.

Negotiations took place between the nine jurisdictions and the client (ABS) to develop suitable contractual arrangements that would protect the interests of all parties. This complex task was made more difficult by the lack of any national standards and the lack of any homogeneity of content in these jurisdictional data sets. This lack of standards meant that a lot of convincing arguments had to be mounted to allay the fears of the client about what appeared to be an obvious shortcoming.

By utilizing a national spatial database, however, the ABS recognized that it would be able to create new census products that would be significantly more meaningful to the social programmes in each jurisdiction. In addition, the use of digital spatial data would aid census planning and facilitate the collection and dissemination of census statistics for the 1996 and future censuses. These advantages outweighed the ABS's reservations.

Up to that time, there were no fully specified and accepted standards for a NTDB and a NCDB. Draft standards have recently been completed by the ICSM and are undergoing revision following feedback from users, industry, and academia but were not available at that time. How then could the creation of a national data set have been commenced? Hastily drafted, pragmatic, interim standards and data contents were pulled together in a few months and the project commenced immediately thereafter. The first pass was completed on schedule in October 1995 and to date the client is very happy with the end result despite the lack of nationally adopted standards. Plate 11 shows one of the outputs – a sample census collector map showing the combination of cadastral and topographic data. Do we then tend to spend too much time on standards?

Standards

Uniformity of data quality or standards is a key determinant of both the demand for data products and the benefits which might eventually flow through the economy from their application in investment projects.

Australia's recent history suggests that creation or use of many of the proposed national digital spatial data sets under consideration have been held back by a lack of accepted standards. It would seem from the success of the ABS project that we may have been using the lack of standards as an excuse for inaction. If in the ABS case we had insisted on waiting for nationally adopted standards, the opportunity would have been lost and no 'first pass' NSDI would now exist. The data sets developed within the specifications for the ABS Project are not wildly at variance from the draft standards recently distributed for comment. Over time the ABS data sets can be upgraded to meet these new standards without significant increases in overheads to the data custodian and with little disruption to the client. It would be naïve to think that, even if precise standards were in place today, that these would not change over time and thus require upgrading of the present data sets. It does not seem logical therefore to allow the lack of fully accepted standards to be used as an excuse for inaction. In fact, it could be argued that until a real project is used to test 'theoretically' developed standards, there is no guarantee that an appropriate standard has actually been developed.

Indeed, there are those who would argue that rigorous standards imposed on particular undertakings can be counter-productive. They can stifle innovation and creativity, remove competition and could result in inefficiency. For example, if a single strict standard had been implemented in the early days of computing, the innovations that have ensued from competing computer firms, say Apple and Microsoft, would have been unlikely to occur so rapidly. Market forces are now ensuring that these once-divergent technologies are now converging.

Perhaps in the spatial information industry as in much of the IT world rigid standards should be replaced by a more flexible approach that allows market forces to shape the final outcome. In the ABS example, the client (market force) drove the first pragmatic standards which are now being upgraded by the demand of other national users (market forces) which will move the data sets towards the draft national standards being promulgated by the ICSM. Perhaps market forces will never drive the data sets to reach completely the national standards developed through the ICSM. That could be more of a reflection on the inadequacy or relevancy of the standards developed through the ICSM than reflecting a fault in the logic of the more flexible approach. In the end, it will always be the cost/benefit that will be the determining factor on how far individual organizations or jurisdictions will go in meeting externally developed standards.

Given the different priorities and resources of the major players in the Australian spatial information industry, how has the industry managed to achieve the successes so far?

National co-ordination

The public and private sectors of industry in Australia must both contend with the political issues which arise from a set of relationships within and between the different levels of government. These relationships are complicated by the tiered federal/state structure of government. National initiatives require action by up to nine governments, while the dual presence of the states and the Commonwealth generates at least twice the amount of complexity, instability, and uncertainty for operational agencies. Public sector initiatives are subject to the policies of the state which, in turn, often depend upon the federal government's allocation of funding (Grant and Krogh 1994).

Spatial data collection has become more focused on state government agencies, or on Commonwealth/state collaborative arrangements, rather than on Commonwealth arrangements alone. This is in keeping with the emerging trend in Australia of the Commonwealth concentrating on policy development whilst leaving operational issues to the states. Collection of fundamental data such as geodetic, cadastral, and topographic have followed this trend.

The major mapping agencies are now the Royal Australian Engineers, the Royal Australian Navy Hydrographic Service, the Commonwealth's Australian Survey and Land Information Group (AUSLIG), and those in the states and territories. The Hydrographic Service is responsible for charting Australian waters. AUSLIG and the Army have produced small- and medium-scale maps over regions of Australia for many years. In tandem, the states have conducted the large- to medium-scale mapping of their jurisdictions, with the exception of Queensland and Western Australia which relied upon the Commonwealth agencies for map coverage of the less populated parts of their large territories.

The mapping of Australia by these agencies and the consequent duplication of effort could, perhaps, be justified in the days of paper maps but in the digital era, scale has lost its significance. Small-scale maps can be extracted from large-scale databases by a variety of techniques, including the reduction of point density and the removal of selected detail. In the light of on-going budget restraint, rationalization appears the obvious solution to this duplication. Perhaps in recognition of this, the Australian Army's strategic mapping function has been devolved to the Army Topographic Support Establishment, staffed largely by defence civilians from the former Royal Australian Survey Corps. As of 1 July 1996 the tactical mapping function was to be completed by 'geomatic technicians' of the Royal Australian Engineers. In another initiative, AUSLIG, in common with other national mappers like Ordnance Survey and Land Information New Zealand, has been set cost-recovery targets. AUSLIG's targets have been difficult to achieve. At the time of writing, staff at AUSLIG are analysing the relevant sections of the 1996 federal budget with respect to the promised reforms of the public sector by the recently elected government. These reforms include substantive withdrawal from commercial operations by government organizations in favour of the private sector. The reforms also include market testing of the non-commercial community service obligation activities with a view to competitive tendering of this work.

Recent changes to the structure of the mapping organizations of Victoria, New South Wales, and New Zealand also reflect the changing expectations of the public service. For example, in New South Wales the statutory/

regulatory activities of the government mapping authority – the Land Information Centre – are being divided from the operational/delivery functions. These changes are consistent with the funder/provider model for the delivery of public goods and services, and also support competition policy for activities that fall outside the bounds of public goods. In the future, the mapping requirements of the states, the territories, and the Defence Forces will probably be completed by a combination of in-house and private sector operators under the co-ordination of the public sector mapping organizations.

Effective co-ordination of land and Geographic Information at the national level offers the advantages of clearly prioritizing data projects for government funding and avoiding any unnecessary duplication of effort. With this aim in mind, Australia has seen the creation of a number of separate national co-ordinating and policy bodies for the surveying and mapping industry.

The Australian Land Information Council (ALIC) was formed in 1986 as the peak co-ordinating body for land information policies at the national level. Now including New Zealand, ANZLIC comprises the heads of government agencies co-ordinating activity in each jurisdiction – as opposed to the heads of those agencies responsible for delivering and maintaining governments' surveying and mapping activities, the ICSM. An Advisory Committee is ANZLIC's executive arm, implementing a programme of work determined, monitored, and supported by the Council. ANZLIC has performed a valuable role, most importantly in airing issues such as pricing, custodianship, and privacy related to information activities and in sponsoring the creation of data standards, most notably the Australian Spatial Data Transfer Standard (ASDTS). The membership of ANZLIC was originally sourced from jurisdictional land management portfolios. Accordingly, there is a perceived weakness by some within the spatial information industry that it does not embrace nor reflect an holistic view.

The Intergovernmental Committee on Surveying and Mapping replaced the National Mapping Council which was set up immediately following World War II to assist national development. The ICSM now concentrates on delivering and maintaining the fundamental components of the NSDI, including the geodetic framework which underpins the whole infrastructure. However, as governments enforce budgetary cuts and consider the privatization path for traditional activities, the functions of the ICSM members have changed. In some instances representatives are no longer able to address all aspects of ICSM activity with authority. These functional changes are the result of a blurring of disciplines between surveying, cartography, and computer science, and are forcing wider changes in traditional organizational structures.

The creation of the Public Sector Mapping Agencies, born from the ICSM in 1992, is a manifestation of these functional changes. The PSMA realizes the high-level policy decisions of ANZLIC, with the technical directives provided by the ICSM in an operational environment, to deliver national data products. Given the success of the PSMA's initiatives, the group is under increasing pressure to provide additional national data sets. The PSMA is progressively upgrading the data collected for the ABS to a common standard and seeks to satisfy new clients' demand for national digital cadastral and topographic data. To this end, a national workshop was conducted in August 1996 to define the common characteristics of each jurisdictional cadastral database and the means of ensuring nation-wide revision to a common standard. Figure 13.1 shows the results of all these co-ordination actions and concepts – an emerging schema for an Australian Spatial Data Infrastructure

Each of these organizations has expressed a firm commitment to the development of a spatial data infrastructure for Australia. Yet not one of these bodies has executive power over all jurisdictions. This is perhaps the telling factor in why, despite such national co-ordination, each jurisdiction has proceeded in developing its own system, only loosely related to those in other jurisdictions. Undeniably, individual operational imperatives will remain the defining factor in directing spatial data developments in each state and territory. However, the willingness of jurisdictions to co-operate and co-ordinate their activities, demonstrated through the PSMA, enhances the prospects of future successes in the creation of a NSDI.

Fig. 13.1 Emerging scheme for an Australian Spatial Data Infrastructure

Competing fundamental data sets

With the widespread support for a national competition policy for Australia, why not allow competing national data sets? It is argued here, however, that the base layers of a NSDI are so fundamental to the strengthening of the overall spatial infrastructure framework that they should not be jeopardized by competing, hybrid base layers. This notion is put forward in the belief that, if the foundations of the system do not have sufficient integrity, the spatial data layers built over these foundations will begin to 'float in space' and finally the system will collapse.

Most experienced participants in this industry would agree that the above statement appears to be logical and reasoned. However, this same level of agreement as to what constitutes the base layers has not been achieved. In New South Wales, the contention is that these base layers include the cadastre, the transportation and drainage layers, and the surface (or digital terrain model) of the landscape. This is shown in graphical form on the diagram of the New South Wales Natural Resource Inventory and is represented by the primary spatial database layers (see Plate 12). The baseline satellite imagery is included as a reference set for state-wide environmental monitoring. Naturally all of these layers are underpinned by the geodetic network. Rather than argue what should or should not be included in these base layers, it is sufficient to recognize that, without one agreed framework of some dimension and on which to overlay other spatial data sets, the system would collapse. For example, it would be difficult to imagine how the system could be sustained if it was not, at the very least, underpinned by a geodetic network. This network fixes the geographic location of what would otherwise be floating data sets. One area of ongoing co-operation between the Commonwealth and the states is in the provision of this national geodetic network and national datums. Re-measurement of the Primary Survey Network using Global Positioning Technology and a readjustment of the entire network to remove existing anomalies was to be completed in September 1996. Australia is now well placed to move to a geocentric datum by 2000.

This is not to say that there should not be competing data sets which 'overlay' the primary database. It would be quite appropriate to have competing data sets for, say, land capability data – perhaps one produced by the public sector and another by the private sector. Whilst both these could have been developed from a different perspective, they could both be overlaid on the basic framework for comparison and analysis. Another example could be the different information- and value-adding that can be attached by competing groups to the transportation layer. This is quite appropriate and does not endanger the integrity of the framework. However, if different groups duplicate the transportation layers to different spatial accuracies, problems will soon arise for future comparison and analysis of multiple data sets which are attached to two different base layers.

The 'first pass' data set for Australia completed for the ABS provides a base layer NSDI. It is not forcing a rigid, prescriptive infrastructure, but rather it provides a framework upon which a multitude of users can place other data sets in whatever configuration suits their needs. This common base infrastructure also enables ease and fluidity of access for an endless number and variety of users. Despite this, there already exist several competing infrastructures in the base layer area in Australia. These are restricted mainly to the transportation layers and have been developed for different purposes from those for which the 'first pass' infrastructure was created through the PSMA. Some have arisen from a road directory approach and others as a data source to complement GIS software sales. The coverage of these alternate sets is, in some cases, not complete. However, if they are widely adopted, they offer hybrid solutions which could endanger overall national benefits.

The greatest long-term benefit of the ABS project lies in the fact that, because government data sets are being used, it is likely that most federal, state, and local government organizations will all be using this same fundamental spatial data. There is sound logic for this: common data sets allow integration of data and applications between the three levels of government. Initial users of the PSMA product are enthusiastically promoting the adoption of this data set as the official national information base for the federal bureaucracy. The end results are likely to be that national co-ordination and integration can be realized and, as a consequence, that some at least of the alternative frameworks will fall into disuse.

It should be emphasized that PSMA's actions are not to enforce a total monopoly over the data infrastructure. Theirs is merely an attempt to gain consistency, at least in the very fundamental base layers of the infrastructure. Even if that is accepted, who then should be responsible for the creation and maintenance of the base level of data?

Infrastructure responsibility

Prior to the emergence of the digital era, the responsibility for standards and regulations, custodianship, collection, maintenance, and delivery, and the value-adding of surveying and land-related information was clear cut. However, given the functional and structural changes of the traditional surveying and mapping organizations, these roles are no longer clearly defined in many jurisdictions. In New South Wales there has been a recent re-affirmation that all this is the role of the Surveyor General. In contrast, several other jurisdictions have shared these responsibilities across more than one agency.

As the very argument for having a single consistent base level of data implies a single trusteeship, it follows that this would probably be more appropriately provided by government as a public good. With the government as custodian, wastage through duplicate collection, ambiguities resulting from widespread and uncoordinated data acquisition, and issues of product monopoly and data-sharing can be avoided. Importantly, no monopoly rents should be extracted from this one source of supply of the base data. It further follows that the other data sets placed over these base layers can be for private good and can fall more readily into the arena of the private sector. There will always be some friction generated in discussions of where the continuum of public and private good starts and finishes. Nevertheless, this tension could be considered to be a positive force to help in determining the break- or sheer-point.

Public ownership of the framework does not necessarily mean that the taxpayer has to fund all of its maintenance. In Australia the PSMA is responsible for the 'first pass' base layer data creation and it could be concluded that what has been created is a public good. However, that does not preclude the PSMA from sharing in some of the monopoly rents that commercial users may extract when combining the PSMA data with these private goods that are sold into the market place.

Pricing

Arising from the above discussion on the appropriateness of governments to be the trustees of the NSDI, it follows that the amount of government revenue extracted from this infrastructure should be consistent with other government pricing policies for public goods. To date, individual jurisdictions have found it difficult to clarify their position regarding the pricing of land-related information. National co-ordinating bodies have therefore been unable to generate sufficient support for their pricing policies to be nationally adopted.

In line with the Hilmer Report (1993) on national competition policy, data suppliers throughout Australia must also consider the establishment of a framework for facilitating competition in data supply and ensuring that users have access to critical or essential data on fair and reasonable terms. This can be pursued through government-owned data suppliers improving their delivery of metadata. Metadata is an essential input for firms in the private sector wishing to become suppliers of value-added products. The promulgation of a set of basic conditions for access to data and the establishment of reasonable prices for products subject to little or no market competition, such as environmental data, is also important (PW 1995).

The role of environmental data in aiding the efficient, effective monitoring and management of our natural resources has been recognized, and a greater government commitment to environmental affairs is claimed at both the state and federal level in Australia. The Intergovernmental Agreement on the Environment, signed by the Prime Minister, State Premiers, and Chief Ministers in 1992 provides for the development of a national approach to the collection and handling of land-related information. ANZLIC has subsequently endorsed the approach that natural resources data to be used for non-commercial applications be supplied between governments at the cost of transfer. At the date of writing this chapter, ANZLIC has not achieved full agreement on this principle from all of the governments of the states, territories, and Commonwealth.

Initial investments in data, systems, expertise, and organizational structures are immense. However, any data set quickly loses value if it is not maintained. Thus an important but frequently neglected factor in the 'cost recovery versus cost of dissemination' debate is maintenance costs. The current proposition is to fund the cost of maintaining the currency of the data by factoring these costs into the price of the data or by obtaining separate community service obligation budgetary funding from government.

CHALLENGES AHEAD

The market place, micro-economic reform, and recession have all acted to reduce duplication of data collection. At the same time, real user needs have driven national data collection programmes, forcing key data source agencies to act in concert.

A change from collection activities to data analysis, dissemination/maintenance, and update/upgrade has caused re-orientation of our thinking from the 1970s, 1980s, and 1990s. The hard work of creating the fundamental spatial reference data sets is in hand and will plateau in the next few years. As data become more readily available, the market place is undergoing rapid expansion. More sophisticated application of spatial information – for example, in asset planning and management for the telecommunications sector – is placing new demands on the data supplier and creating new opportunities in the field of data integration.

Given all this, government organizations need to move from discrete work practices to an integrated environment to provide the value-for-money service the public now demands. Technology is the enabling tool for this integration, and happily the technology vendors have an impressive range of tools that can assist. Rationalization of institutional structures, combined with improved management practices, is necessary to eliminate much of the duplication of activities. This will lead to the concentration of both expertise and resources and permit the integration so desperately needed.

Until recently, most private sector involvement has been tied to government initiatives. Significant commercial interests have entered the market place either as suppliers of value-added data or as major users of the government data (Figure 13.2). There is demonstrably a need for wider intellectual and technological transfer between the public and private sectors.

The PSMA have taken advantage of opportunities to support the development of the private sector. The private sector has been involved in the digital capture process for the ABS project, the design and implementation of software and systems, and the production of census collector field maps from the digital data. The private sector will be able to compete for value-adding of the database to create dissemination products such as CDATA96 on CD-ROM. This value-adding by the information broker and the joint development of the relevant application for use in, *inter alia*, the transportation, health, law enforcement, and demographic environments

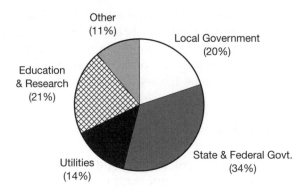

Fig. 13.2 Australian spatial information systems users by industry sector
Source: PWU and AISIST 1994

will ensure maximum exploitation of these fundamental data sources and a significant monetary return to government. We contend therefore that the role of the federal government in surveying and mapping should be to provide policy, co-ordinate the efforts of the states, set appropriate standards, and stimulate mapping programmes by the provision of funding where necessary.

Data access mechanisms still present problems. The current work on standards will provide some of the answers. But the problem goes far beyond technical issues: information professionals must conform to a set of ethics which dictate that they develop data access mechanisms which ensure equity of access but protect individual privacy. A national (or international) code of practice on data access is needed to address these and allied issues.

CONCLUSIONS

The benefits of a NSDI to Australia are to a large extent self-evident. The savings in duplication, the increased efficiency, and the potential for higher-quality decisions are no less in the national sense than those that are already well documented in the individual jurisdictions. To realize these benefits fully it is necessary to have, as a minimum, homogeneity in the base level data sets that underpin the NSDI.

It does not follow that we need to have rigid prescriptive standards and only one available data set for each of the non-basic themes within the infrastructure. Naturally, interoperability and co-operation are desirable but it is more efficient, in an economic sense, to allow market forces to drive these aspects. Without some level of government intervention to provide co-ordination and control of the base level infrastructure in the public good, it is unlikely that the overall infrastructure would be as flexible, sustainable, or profitable even for the private sector. In addition to increasing national and international co-ordination, the challenge for government agencies is to aid the development of the market place by encouraging the formation of a data brokerage and value-adding sector. This sector will then provide the stimulus to direct data flows and develop new products, leading to a mature spatial information industry.

This need for flexibility and individualism, built on a sound homogeneous spatial data infrastructure, is being highlighted more each day as this spatial framework becomes enmeshed with the 'information super highways' of the immediate future. Finally – and as shown elsewhere in this book – the growth of digital spatial data activities has taken place in the wake of the technological revolution. But we are only beginning to come to grips with the cultural revolution that follows. We may have mastered the technology but have only just started developing the applications and processes that will lead to efficient use of spatial information (Kelly 1993).

REFERENCES

Clinton WJ 1994 Executive Order 12906. *Co-ordinating geographic data acquisition and access: the National Spatial Data Infrastructure*. Washington, DC, April 11

Grant DM, Krogh BJ 1994 Cadastral development in New South Wales – philosophy, politics and polarisation. *Proceedings International Federation of Survey's Congress XX Commission VII*. Melbourne, 5–12 March 1994: 703.1/1–703.1/12

Grant DM, Mitchell CJ, Krogh BJ 1994 Spatial information systems in New South Wales – concepts and implementation. *Proceedings NALIS 94 Symposium and Exhibition*. Kuala Lumpur,14–16 November 1994: TS2.4, 1–15

Grant DM, Mooney DJ, Gatenby I 1991 Funding spatial information reform in a tight monetary environment. *Proceedings Champlain Forum on Land Information Policy*. New Brunswick, Canada, 26 August 1991

Independent (Hilmer) Committee of Inquiry 1993 *National competition policy*. Canberra, Australian Government Printing Service

Kelly PC 1993 A National Spatial Data Infrastructure. *Proceedings AURISA 93*. Adelaide, 22–6 November 1993: 55–65

Mobbs JD, Mooney DJ 1994 Extracting the digit. The public sector mapping agencies and the 1996 Census – A national project. *Proceedings AURISA 94*. Sydney, 21–5 November 1994: 485-502

Mooney DJ, Grant DM 1995 National Spatial Data Infrastructure. *Proceedings Cambridge Conference for National Mapping Organizations*, Session C, 25 July – 1 August 1995. Southampton, Ordnance Survey

PW 1995 *Australian Land and Geographic Data Infrastructure – ANZLIC benefits study*. Canberra, Price Waterhouse Economic Studies & Strategies Unit

PWU 1990 *A cost benefit study into the provision of an up-to-date framework and digital mapping database for use in NSW land information systems*. Sydney, Price Waterhouse Urwick

PWU, AISIST 1994 *The Australian spatial information systems industry survey*. Sydney, Price Waterhouse Urwick (contact Pierre Oosthuizen)

CHAPTER 14

Towards a European policy framework for Geographic Information: a working document

Editor's note: this document is the summary of a 26-page document produced by the European Commission, the public service of the European Union. The aim of the Commission staff was to describe what is happening in the field of Geographic Information in Europe and elsewhere and indicate the need for Community actions to ensure that Europe was competitive in this area, that the private sector prospered, and citizens had the maximum access to data possible consistent with privacy and commercial confidentiality issues.

SUMMARY

A European policy for Geographic Information is needed by the European information society. The policy will contribute to providing better and more efficient government, more effective management of scarce resources, and new business opportunities. The policy is necessary to ensure important cross-border initiatives are nurtured and managed cost-effectively.

This communication explains what Geographic Information is and why it is important for Europe to have a European policy framework for Geographic Information under which the market for European Geographic Information content can develop and prosper. What is so important about Geographic Information content that we need to take affirmative action at European level?

A major flood occurs for the third consecutive year on a major European waterway, hundreds of towns and villages are devastated, thousands of farms are inundated, the damage is estimated to run into billions of ECU and will take years to rectify. Not all of the damage can be repaired – loss of life was mercifully small.

Surely cross-border, regional flood control, and civil protection systems can already cope?

Your morning paper brings appalling news which will directly impact you, your family, your friends, your business, and perhaps even your national economy – 'Chernobyl 2' has happened. Civil protection forces, environmental groups, agricultural and fisheries departments, hospitals and medical associations – everyone is asking the same questions. When will the fallout arrive? How bad is the situation? How long will it take us to recover? How much economic damage can be expected? How many people will die?

Yet this has happened before, so one expects that emergency services, analytical teams, disaster relief organizations, and the like are all well prepared. But can they exchange information quickly and efficiently to facilitate co-operation?

Less dramatic, but still important, how does an international distributor of goods develop a 100 million ECU regional plan for placing a series of major goods outlets in the most appropriate locations, a project spanning the next decade, with major direct and indirect impact on employment, on transport infrastructure, and on environmental issues? Or what about the proposal for a new dam on a river which controls a watershed covering millions of hectares, touching several national boundaries; or the plan for that next industrial complex, to be built near a convenient port – which also happens to lie in an estuary of special environmental importance?

What these scenarios all have in common is the need for cross-border Geographic Information. The sort of information needed to manage the European integration, trans-European networks or smaller cross-border infrastructure projects, business development, marketing, to prepare for and clean up after major disasters, to manage today's road traffic chaos, or to plan for the next century's land use at local, national, and regional level, is *European Geographic Information content.*

Such information, in the form of paper maps showing locations, boundaries, and relationships, has been instrumental over the past centuries in the development of the nation state. First it was an essential aid to territorial conquest, the exercise of territorial sovereignty, and defence. Subsequently it has been used for governing and managing territory in times of peace. Today, and even more so in the future, it will be the key to planning for optimal use of limited resources under pressure from expanding populations to maintain sustainable development. As European integration advances and the world goes digital there is an increasing need for cross-border and European Geographic Information at all levels of society, especially in digital form. The need is also broadening to encompass much more information than just traditional map data – such as environmental data, business demographics, traffic information. At present such digital information is scarce and hard to obtain. What does exist is national and/or application specific in scope. It does not fit easily together with similar data from other Member States nor is it easily transferable to other application areas. In addition, there is a difficult transition from the national/military scene to the tradable market, where one key issue is open and fair access.

Geographic Information is a complex, rapidly growing, and important part of the information society. New Geographic Information technologies are developing rapidly. The great advantage is that it has the capability of summing up and visualizing graphically what vast amounts of data are trying to tell you. There are many applications in international, national, and local government, business and research, and culture. Geographic

Information is important because of its value for planning, land management, marketing studies, environment, renewable energy resources, emergency services, health care, political analysis, and many other uses. Unfortunately, future growth in Europe is hampered by major differences in the way this unique type of information is collected, stored, and distributed in different countries and in different sectors of government and commerce. Collecting and disseminating Geographic Information has been a specialized activity organized by individual nations and professions in different ways, making it difficult to combine and exchange national data to create European Geographic Information.

Geographic Information content is also a growing part of multimedia content, which is the key to growth and employment. At present the European content market is worth 150 billion ECU and employs 2 million people. Over the next ten years this sector is expected to generate 1 million new jobs. A proportion of this will be related to the provision of Geographic Information.

Following nearly two years of wide-ranging consultation among major Geographic Information suppliers and users, a need has been established to formulate a European policy framework for Geographic Information through which European Geographic Information can be created, combined, marketed, used, re-used, and shared in a cost-effective manner for the benefit of the European information society. It has the potential to provide better and more efficient government, more efficient management of scarce resources, and new business opportunities for the nascent European Geographic Information industry.

The major impediments to the widespread and successful use of Geographic Information in Europe are not technical, but political and organizational. The lack of a European mandate on Geographic Information is retarding development of joint Geographic Information strategies which causes unnecessary costs, is stifling new goods and services, and is reducing competitiveness.

What is required is a policy framework to set up and maintain a stable, European-wide set of agreed rules, standards, procedures, guidelines, and incentives for creating, collecting, updating, exchanging, accessing, and using Geographic Information. This policy framework must create a favourable business environment for a competitive, plentiful, rich, and differentiated supply of European Geographic Information that is easily identifiable and easily accessible.

The benefits include efficiencies of scale in a unified market, reduced problems for cross-border and pan-European projects, efficient technical solutions for future growth, increasing use of European skills, improved market position in Geographic Information, and better results of European-wide planning and decision-making.

Europe has the *means* but needs to *demonstrate the will* to create a policy framework for Geographic Information that will benefit the market place and EU citizens. It must include the legal aspects of Geographic

Information to ensure the creation and use of EU-wide data sets and standards. It must also stimulate and challenge private companies and public bodies to invest in the creation of such data sets and to co-operate where appropriate.

The most important political actions needed are to achieve agreement between the Member States:

- to set up a common approach to create European base data, and to make this generally available at affordable rates. This must include the adoption of the newest co-ordinate and projection systems on a Europe-wide basis applicable to European Geographic Information;
- to set up and adopt general data creation and exchange standards and to use them;
- to improve the ways and means for both public and private agencies and organizations to conduct European-level actions, such as creation of seamless pan-European data sets;
- to ensure that European solutions are globally compatible.

To initiate these actions, the Commission intends to create a GI2000 High Level Working Party. It will involve representatives from all the leading players in the public and private sectors including user representation and will be chaired by the Commission. The approach is the same as that adopted by the Telecommunications Council of 27 November 1996 to set up a working party to combat illegal content on the Internet.

The working party will elaborate a detailed action plan to implement the policy. Subsequently, it will provide the political leadership and vision required to guide the implementation of the action plan. The High Level Working Party will also provide the focal point for promoting a sense of unity across disciplines and national borders.

The role of the Commission is to provide the European dimension to actions at national level, acting as a catalyst, to co-ordinate Member States' policies building on existing national information holdings and structures. Neither new European organizational structures nor any form of central Geographic Information data storage are proposed or envisaged. The basic collection and storage of Geographic Information, creating and dissemination of metadata, and performance of other basic actions, must remain national tasks. The Commission will ensure co-ordination in regard to global Geographic Information policy and projects, such as those proposed via the G7 and with regard to the discussions being initiated at global level by the US Secretary of the Interior.

CHAPTER 15

Geographical data infrastructure in Asia and the Pacific

Dató A Majid Mohamed

SUMMARY

A number of nations within Asia and the Pacific have recognized the changing needs of their governments and peoples in terms of geographical or spatial information. They have set out to create an Asia and the Pacific Spatial Data Infrastructure (APSDI) through the formation of the Permanent Committee on GIS Infrastructure for Asia and the Pacific. This chapter describes the work thus far and the aims and objectives of the participants. It is concluded that there are many parallels with work in the USA and Europe, not least in the changing roles of national mapping organizations (NMOs).

THE ORIGINS OF THE COLLABORATION

The surveying and mapping organizations of Asia and the Pacific meet regularly under the auspices of the United Nations Regional Cartographic Committee (UNRCC). These meetings consider a wide range of topics of mutual concern. Discussions also cover activities in survey and mapping elsewhere in the world. At the 13th UNRCC for Asia and the Pacific in May 1994, Resolution No. 16 passed by the delegates committed the organization to set up a Permanent Regional GIS Infrastructure Committee in the following words:

> Recommends that within a year from now, with the initial administrative support of the United Nations Secretariat, directorates of national survey and mapping organizations in the region form a permanent committee to discuss and agree on, *inter alia*, geographical information system standards, geographical information system infrastructure and institutional development, and linkage of the prospective committee with related bodies in the world.

This recommendation was turned into reality at the International Meeting on the Formation of a Permanent Committee on GIS Infrastructure for Asia and the Pacific, held between 12 and 14 July 1995 in Kuala Lumpur. Attracting an attendance of 169 participants from 23 countries, it resolved not only to establish the Permanent Committee on GIS Infrastructure for Asia and the Pacific but also to elect an Executive Board to plan and co-ordinate the Committee's work programme. The initial membership of the Executive Board is set up in Table 15.1.

Table 15.1 Executive Board of the Permanent Committee for GIS Infrastructure for Asia and the Pacific

PRESIDENT	Dató A Majid Mohamed, Malaysia
VICE-PRESIDENT	Prof. Yang Kai, China
SECRETARY	Mr Brendan Godfrey, Australia
MEMBERS	Mr Tony Bevin, New Zealand Mr Rudolph Matindas, Indonesia Mr Kim Won-Ik, Korea Mr Abbas Radjabi Fard, Iran Mr José G Solis, Philippines Mr Kunio Nonomura, Japan Colonel Nukool Ratankarn, Thailand

THE COMMITTEE'S AIMS AND OBJECTIVES

These aims and objectives are best summarized by citing the key elements of its Constitution.

Article 3 of the Constitution: The aims of the Committee are to maximize the economic, social, and environmental benefits of Geographic Information in accordance with Agenda 21 by providing a forum for nations from the Asia and the Pacific to:

- co-operate in the development of a regional Geographic Information infrastructure;
- contribute to the development of the global Geographic Information infrastructure;
- share experiences and consult on matters of common interest; and
- participate in any other form of activity such as education, training, and technology transfer.

Article 4 of the Constitution: This defines the GIS Infrastructure referred to in Article 3 as comprising:

- the institutional framework which defines the policy, legislative, and administrative arrangement for building, maintaining, accessing, and applying standards and fundamental data sets;
- the technical standards which define the technical characteristics of fundamental data sets;
- the fundamental data sets which include the geodetic framework, topographic databases, and cadastral databases;

- the technological framework which enables users to identify and access fundamental data sets forming the basis of a national or regional land administration, land rights and tenure, resource management and conservation, and economic development. This framework supports the organization and the analysis of a range of spatial and related information for a wide range of social, economic, and environmental purposes.

Article 5 of the Constitution: the Committee shall endeavour to achieve, *inter alia*, the following objectives:

- develop guidelines for the nature of the legislative and administrative procedures and orders appropriate to the acquisition and sharing of spatial data;
- define the nature of a regional Geographic Information infrastructure that each country of the region can make available to meet regional mapping requirements as they relate to global mapping requirements, principally consisting of a regional geodetic framework, topographic features, and geographic names;
- define a framework for the documentation of the status of fundamental data sets and key agencies in each member nation, and for the exchange of such information;
- design a strategy for the development of a regional geodetic framework and topographic databases as the basis of regional GIS activity;
- prepare guidelines and strategies to assist member nations in the development of digital cadastre databases and where necessary for the implementation of cadastral reforms to meet individual member nation needs; and
- determine the need for research, training, and technology exchange in relation to the beneficial impact of Geographic Information on the social, economic, and environmental objectives of member nations of Asia and the Pacific region.

At a meeting of the Executive Board of the Permanent Committee, held on 14–15 May 1996 in Kuala Lumpur, the proposed Operational Statutes and Rules of Procedure were considered and approved. Preparation was also made for the Meeting of the Permanent Committee in Sydney in September/October 1996. The Sydney meeting attracted 77 participants from 17 countries in the Asia Pacific region. They formally adopted the Committee's Statutes and Rules of Procedure. In addition, four Working Groups met.

Working Group 1 deals with the 'Geographical Information Infrastructure and the Institutional Framework'. Its objectives are to:

- produce a schedule of activities with milestones and completion dates;
- research and document the key agencies dealing with spatial information in each member nation;

- define 'the Asia-Pacific Spatial Data Infrastructure' and its development rationale;
- define the model to be adopted for the Asia-Pacific Spatial Data Infrastructure, including purpose, fundamental data sets, and operational use;
- research and document the status of fundamental data sets within each member nation; and
- prepare a paper on the justification for developing a national GIS, including benefits, costs, and case studies.

Working Group 2 deals with 'Issues relating to cadastral survey' whilst the third Group is concerned with 'Geodetic networks for Asia and the Pacific Region' and Working Group 4 is tasked with 'Legislation and administrative arrangements for the acquisition and sharing of spatial data'.

The results of the meetings of the Working Groups in Sydney are summarized in a number of definitions, recommendations, and resolutions. The definition of the Asia and the Pacific Spatial Data Infrastructure (APSDI) which was adopted is that it comprises an institutional framework, technical standards, fundamental data sets, and a distribution network. Through these mechanisms the APSDI provides a network of databases, located throughout the region, that together provide the fundamental data needed to achieve the region's economic, social, human resources development, and environmental objectives.

The resolutions agreed in Sydney are:

Resolution 1: that the Permanent Committee seek Class A Liaison status with the International Organization for Standards Technical Committee on Geographical Information Standards (ISO/TC 211);

Resolution 2: that the PC foster a close liaison with appropriate international professional and co-ordination bodies, such as the ISPRS, FIG, ICA, IHO, IAG, ICAO, and UNGEGN, and with regional and development initiatives such as Global Mapping, SPREP (South Pacific Regional Environmental Programme), SEMIS (Subregional Environmental Monitoring and Information Systems), and SOPAC (South Pacific Applied Geoscience Commission). The purpose of this collaboration is to ensure that the Asia and the Pacific Spatial Data Infrastructure (APSDI) is compatible with other regional and global initiatives and that duplication of effort is avoided;

Resolution 3: that the PC endorse regional training initiatives on Geographic Information infrastructure issues, such as the toponymy training course to be held by UNGEGN in Darwin, Australia, in mid-1997, and encourages member nations to participate in those initiatives;

Resolution 4: that the PC establish a liaison with the European Umbrella Organization for Geographic Information (EUROGI) and similar regional co-ordinating bodies;

Resolution 5: that the PC prepare a statement to the 14th UN Regional Cartographic Conference for Asia-Pacific to be held in Bangkok in February 1997, noting the importance of making use of the services of the public, academic, and private sectors for the development of jurisdictional cadastral infrastructure and cadastral management systems;

Resolution 6: that the new Defense Mapping Agency geopotential model is adopted as the reference geoid for the Asia-Pacific region but that individual countries are encouraged to continue their gravity, GPS, and levelling activities for the development of an improved geoid;

Resolution 7: that the ITRF is adopted as the reference frame for geodesy in the Asia-Pacific region and that the values produced can be regarded as WGS 84 for practical purposes for spatial data;

Resolution 8: that the co-operative Asia and the Pacific Regional Geodetic Project is supported as a step towards the establishment of a regional geodetic infrastructure and the maintenance of a regional geodetic network for GIS application.

At the subsequent meeting held in Bangkok in February 1997, some 81 individuals from 13 countries in the Asia and Pacific Region attended, along with observers from five other countries and representatives of various specialist agencies. One important outcome was the setting up of a World Wide Web site at http://www.percom.apgis.gov.au/pcg

CONCLUSIONS

Even though the work of the Permanent Committee on GIS Infrastructure for Asia and the Pacific is at an early stage, progress so far has demonstrated an impressive commitment to collaboration amongst the nations of the region. The Executive Board is sufficiently confident of continuing collaboration to have organized other meetings in Tehran (1998) and Beijing (1999). The participants have recognized that there are many advantages in defining and sharing a common infrastructure and a recognition of the wider role which National Mapping Organizations can – and must – now play. To that end, all NMOs in the Asia-Pacific region are encouraged to participate in the meetings of the Permanent Committee on GIS Infrastructure for Asia and the Pacific. In this way, they can help to develop the Asia and the Pacific Spatial Data Infrastructure in parallel with equivalent developments in other areas of the world.

SECTION 4

Re-inventing government and national mapping organizations

Thus far, the emphasis in this book has primarily been upon the nature of the geographical framework both nationally and at global level, plus how technology and customer needs are changing the situation so far as the creators of the framework are concerned. But these creators have hitherto largely been National Mapping Organizations (NMOs) (or military bodies, sometimes both) and all of these have long been arms of the state. Yet – in some parts of the world at least – the state is under siege and quite different approaches are being sought from its components. The spread of the New Public Management has been surprisingly contemporaneous in many countries as far apart as New Zealand and Denmark. Whilst its local manifestations differ greatly, it is typified by the search for efficiency and high quality of service: the user is seen as customer and often pays for the service in whole or part, thereby gaining much leverage over the service providers. In some countries this has extended to the quasi-privatization of several state bodies.

The opening chapter of the section, by O'Donnell and Penton, describes the huge changes, including massive 'downsizing', involved in agencies responsible for mapping and the framework in Canada's federal government. They argue that:

> the traditional surveying and mapping organizations are threatened with extinction. Their survival will depend on our ability to understand and adapt to the trends that are forging our future directions.... Leading these trends are the changes in the world economy, with emphasis on governmental deficit reductions, downsizing the public services, and increasing demands for more value for tax dollars. Globalization of the economy and of the marketplaces is well underway, leading to a global arrangement of interdependent nations. Client demands will, more than any other factor, influence where National Mapping Organizations (NMOs) are headed. Our clients are no longer satisfied with the traditiona content, scale and relevance of our paper maps.

A more restrained and subtle French approach is set out by Grelot. He reviews the implicit way that the Institut Géographique National (IGN), the French NMO, has moved towards the users and the market in recent years. Grelot describes the historical situation and the funding dilemma which IGN faces in building, up-dating, and exploiting its cartographic and topographic databases. The general objectives set for IGN by government and the contract which expresses these are discussed, together with the form of copyright protection which exists in France and IGN's pricing policy. The chapter concludes by describing the evolving relationship between IGN and the private sector.

In Sweden, the government and Parliament have recently made very substantial changes to the way in which the state operates. This has involved many reductions in funding for social welfare and in government spending to reduce fiscal deficits. This characteristic is shared by many European nations as they struggle to accommodate to the convergence terms of the Maastricht agreement which may bring a single European currency and official banking system. Sandgren describes the 1996 merger of the National Land Survey (NLS) and the Central Board for Real Estate Data (CFD). The new body has three main tasks: to provide cadastral services, land and Geographic Information services, and commercial services. At the same time, some 120 County Survey Authorities, Real Estate Registration Authorities, and Real Estate Formation Authorities were merged into 24 new County Survey Authorities. Services carried out on a commercial basis have been organized separately from those for the public interest. The intention is that these commercial services should later be fully moved from the authority into one or more companies. The first manifestation of this is that, from 1 July 1995, the real estate valuation service which was carried out on a repayment basis has been moved from the NLS into a new government-owned limited company. His chapter summarizes the main reasons for the organizational changes, the processes which were involved, the tasks of the new organization, and how it will be financed.

New Zealand has been a pioneer in the New Public Management, changing the very nature of the society and its economy in the process. Robertson and Gartner describe how these changes began with the major reforms of the public sector from 1986 onwards, requiring the Department of Survey and Land Information (DOSLI) to adopt a cost-recovery regime. The changes have been ongoing, and the latest restructuring in 1996 separated out the regulatory from the commercial functions through the creation of two new organizations. Over this time, DOSLI was involved in the management of major change, the mix of commercial and regulatory functions, the definition of its core business, and alignment with government's needs from a survey and mapping organization. This process culminated in government reaffirming its ongoing needs for an organization such as DOSLI. Their chapter describes the rationale for the reform process and how it was managed.

Successful change is achieved not by abstract thought but through people. Peter Jakobsen's chapter sets out how the national responsibility for topographic mapping, nautical charting, cadastre and basic geodetic research in Denmark has since the end of the 1980s been placed in one governmental organization: Kort & Matrikelstyrelsen (National Survey and Cadastre – Denmark). This is still somewhat unusual compared to many other countries, where these activities are undertaken by several different official organizations. The creation of KMS as a market-orientated organization and preparing it for a life under conditions similar to those in the private industry have been – and still are – a major challenge. He has been responsible for great organizational and technical changes in KMS since the beginning of the 1980s. In this chapter, he focuses on these experiences in order to ensure others benefit from the mistakes he made and the lessons he learned. The main things to be learned are that:

- all organizational processes take longer than you expect;
- if you want to change something in an organization, you must make it clear to yourself and to the organization what you want it to do;
- the customers/users are your long-term guarantee for survival; and
- you must be prepared to change to survive.

The final chapter is by the editor of the entire book. He attempts to demonstrate how many of the issues identified in the rest of the book were faced by Ordnance Survey (OS) in Great Britain. These include the challenges of the UK government's commitment to competition and privatization, the threats and opportunities posed by new technology, the growth of globalization in the business, and the rapidly changing needs of customers. He describes the situation in which OS existed in 1991 and the reasons why radical change was essential. The chapter sets out how OS has reformed itself, both structurally and in performance terms, in the last five years: the databases and hence the national geographical framework are more up-to-date than ever before and are all in computer form. The cost of operating OS to the taxpayer is also significantly less and OS products and services are more widely used. For OS, however, change is now an unending process. Key issues in making such change beneficial include organizational culture, the need for continuing investment, and the assessment of future customer needs. These too are discussed in this chapter, together with staff skills and motivation and other human resources factors crucial to success.

CHAPTER 16

Canadian perspectives on the future of national mapping organizations

J Hugh O'Donnell and Cyril R Penton

SUMMARY

This chapter speculates on the roles and responsibilities of national mapping organizations (NMOs) in the future. What we can be certain of is that the traditional surveying and mapping organizations are threatened with extinction. Their survival will depend on our ability to understand and adapt to the trends that are forging our future directions.

Leading these trends are the changes in the world economy, with emphasis on governmental deficit reductions, downsizing the public services, and increasing demands for more value for tax dollars. Globalization of the economy and of the market places is well under way, leading to a global arrangement of interdependent nations. Client demands will, more than any other factor, influence where NMOs are headed. Our clients are no longer satisfied with the traditional content, scale, and relevance of our paper maps.

The ability to harness emerging technology in delivering our programmes has always been a major strength of our organizations. However, technology development is becoming so rapid that our near-future clients will demand only basic, geographically referenced data from us and will have the capacity to produce the customized and personalized products they will require.

These forces together are driving entrepreneurial government, where NMOs recover costs and generate revenues in a move towards at least partial self-financing. Coupled with this is the trend to move those activities that can best be done by the private sector out of government. Privatization is more than a trend, it is a reality. In Canada, the popular phrase is 'the business of government is getting out of business'.

But NMOs can create their own, preferred future. That lies in leading the creation, maintenance, and adherence to national standards of a national spatial data infrastructure, linked to other NSDIs of the world via the Information Highway. We will no longer simply accumulate data but will be involved in transforming those data into information and, ultimately, into knowledge. We will also be leaner, meaner, and more clearly focused organizations in terms of the service we will provide.

INTRODUCTION

Trying to forecast the future activities of NMOs even for the next year or two is fraught with uncertainties and imprecise projections. Stretching that forward look two to five years down the road, the essence of strategic planning, is an exercise in educated guesswork. Beyond five years, trying to define accurately what the future will bring is a combination of good judgement, based on the best available information, good luck, and a generous amount of clairvoyance. Unfortunately, we cannot claim to be clairvoyant. How then do we predict the position of NMOs at the turn of the century? To do so, we must first attempt to describe the changing environment that is influencing our future direction. If we can understand the forces involved, we stand a better chance of projecting where they will take us. But first, a brief look at vision is in order.

IN SEARCH OF A VISION FOR NATIONAL MAPPING ORGANIZATIONS

NMOs are as diverse as they are numerous. Their structures and organizations differ widely, as do their size, accountability within their respective nations, and their roles and responsibilities. They do, however, share a common mandate to provide the basic geodetic and topographic information for their country.

Each of these organizations is struggling to define a vision and to establish the goals and measures that will be needed to get there. This is a traditional approach, but one that is doomed to failure if we do not account for the paradigm shift that NMOs are encountering. The forces driving that shift will make the traditional surveying and mapping organization an obsolete entity by the end of this decade. In another chapter of this book, Morrison claims that part of the shift is a questioning of the very need for a national mapping agency.

Some authors have argued that many of the activities associated with geomatics, which includes surveying and mapping, will be taken over by other, non-geomatics professionals. Trinder and Fraser (1994), for instance, have proposed a contrived future under the geomatics banner where the surveying and mapping sub-disciplines thrive under a much broader umbrella across spatial information management and science as a whole. Ellyard (1994) was more direct when he said that it is likely that the surveying and mapping profession will continue to decline in significance if things continue as they are. He referred to such a future as a 'probable future'. However, the future which the profession can create for itself he calls the 'preferred future'. The same argument can be extended to NMOs: if these are not pro-active and design their own preferred future, they risk an imposed one – where they decline in importance and value to society.

EXTERNAL INFLUENCES

To create that preferred future, we must understand and account for the influences that are driving the paradigm shift that our agencies are undergoing. Those influences are many and complex, so we will deal only with those which are the most critical. They are the world economy, globalization, changing client needs, organizational changes, environmental issues, the Information Highway, and technology change more generally.

The world economy

At the time of writing (1996), the industrial nations of the world are just emerging from the 1990–92 economic recession. The recovery is the weakest from any recession that we have undergone. That recession was the longest and second deepest since the Great Depression. The economy, for all practical purposes, was in decline for more than two years. Businesses saw demand for goods and services plunge drastically as consumers, fearing further debt and job loss, cut back on their spending abruptly and severely. As a result, corporate profits tumbled to a post-Great Depression low. Compounding the situation, inflation forced interest rates to near-record real levels in many countries. Many national debts reached crisis proportions. As one example, New Zealand was forced to implement very serious budgetary measures to control its economic problems. Canada has been facing a similar situation.

National debts are a priority of governments today and will be so for the rest of this decade. Governments around the world are scaling back programmes. They are undergoing, or have undergone, major downsizing and re-organization exercises. Alongside this reduction in government spending are measures to increase revenues. Both of these have impacted directly on NMOs and these will continue to be among the agencies most affected.

In Canada, we completed Programme Review in 1995. This was the most comprehensive review of federal government activities ever undertaken in our country. It culminated in the 1995 budget, which demonstrates Canada's commitment to deficit reduction, economic growth, and responsive and efficient government. Departments are seeking new ways to deliver programmes and services at lower cost to Canadians. Programme Review has been the catalyst for this renewal. The budget announced significant reductions in funding. For example, Natural Resources Canada (NRCan) will go from a C$1.1 billion budget in 1994-95 to approximately C$435 million in 1997–98. Geomatics Canada, a part of NRCan, will see a budget reduction of C$23.7 million in that same time frame. This represents a 31 percent reduction from the 1994-95 budget.

The paradox is that, at the same time, the world is moving towards an economy in which information is of primary importance. Government is a key provider, user, and custodian of information. In particular, NMOs are the holders of the fundamental Geographic Information for their respective nations. Thus they can shape their own destiny and thrive in the emerging information society – but wider events dictate that they do this at less net cost to the taxpayer.

Globalization

The economic situation is driving a globalization process, one that goes beyond regional economic arrangements. It has created a climate of interdependence between nations, one that impacts on both the public and the private sectors. This globalization of the market place is well under way. Nations are moving from independent states dependent on trade within a small group of nations to interdependent states buying and selling in a global trading system. A new European Community has emerged. Poland, Hungary, and Czechoslovakia have established a Free Trade Zone. The Asia-Pacific region is moving towards increased economic integration. The Concorda Agreement sets the stage for free trade between Brazil, Argentina, and Uruguay and is seen as the precursor to a Pan American Economic Community. Mexico, the United States, and Canada are partners in the North American Free Trade Agreement. Ellyard (1994) has foreseen that 'a century of the planet is at hand' and 'a new planetary culture is being moulded by an unstoppable combination of political, economic, technological and ecological forces'.

Changing client needs

NMOs have long enjoyed a position of power and authority. Spatial data, in analogue, and later in digital form, has been their realm, their speciality. In earlier times, their clients were well served when they were provided with paper maps to describe the geoscience, topography, and topology of the land. However, that position is coming to an end.

We are already witnessing a revolution from our clients. They are demanding a higher quality and a wider range of products. They are no longer content to put up simply with what is already available. Clients are also looking for governments to provide 'one-stop shopping' for the multiplicity of national spatial data produced by separate government departments. As a consequence, a current emphasis in our respective national organizations is on user surveys – identifying not just who our clients are, but also what are their requirements. Not only must we be client-focused, but we must also provide dynamic products that are adaptable to clients' changing needs.

Until the 1980s, NMOs were *the* collectors of topographic data. In many cases, only they could afford the equipment and infrastructure required to map on a national scale. As the technology improved and became more accessible, however, private sector capabilities emerged and some NMOs progressively shifted from data gatherers to data managers. As the 1990s play out, the performance and simplicity of computer hardware and software, coupled with dramatically decreasing prices and increasing accessibility, will ensure that our clients will need only access to data to produce the customized products they want rather than buying them from NMOs. And, if we cannot supply those data or that information quickly enough, or with the desired quality or relevance, those clients will seek other suppliers.

Many NMOs have existed for hundreds of years. Yet, within a span of 20 years, we are witnessing a paradigm shift with respect to our clients. We have seen the emphasis go from providing products to providing data, and now from data to information. By the turn of the century, the emphasis will pass from information to knowledge, where knowledge is defined as the application and productive use of information. A significant aspect of our preferred future is becoming a knowledge-based organization. That means understanding how to convert our Geographic Information into knowledge which has immediate value to our clients. This in turn needs cultural, organizational, skills, and many other implications for the organizations involved.

Organizational changes

The economic trends, coupled with the reduction in government budgets noted earlier, necessarily implies that the role of government in spatial data production and management is changing. Some suggest that national mapping agency roles will be reduced to co-ordinators of government activities and national standards, with the production of spatial data taken over by the private sector and non-government organizations. Privatization is a popular policy in many countries as governments seek ways to reduce the size and cost of the public service.

Other chapters in this book cite examples of financial pressures on and organizational change affecting NMOs. As Rhind shows, the Ordnance Survey is a prime example of the 'user pays' principle. The OS reported in 1995–96 that 78 percent of the overall budget came from the sales of products and services, with the remaining 22 percent from government appropriation or being nominal items. Robertson and Gartner describe how the Department of Survey and Land Information (DOSLI) of New Zealand has seen cost recovery objectives rise steadily from 30 percent in 1987 to

70 percent in 1995. Most recently, New Zealand took the commercialization approach a step further. DOSLI is no more, having been divided into Land Information New Zealand (LINZ) and Terralink New Zealand Limited. LINZ is a new government department responsible for core land information activities. Terralink is a state-owned enterprise, providing the essential survey services, mapping, property services, and GIS solutions on a commercial basis.

It is no exaggeration that many NMOs are being challenged on their mandates and their very need to exist. The systematic, long-term, and comprehensive topographic mapping of a nation at specified map scales no longer meets the needs of an information-hungry society. Digital topographic data, unbounded by scale or area, is a basic information need. The National Mapping Division of the US Geological Survey is seeing its mandate move from a provider of topographic maps to a responsibility for the national spatial data infrastructure.

In Canada, as a direct result of Programme Review, a study has been conducted into the potential integration of federal mapping activities. Aside from Geomatics Canada, there are eight other government agencies involved in mapping, ranging from the hydrographic charts of Fisheries and Oceans Canada to the military maps of National Defence. The study examined the common expertise, technology, outputs, and client bases to determine how the respective agencies might work more closely together to deliver federal government mapping programmes effectively .

Beyond structural reform, the global trend is also towards entrepreneurial government. The challenge is to use public finances more effectively and to subject government operations to the laws and forces of the market place. The response is taking the form of:

- reductions in the size of the Public Service;
- commercialization of certain government activities;
- restructuring of the government machinery; and
- a redefinition of the process for developing public policy and the role of the various players involved in this process.

In these circumstances, NMOs will have to be entrepreneurial to survive. The Executive Agencies of the United Kingdom, the state-owned enterprises of New Zealand, and the Special Operating Agencies of Canada are typical of the new models for programme delivery. In the mid-1990s, the effective, efficient, and economical delivery of government programmes has been under intense review in Canada. One of the results is the evolution of a series of alternative mechanisms. Every government programme, depending on its mandate, degree of autonomy requirements, market responsiveness, and financing capability can fit into one or more of these mechanisms, which are shown in Figure 16.1. The further to the left of centre, the more involvement one sees in delivering a public good service, one that requires increasing degrees of policy input and also financing from the public purse. To the right of centre in Figure 16.1, the consideration of national issues and policy becomes less and less. Moving up from the centre one sees an increase in the autonomy of organizations from central government, coupled with increased commercialization capability. At the lower left, we find the traditional government department, where control by the central government is at a maximum and commercial capability is minimized. At the top right is the private enterprise, with minimum government involvement and maximum commercial capability. In practice, of course, government regulation of quasi-private sector monopolies may still be required.

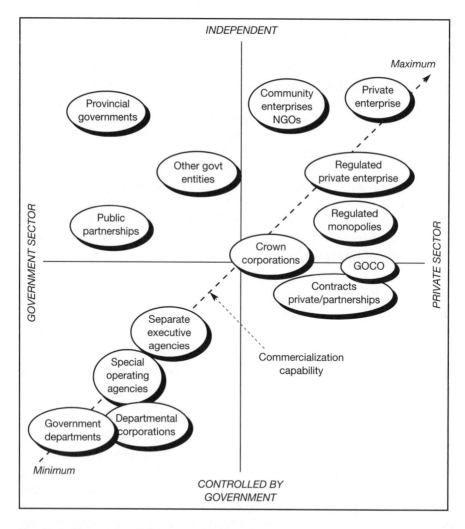

Fig. 16.1 Alternative delivery mechanisms

Thus the core activities of NMOs are under minute scrutiny in many countries as part of a wider-ranging review of the role of the state. Yet the products and services produced by NMOs are fundamental to the needs of the state and to commerce; it is also widely held that governments must provide at least some of them to citizens and that some are necessarily funded out of the tax base. The trend in recent times is to strip away all those activities that are not certified as part of the core responsibilities. Such activities are made self-sustaining, devolved to the private sector, or eliminated. The Honourable Paul Martin, Canadian Minister of Finance, has summarized all this in proclaiming: 'The business of government is to get out of business.' There is a wider rationale for the reduction of government activity: geomatics companies will only succeed in the international market place if domestic markets operate efficiently and provide them with a strong domestic base.

The environment

Ameliorating the accumulative damage that has been and continues to be inflicted on the planet is a current preoccupation of many citizens and governments. This view seems certain to continue. Sustainable development of natural resources is certainly one of today's priorities of the government of Canada. A new planetary environmental order is being realized, and NMOs can play a prominent role in that order. As Htun has indicated elsewhere in this book, the spatial information needed to support sustainable development fully is lacking in most parts of the world. By virtue of their historical role, NMOs collectively have the key spatial data that decision-makers need. These organizations represent the most effective means to monitor the state of the environment on a continuous basis. Thus NMOs must be a part of the implementation of Agenda 21, the action plan that came out of the Rio earth summit to which most of the world's governments subscribed. It encourages nations to develop internally acceptable methodologies for databases of land use and to develop and maintain databases for management of coastal areas.

Technology

Mapping organizations have always been and will remain technology-dependent. Our organizations have a rich history of successfully exploiting emerging technology to deliver programmes. In future, the major technological trend for geomatics will involve linking the multitude of existing spatial databases, as we move towards integrated, total solutions to geomatics markets. Information will be our primary commodity and the growth potential will be in developing value-added applications and uses of that information. Technological innovations will also affect the structure of our organizations and the conduct of our work, as well as the management of our organizations.

The following are but a representative sample of the changing technologies that are driving the future of geomatics:

- custom maps will be made using public domain software running on desk-top computers linked to the Internet. Low-volume maps will be printed on demand, at user-specified scales and boundaries;
- small-scale map coverage will increasingly be provided by automatically processed imagery from satellite remote sensing systems. Technology already under development will extend this to fully automatic topographic mapping at medium scales. Remote sensing technology will inevitably provide the data for compilation and revision of maps at all scales;
- aerial photography will remain a viable data source for photogrammetric mapping at certain scales. However, easy access to high-accuracy, high-resolution satellite imagery will change the way that public and private mapping agencies – as well as end-users – will view the task of mapping. Satellite sensor systems for mapping from space are currently under rapid development. Higher-resolution sensors with stereo capability, as well as increased spectral possibilities, are becoming available from various nations. Radar imaging and radar interferometry are emerging as significant new tools. In September 1995, for instance, Canada launched RADARSAT, the world's first fully operational satellite dedicated to radar applications;
- Geographic Information Systems (GIS) and related applications will also continue to enjoy substantial growth. It is suggested that funds spent on GIS are growing at an estimated 30 percent per year (Trinder and Fraser 1994). While the cost of GIS workstations and software is dropping significantly, the high cost of getting data into the spatial databases will continue to impede the growth of GIS. This impediment is the cause of the large gap between the potential of GIS and actual use;
- Differential Global Positioning System (DGPS) services are being established and will grow in importance and extent. GPS will be inextricably entwined with GIS in the future, providing the positioning element of real-time spatial data acquisition. And GPS will move on from being a military-based to a global, civilian-controlled satellite positioning system;
- interoperability is a cornerstone of tomorrow's GIS; without the ability to connect systems together, much of the added-value potential benefits of GIS cannot be realized. This capacity, being realized through much work across the world, will define the pathways for linking currently disparate and isolated spatial information systems. It will also imply the existence of common user interfaces that support the integration of consistent, reliable data sets. *(Hecht 1995)*

The Information Highway

The need for the Information Highway has been growing for some time. Since the early 1960s, foundations for the highway have been laid with the development of computer technology to manage spatial data. Traditional mapping gave way to an new era of computer-assisted mapping. The 1970s saw the creation of the Canadian Geographical Information System, the world's first national database of spatially related data. Through the 1980s software development had evolved to a situation where digital spatial data bases became commonplace. These were generally independent and isolated. Widespread frustration resulted from trying to link data that did not conform to common standards.

As Tosta explains elsewhere in this book, an important task is now to link those databases into a national spatial data infrastructure, or NSDI. Externally to any one nation, the task will be to link the various NSDIs to develop spatial data market places, accessible via the Information Highway. This is already spanning continents. Constraints of physical separation or time differences are no longer significant. As a result, the fusion of computer and communications technologies is bringing about a major social transformation with dimensions so vast that they are difficult to discern. The NSDIs of the world will form the major nodes of that highway. Those nodes are essential if spatially related data are to be readily transported, integrated and used by the decision-makers of tomorrow. We see the future of NMOs as not just participants, but as leaders in the development of national strategies to manage spatial data. After all, it is the database of digital map data that underpins all other national spatial data.

To be successful, NSDIs must maximize the accessibility, availability, and application of geographically referenced data. To this end, Geomatics Canada began in 1994 the development of GeoExpress, a potential model for a Canadian NSDI. The objective is simply to facilitate the retrieval and use of geographically referenced information from a host of separate databases. These databases are produced by various levels of government, by the private sector, and by other non-government organizations. They cover topics ranging from natural resources and the environment to social and economic data. Integration of these disparate databases will provide information decision-makers need, easily and cost-effectively. For example, topographic contour information, soil maps, forest cover data, and hydrology can be combined to identify fragile areas where prudent forestry is needed to prevent soil erosion and avoid damage to the water system. The resulting map of fragile areas can be further combined with administrative maps to identify zones of management responsibility. Canada has also established the Mapping 2000 Alliance, bringing together expertise from the public, private, and academic sectors. One development of the Alliance is ChartNet, a client/server software application for the collaboration, production, maintenance, and distribution of electronic hydrographic charts in a high-speed, wide-area network environment.

Building an NSDI is much more than developing the translators, standards, and communication protocols to link disparate spatial databases. It requires building a complete national infrastructure. This involves a national network linking local, wide-area, and international networks. This national network must not only be widely accessible but also be simple to use, and transparent to the user. Technical problems will be a relatively minor concern in building an NSDI. Dealing with the political, organizational, and financial issues will be the central concern. A functioning NSDI involves accessibility to data which were previously coveted and jealously guarded by institutions. This raises the problems of ownership of data, copyright, licensing, data distribution, security of data, liability for the deficiencies of data, and so on. The inherent right of citizens to access and use public data on a free or low-cost basis is drastically opposed to the right of public institutions to generate revenue from the use of those data. All of these fundamental issues must be addressed for NSDIs and the Information Highway to be effective.

DEVELOPING STRATEGIES FOR THE FUTURE

Joint ventures or strategic alliances involving private companies, universities and public agencies will give access to research, to the efficiencies of the private sector, and to the public sector's abilities to manage complex projects. A large part of alliances between the public and private sector will result in commercially viable value-added products and services. *(Ryttersgaard 1995)*

While the activities funded by public money are continually being streamlined, there is a concurrent pressure for NMOs to look for new areas of activity that will generate the revenues needed to supplement government appropriation. This has created another problem, the lack of marketing expertise in some such agencies. In the recent past, such marketing has been avoided, simply because any increased revenues went to the public accounts and could not be used even to offset the cost of marketing. The current emphasis on cost recovery and revenue generation is instilling another element of cultural change in NMOs.

NMOs are also faced with new challenges in trying to explain to bureaucrats why it is essential to continue to fund core activities. In the main, NMOs are not very good at promoting what they do or getting the media's attention for success stories. Indeed, NMOs seem deliberately to avoid the media and to maintain a low profile. The need now to 'wave the flag' and to demonstrate their value to society is another element of the paradigm shift they are experiencing.

CONCLUDING REMARKS

NMOs are undergoing the most intense review ever of their *raison d'être*. Economic realities are driving downsizing, streamlining, privatization, budget reduction, and revenue generation. Yet, in spite of all this, the future for our agencies can be as bright as we want it to be. NMOs collectively control or strongly influence the creation of most of the world's spatially related Geographic Information, a commodity that will be the basis for the knowledge-based society of the twenty-first century. They can continue to exercise that control or influence for the benefit of society. But it will be taken away if they do not adapt to the changing realities. Our preferred future is at hand. It is up to us in the NMOs to design and implement it. Otherwise, we face the uncertainties of an imposed future.

REFERENCES:

Ellyard P 1994 The emerging planetary paradigm: professionalism for an interdependent planetary 21st century. *International Federation of Surveyors International Conference*, Melbourne, 5–12 March 1994: 62–79

Hecht LG 1995 Technology development, policy, and GIS interoperability – the process of change. *GIS World* 8 (5): 32–4

Rhind DW 1995 GIM interviews Professor David Rhind, Director-General and Chief Executive, Ordnance Survey. *Geodetical Information Magazine* 9 (5): 55–60

Ryttersgaard J 1995 The surveyor and information society, case study 1. *Geodetical Information Magazine* 9 (5): 28–31

Trinder JC, Fraser CS 1994 The case for a change of name of a discipline in the academic context. *The Australian Surveyor* 39 (2): 87–91

CHAPTER 17

The French approach

Jean-Philippe Grelot

SUMMARY

The chapter reviews the (implicit) way that the Institut Géographique National (IGN), the French national mapping organization (NMO), has moved towards the users and the market in recent years. It describes the historical situation and the funding dilemma which IGN faces in building, up-dating, and exploiting its cartographic and topographic databases. The general objectives set for IGN by government and the contract which expresses these are discussed, together with the form of copyright protection which exists in France and IGN pricing policy. The chapter concludes by describing the evolving relationship between IGN and the private sector.

HISTORICAL ROLE OF FRENCH MAPPING ORGANIZATIONS

As in most European countries, maps produced for the French government since the 1700s have been tools for supporting the policy of central governments. The primary policies have been those for administration, defence and security, and for land registration. Different mapping organizations have been created as government agencies or services to provide cadastral mapping, topographic mapping, and hydrographic mapping. In turn, the information they assembled served as the bases for all other geo-referenced information, from technical information (geology, soils, vegetation, forestry, population, and so on) to tourist information (roads, paths, sites, and so forth). Cadastral mapping is now made within the Ministry of Finance, geodetic surveys and topographic mapping are made by the IGN, which is an agency under the Ministry of Public Works, and hydrographic surveys and charts are made by Service Hydrographique de la Marine within the Navy, Ministry of Defence.

As part of governmental administration, the missions of these organizations have previously been totally funded by the state.

IGN AS AN ORGANIZATION

IGN has a statutory mission to carry out research, teaching, production, public dissemination of information, and management of information. It functions under the Ministry of Public Works but has a link to the Ministry of Finance. The IGN Board of Directors is essentially a steering committee and includes staff representatives and others from various ministries including Agriculture and Defence, from the French space agency, and from other bodies; the Chair of the Board is named by the Minister of Public Works. IGN's Director General is appointed by the Council of Ministers.

The budget is 700 million French francs funded through a five year contract with the state. The state contributes 400 million francs directly. Of the other 300 million, 110 million francs are derived from the public at large, 145 million francs arise from the professional market (80 percent of which is public sector) and 35 million francs are generated from overseas activities.

The state contract sets the grant, the production aims, and the criteria for judging success. These criteria are productivity gains, growth of market income, and the annual financial out-turn. The 2000 staff are paid bonuses if the results are good. A key to producing good results is the creation of additional customers and involvement in many parts of the expanding market place. One way in which IGN helps to create a market is by the loan of IGN France staff to other organizations in France to foster the need for GI. It is strongly involved with other commercial organizations, typically through some form of shareholding: it holds equity in IGN France International (along with IGN Spain), in SPOT Image (the French remote sensing company), in NAVTech (a multi-national enterprise creating technology and data for car guidance systems), and in companies specializing in crop forecasting through remote sensing and in training.

EARLY COMMERCIAL ACTIVITIES OF IGN

Mainly since World War II, however, IGN has been selling paper copies of its base maps and of derived versions of base maps to the general public. The retail price is now several ECUS or US dollars per copy and covers printing, storage, and distribution costs. IGN has no privilege in this activity; it has private competitors especially in regard to small-scale maps and in tourist areas. These are the two main and the only profitable market segments.

IGN has also supplied reproduction material of its maps at all scales to end-users and to a few map publishers. The price charged for reproduction material is approximately twice the direct copy cost. This level of charging, even including a royalty for reproduction in quantity, does not cover survey or compilation costs.

Since the end of the 1960s IGN has been encouraged by the French government to develop and target its products (maps) and 'know-how' (services) towards:

- the general public;
- local governments and public organizations in France and abroad; and
- private companies.

At that time, the market was mainly a supply-led market, as opposed to a demand-led one, and the government did not define specific guidelines for pricing strategies.

DIGITAL ISSUES IN THE LATE 1980s

At the beginning of the 1980s, IGN moved from the production of analogue maps to the capture of digital data. This was dictated by technical considerations rather than by a marketing strategy. But a number of issues quickly arose:

- digital data designed for map production could be used in digital form in geographic information systems (GIS): which product specification should be used and which pricing strategy should be applied?
- existing analogue maps were not the ideal products for and from information systems and decision-making systems; how should the specifications of digital cartographic reference databases be defined?
- as the potential demand for digital databases for professional uses is perceived as much larger than that for analogue maps, the government anticipated the possibility of reducing its funding and for encouraging IGN to find financial resources directly from the market.

However, NMOs cannot simply define their products strictly and solely from market research. They are typically required to produce reference data sets over the *totality* of their national territory and not simply when and where a market demand exists (and is adequate to pay for all the costs involved). NMOs have also to distribute data to a much wider extent than simply through the most profitable channels. Under their remit, they may have to produce and to maintain a basic infrastructure transcending any potential market and they may have to develop research activities for the whole community and wider than their own narrow interests. Moreover, as a public infrastructure, cartographic infrastructure has to conform with public sector obligations of universal service and of equal access to citizens.

THE FUNDING DILEMMA

The funding dilemma facing IGN can be summarized as follows:

- IGN has to spend at least the same money for a similar production each year (modernization will in fact be more costly until complete digital coverage is achieved);
- it sub-contracts very limited volumes and its main expenditure is on its labour force (amounting 65 to 70 percent of total costs). This results in a severely constrained short-term flexibility;

- the production of a nation-wide cartographic coverage requires long-term commitment;
- direct funding by government is decreasing;
- the IGN annual budget can be balanced only if revenues generated from the market increase.

The solution to this dilemma is to identify those activities which may generate sufficient financial resources to balance the costs of operation through time. Typically, sales of products for the general public may increase at a relatively low rate, perhaps 3 to 5 percent per year. It is also obvious that traditional activities previously funded by the government will not be funded from the market if there is only one customer. In such circumstances, the single customer will choose from information sources on a purely competitive basis and the specifications and product cost structure will not always be favourable to an IGN basic product since it is defined to meet the needs of several domains, and whose specifications have to conform homogeneity over all the French territory.

In addition, there is now a strong socio-economic pressure for concentrating the activities of a number of public organizations on public services only, especially in the information area (Chamoux and Ronai 1996).

The inescapable conclusion is that revenues which IGN obtains from the market need to increase to a level sufficient to balance its costs of operation over the years in the context of the governmental funding decrease. But this can only be achieved through and from information products, i.e. from the licensing of digital databases. In addition, this income has to cover not only distribution costs (including but not limited to reproduction costs) but also some part of the capture and production costs. Moreover, for some products and/or areas, the total amount received from licence fees has to be greater than the capture and production costs of these products and/or areas to ensure that the whole territory will receive basically the same cartographic infrastructure irrespective of whether market demand exists in the short term. In other words, there needs to be a cross-subsidy from 'profitable' products and areas to 'unprofitable' ones if government does not recognize this problem in its funding and the NMO remit remains unchanged.

At this stage, there is no proposal for privatization of this service in France. Geographic Information is not perceived as a private market matter but is still seen as a tool for general management. Pressure is applied to reduce the costs of the service to the taxpayer through an agreement between IGN and the government, with a semestrial review of the production programmes and expenses.

THE COPYRIGHT ISSUES

This section refers specifically to the French context. There are some differences between that and its equivalent in other European countries.

The French Law on intellectual property updated in July 1992 under No. 92-597 (Code de la Propriété intellectuelle, 1992: 3-26) gives protection to authors' creations as soon as their designs are being transformed into actual pieces of work. Basically the author is an individual, but all ownership is transferred to the author's organization if the creation is made as part of the normal activity of that author within the organization. The status (whether private or public) of the organization is irrelevant. Facts, ideas, and raw data as such are not protected. The creation has to be original as compared with pre-existing material. Originality is evaluated according to overall characteristics despite any discrepancies in the details.

Protection is given against reproduction, representation, adaptation, and transformation by all means and on all media. It covers two areas:

- 'moral' protection; and
- 'material' protection.

'Moral' protection exists to protect the spirit of the piece of work and the image of the author and of his/her creation from a cultural point of view. It prevents any adaptation of the work to be made which transgresses the intention of the author. Although this protection is specially devoted to literature, arts, and films, it is the key element which recognizes the primary right of the author to allow the use of his/her production in each kind of application.

'Material' protection defines the principles of payment of the author when reproduction, representation, adaptation, or transformation have been allowed. Accordingly, the clearance, or licence, has to define in detail the user, all uses, and duration of use which have been permitted. The author basically has total freedom in giving permission and in setting pricing: in this particular regard, there may be some conflict with other regulations about free and open competition.

For those NMOs which can benefit from such protection, the laws on intellectual property and on copyright give the legal framework for defining licensing policies and for organizing the distribution of data, and for defining the specifications of data to be supplied, the permitted users (end- users versus intermediate users), the inclusion of value-added data, etc. All these clauses thus arise under the framework of a very general regulation which does not depend on the statutes of the individual organization; in that respect they do not infringe the rules of competition.

The primary interest of NMOs is in regard to the 'material' protection area. In that sense, the European Union approach to protecting databases as investments, based on a 'sweat of the brow' principle, has been greatly clarified through the European Directive on the legal protection of databases (European Parliament and Council 1996). It is worth noting that no specific provision has been made for databases compiled by public organizations as opposed to those compiled by private companies.

The 'moral' protection established by the French law, which has often been named 'The French cultural exception', can also be relevant to database quality and maintenance issues. These will be of crucial importance in the future.

GENERAL OBJECTIVES GIVEN TO IGN

The definition of IGN's government-funded programmes combines two basic approaches:

- a financial approach determines how much can be done in each area according to the budget;
- a technical approach determines what should be done in order to meet the needs and expectations of a number of key users.

The final definition of the programmes takes into account the policy of general interest supported by public services: sovereignty, territorial unity, and solidarity; balanced land planning and environment protection; and research of economic and social efficiency in a middle- and long-term perspective. Proposed programmes are presented each year to the National Council on Geographic Information with the volumes anticipated for every type of product. This council was established in 1986 and acts as an advisory body to central government; its members represent the main public producers, all government departments involved in Geographic Information (public works and transportation, environment, agriculture, finances, industry, education, research, co-operation, foreign affairs, defence), public utilities, local and regional governments, and chartered surveyors. The council tries to reach consensus on different matters: it moves from considering technical recommendations to matters of general policy but it has no role in the determination of the budgets of public organizations nor on the assessment of their efficiency.

When IGN has launched its two major database programmes (the creation of a three-dimensional topographic database with 1 m accuracy and of a cartographic database with 10 m accuracy), it showed that the normal annual budget mechanism was not suited to these long-term projects and that the costs would not be covered by government budgets in this difficult period. As a result, three successive agreements have been made between IGN and the state, using a procedure defined for the contracts between the state and the French regions in order to share the financing of major infrastructures. These agreements have been made for the periods 1985–88, 1989–92 and (currently) 1993–97. They define technical and cost objectives for IGN activities in relation to the evolution in demand for basic geographic digital data and to the way users now operate. Under the current agreement, IGN has to achieve approximately 3 percent cost savings per year, and its resources derived from the market have to increase from 47 percent to 51 percent of its operational costs, computed on the same basis as in any private company. IGN reports every six months to the French government but does not publish financial reports to the general public.

The current agreement gives specific objectives for database production; for instance:

- ramping up the availability of the production line of the topographic database (involving about 300 people) from 1997 to achieve an annual coverage of 35,000 to 40,000 square km;
- completing data capture of the land-use categories of the cartographic database in 1995; the database has been made available since 1993 and the updating process began in 1994.

As far as financing is concerned, the agreement states: 'In addition to the activities covered by government funding and listed in the agreement, any other product or service demanded by state administration and other public organization belongs to the market domain and has to be provided against specific payment.'

A fundamental principle of the agreement is that the initial capture and the updating of national reference databases have to be financed from a variety of sources. During the initial phase, state financing is the major source but it has to be supplemented by and transferred to users of any type, i.e. state organizations, local governments, private companies, etc. France is not alone in this: though there are differences because of the type of geographic infrastructure they have to provide, a number of governmental survey and mapping organizations in Europe have to move from funding by government to funding by the end-users. This trend is a general socio-economic policy across many sectors but it also reflects the growing economic role of (digital) Geographic Information in decision-making processes.

Under the current rules, IGN now requires a financial contribution from users from the very beginning in order to cover distribution costs and all services provided in delivering digital products. For analogue maps, the financial scheme remains quite similar to long-established practice: the costs of direct reproduction and printing, of storage, and all sales and marketing costs (including staff) have to be covered by sales revenues. These revenues also have to contribute to the necessary investment (including research and development) and sometimes to the compilation of the maps. In practice, this scheme has been adapted to apply also to the digital products but in this latter case a significant part of the income has also to cover data capture costs.

IGN PRICING POLICY

Geographic and cartographic data is information or represents it. The wider the distribution of it, the greater is the economic impact of these data (Didier 1990). One aim of IGN is that its cartographic products form the reference frame for planning and land management policies. As a result, IGN tries to ensure that it addresses the needs of the largest number of users. Yet the basic characteristics of geo-referenced data imply that, for a given territory, the number of potential users is limited: technical as well as human resources for making the data available to users are still costly, especially because this still-emerging activity requires continuous and time-consuming technical support.

Moreover, the state, and accordingly IGN as a government organization, takes the role of initiator, facilitator, and regulator. As an initiator, it has to ensure the setting up of the production facility; as a facilitator, it completes the production up to a defined minimal content; as a regulator, it guarantees the homogeneity of the cartographic infrastructure all over the national territory in spite of differences between regional economic status. And since the data are intended for both national use and/or local users, the government has defined, through the IGN budget, a mechanism combining national funding and funding by the users, consistent with the logic of public service. One important decision made by the French government was that the cartographic infrastructure is considered globally and not product by product since this results in a smoothing of investment and operational cycles.

The direct economic relationship between users and IGN facilitates the creation of a balance between supply and demand in terms of data specifications, updating and the evolution of products. This technical and economic compromise has to conform with the constraints provided by the need for a national infrastructure: its value is assessed in relation to all services given to end-users, most frequently through an evaluation of costs avoided by the national taxpayer by the charging mechanism.

According to this policy, IGN distributes its topographic and cartographic databases with a licensing system and a price list updated and published every year. The licensing system includes a basic fee depending on the number of users and the type of data, an optional maintenance and updating annual fee, and a royalty when maps are derived from the data set and reproduced in quantities. The user is not allowed to produce maps from IGN material which could compete with existing IGN map series without IGN's prior specific consent.

IGN has defined two integration modes corresponding to two types of users and uses:

- a vertical mode;
- a horizontal mode.

The vertical mode is offered to central organizations acting for their regional offices which, in totality, cover all or a significant part of the country. A model agreement is defined between the central organization and IGN and every regional office makes a specific agreement using the technical and pricing specifications of the model agreement. The price is determined by taking into account the area covered by the central organization and an appropriate discount is applied either to the first regional office or when a sufficient number of regional offices have signed the agreement in order to cover a given area. The user is generally involved in the updating process through providing relevant information.

The horizontal mode corresponds to the building up of local servers addressing a number of different public users (such as local governments and regional offices of the central government) at regional level. IGN has a single contact point which is responsible for every member of the group of the users. This contact point is provided with a multiple licence covering all users and the relevant number of workstations for each of them.

In addition to this scheme, IGN is developing relationships with a number of value-added resellers, including the suppliers of GIS. The tendency now is to address application domains through resellers (transportation, telecommunications, etc.) while multi-purpose activities and regional and central government levels are directly addressed by IGN itself. This seems an appropriate way to combine co-operation with the private sector with meeting the general objectives on the cartographic infrastructure laid down by the national government to its NMO.

REFERENCES

Chamoux JP, Ronai M 1996 *Exploiter les données publiques.* Paris, A Jour
Code de la Propriété intellectuelle 1992. Paris, Direction des Journaux Officiels
Didier M 1990 *Utilité et valeur de l'information géographique.* Paris, Economica
European Parliament and Council Directive 96/9/EC of 11 March 1996 on the Legal Protection of Databases 1996 *Official Journal of the European Communities* No. L (77): 20–28

CHAPTER 18

Merger, government firms, and privatization? The new Swedish approach

Ulf Sandgren

SUMMARY

The National Land Survey (NLS) and the Central Board for Real Estate Data (CFD) were merged into a new organization from 1 January 1996. The new body has three main tasks: to provide cadastral services, land and Geographic Information services, and commercial services. At the same time, some 120 County Survey Authorities, Real Estate Registration Authorities, and Real Estate Formation Authorities, were merged into 24 new County Survey Authorities.

Services carried out on a commercial basis have been organized separately from those for the public interest. The intention is that these commercial services should later be fully moved from the authority into one or more companies. The first manifestation of this is that, from 1 July 1995, the real estate valuation service which was carried out on a repayment basis has been moved from the NLS into a new government-owned limited company.

This chapter describes the main reasons for the organizational changes, the processes which were involved, the tasks of the new organization, and how it will be financed.

THE OPERATING ENVIRONMENT FOR THE NEW ORGANIZATION

The main reasons for the organizational changes that are in process in Sweden today are:

- the changes in user needs;
- the impact of new technology;
- the need for reform to improve efficiency and bring about cost reductions.

Additional factors include political decisions to separate official duties from commercial services and to prepare the organization for greater levels of contracting out.

To meet those demands, a total reconstruction of the organizations involved was a necessity. However, to understand what has been done, it is first necessary to give a brief overview of the previous organization of surveying and mapping in Sweden.

A SHORT HISTORY OF SURVEYING AND MAPPING IN SWEDEN

Surveying and mapping have deep roots in Sweden: the NLS can trace its lineage back to 1628, when the first systematic mapping of the country was begun. Anders Bure was then commissioned by King Gustav II Adolf to establish an organization for surveying and mapping. The king was then extending the boundaries of his state and was in need of funds to finance his war actions. The goal of the first mapping was to lay the foundation for a national property taxation system. Mapping was then – and still is – also an important instrument for fostering economic growth and development of the country.

Great land reforms took place in our country during the eighteenth and nineteenth centuries. They ensured, among other things, that earlier state land or jointly used land was divided into privately owned lots. These reforms remain contentious today. But there is no doubt that they have been of great importance in developing new and efficient agricultural methods and, consequently, for the growth in wealth of Sweden.

At the beginning of the nineteenth century, the Swedish armed forces started topographic mapping of the country to fulfil their own purposes. Later on, they also took over the economic mapping. So, for a long period of time, most of the official mapping in Sweden was a task for the military organization. In 1937, however, it was handed over to a new civil agency, the Geographical Survey Office. This agency had, as the NLS still has, the responsibility both for military and civil mapping. This integrated organization seems a unique but very convenient arrangement.

As described earlier, mapping activities have always been connected to real property formation. Thus mapping was also a task for the NLS which carried it out at a variety of scales on a repayment basis. In principle therefore, there were many good reasons to merge the NLS and the Geographical Survey Office. This organizational reform took place in 1974. As a result of the merger, the organization for real estate formation gained access to advanced technical resources at the former Geographical Survey Office. At the same time the official map-makers gained access to a regional and local organization with established contacts with customers.

In 1966, an official report recognized the need for a reform of the real property registration and the land/title registration. In 1968 Parliament decided to establish the land data bank system by use of computer technology: the Central Board for Real Estate Data (CFD) was established the same year. The conversion of the real property register and the land/title register was started in 1971 and was completed in September 1995.

The organization up to now

Before the organizational changes in January 1996, the NLS had three basic tasks: to carry out cadastral survey and land consolidation, to produce official mapping, and to provide applied services on a repayment basis. It was a three-tiered organization with a central office in Gävle some 150 km north of Stockholm, 24 regional offices, and 110 local offices. The total staff was of the order of 3000.

Cadastral survey, real estate formation, and land consolidation were carried out by the local offices (called Real Estate Formation Authorities). The local organization also supplied individuals, municipalities, industrial and forest companies, etc. with various kinds of services on a repayment basis. These services included, for example, preparation of maps at a variety of scales for different purposes, setting-out and control of the location of buildings, real estate judicial investigations, and valuation of land and buildings. Outside the main framework of the state organization, there were also special urban development units in 41 of Sweden's 286 municipalities.

In every one of the 24 counties there was a County Survey Authority, which was the head authority for the local land survey organization. With their technical resources, they also served as links between the central office, as the producer of official maps, and various map-users. The real estate registration was a task for the Real Property Register Authorities. These were, in practice, integrated in the County Survey Authorities. In 29 of the municipalities with Real Estate Formation Authorities for urban development, there were also municipal Real Property Register Authorities.

Land registration was, and still is, performed by 94 Land Register Authorities. These authorities are part of the general lower courts and are administratively supervised by the National Courts Administration.

The Central Board for Real Estate Data (CFD) had the main responsibility for development, implementation, and processing of the Swedish Land Data Bank System. The work was carried out in close co-operation with the land survey and the court organizations.

A SUMMARY OF THE REFORM PROCESS

In 1992 the NLS proposed to the government a far-reaching organizational reform. It proposed that, on the central level, the Central Board for Real Estate Data (CFD), the Survey itself and those parts in the National Courts Administration responsible for the supervision of the Land Register

Authorities be merged into a new single organization. On the local and regional level, the proposal was that the Real Property Formation Authorities (157), the Real Property Register Authorities (53), and the Land Register Authorities (94) be merged into 24 new authorities, one for each county. These were to be given responsibility for real estate formation, real estate registration, land registration, and tax assessment valuation. The proposal also included a clear division between official duties and services provided on a repayment basis, but still organized within and by the central and regional authorities.

In 1993 the government set up a committee with the task of investigating the organization of land survey, real estate data, land registration, etc. The committee had also to explore the possibilities of a closer co-operation between the national mapping and the production of marine charts. The instructions did *not* include the organization of tax assessment valuation.

The terms of reference for the committee stressed the following goals for the future organization:

- cadastral survey, land consolidation, and official mapping are important parts of the infrastructure in society. Because of this, any new organization should promote an efficient real estate market and land use and meet the needs for maps and spatial information in society;
- the organization should be characterized by quality, efficiency, and competence;
- on-going improvements in efficiency and development should be actively promoted;
- total costs should decrease;
- the new organization should be easy to understand;
- the organization should, as far as possible, be uniform for the entire country;
- it should be a decentralized and market-focused organization with few hierarchical levels;
- official duties should, in principle, be separated from commercial services. The official duties should be operated under the rule of law while other services should be prepared for open competition.

In October 1993 the committee presented its first proposals concerning a new organization. Nine months later it produced its report on financing, co-ordination, and regulation, but a key recommendation in the first report was that official duties should be separated from services provided on a commercial basis. The latter should be organized within a limited company owned by the government. All technical resources for official mapping, as well as those for cadastral survey and land consolidation, should be moved to the company. The new official authority should concentrate on official duties and buy technical services on the open market. The proposed company would then compete with other enterprises within or outside the country. The company should have offices covering the whole country.

The new central, official authority should be established by merging the official duties parts of both NLS and CFD, as well as the parts in the National Courts Administration responsible for the supervision of the Land Register Authorities.

On the regional level, new authorities were proposed to be established by merging the County Survey Authorities, the Real Property Registration Authorities, the Real Estate Formation Authorities, and the Land Register Authorities. At the same time, all tasks within these pre-existing bodies that not are defined as official duties should be moved to the company. The municipal Real Estate Formation Authorities and Land Register Authorities were proposed to be discontinued and the responsibility for these tasks completely transferred to the governmental organization. A new administrative form for municipal handling of real estate formation within the planning process was proposed.

The report from the committee was referred to 120 organizations for consideration. No fewer than 230 responses were received! That shows that these matters are of great interest to many sections of society. Following this public consultation, the government presented its proposals to Parliament in March 1994. In comparison with the proposals from the committee, the government wanted to proceed more cautiously. The Land Register Authorities were, for the time being, to remain within the courts administration. It concluded that the issue of completely moving the responsibility for real estate formation and land registration from the municipalities to the state needed to be considered more deeply. Only some parts of the commercial services were considered to be ready for transfer from the official authority into new companies. Government considered that two companies should be established: one for valuation of land and real property and another for the publishing of maps and cartographic production of tourist maps, etc. It was, however, clearly expressed that other types of repayment services should be organized separately from official duties and must be prepared to be carried out in a company. At the same time, it was recognized that certain repayment services in the future should be carried out by the authorities, especially on the regional level.

Parliament decided in June 1994 as the government had proposed. A few weeks later, the committee presented its final report with proposals concerning financing, co-ordination between agencies, and the regulation needed for the implementation of the new organization. This report was also referred to a great number of organizations for consideration.

In August 1994, the government appointed a new committee to make the necessary preparations for establishing the new organization. The committee was charged with demarcating the activities that should be moved to the companies from the authorities, with working out the organizational structure in detail, and with other tasks. In December, the committee also got the commission to investigate whether a third company should be established for the handling of real estate data.

In February 1995 the government presented a bill on financing the various bodies based on proposals from the two committees. It was then agreed by government that only one company should be set up – that for real estate valuation. The main reason for this decision was that real estate valuation on a repayment basis could mean that the public might lose confidence in the authority's official duties. Other types of repayment services were to be prepared for incorporation in a company at an unspecified time. One important decision by government that real property formation, land registration, and the information in the Land Data Bank System and in official maps and geographic databases were important parts of the infrastructure in society. The basic costs of these activities must, therefore, be covered by the state. On the other hand, the government proposed that the users of the information to a greater extent than earlier should contribute to the costs for management and development of the information systems. Furthermore, the same principles should also be applied to different kinds of information. It was anticipated that this would lead to higher charges for printed maps and the use of information from the Land Data Bank System, but lower charges for the use of databases containing Geographical Information. A new pricing policy, based on these principles, was inaugurated by the NLS on 1 January 1996.

THE NEW NATIONAL LAND SURVEY

From 1 January 1996 the NLS was merged with CFD into one new agency. This involved some loss of functions. From 1 July 1995 real estate valuation on a repayment basis was moved from the NLS into a new state company called SVEFA, Svensk Fastighetsvördering AB (Swedish Real Estate Valuation Ltd). Just over 100 NLS real estate valuers have joined the new limited company. The company is now the biggest of its kind in Sweden, with its head office in Stockholm and offices in 25 different places around Sweden.

The key aims when organizing the new agency were to facilitate the renewal of the cadastral services, to focus on the organization's role as a provider of information and co-ordinator of the handling of land and geographic information in Swedish society, to focus on official duties and develop the business-like activities separately from these duties (including preparation for future moves of the more business-like activities from the state agency to a limited company), to simplify the complex and expensive administrative structure, to pay close regard to some partially new financial aspects, and to exploit advances in technology.

To achieve these aims, the organization has been divided into three main areas of activity:

- cadastral services;
- land and Geographic Information services;
- repayment services.

To support these main departments, there is one Research and Development department, one service department, and a staff unit.

Cadastral services

On the central level, the department of cadastral services has the responsibility for the supervision of, and for giving support to, the new regional Land Survey Authorities. Its most important task is to support the renewal of the real estate formation process. That includes an increased concentration on rule of law, quality, competence, shortening of the time period required to handle cases, and a reduction in cost. Integrated systems based on computer technology are being developed and the register maps are being transformed to cadastral databases linked to the non-graphic real estate information in the Land Data Bank System. The merging of NLS and CFD has facilitated these efforts.

The main task for the regional Land Survey Authorities is to carry out the cadastral services. Beyond this, they have an important role as co-ordinators on the local and regional level in regard to the updating and use of land and Geographic Information. They also have other official duties and provide some kinds of services on a repayment basis, provided these are closely linked to their official duties. They are, for example, still able to provide a house-builder with a site map derived from a cadastral survey.

The land and Geographic Information service

The new organization has an important role in providing society with basic land and Geographic Information. The most important tasks for the department of land and Geographic Information services are to utilize the benefits of the co-ordination of land and Geographic Information, to tailor the information to the users' needs, and to make such information easily accessible, quality-marked, and good value for money. At the same time, more efficiency in handling of information through co-ordination with other agencies must be sought; for example, in the updating of different databases.

The responsibility for *all* kinds of information services lies with the new department – archives, registers, maps, databases – but the department does not have production resources. The department works out the technical specifications needed and purchases the production from Metria (the commercial department) or from other providers. The intention of this kind of arrangement is to ensure a focus on the authority's role as provider of information and co-ordinator of the provision of information in society, as well as the creation of competition and reduction of costs. It is intended that this will ensure that the commercial part of the organization is better prepared to provide other kinds of commercial services on the open market.

Metria

The department for commercial services is called Metria. It provides on a business-like basis the department for information services with air photography, orthophoto production, maintenance of the fundamental national geodetic networks, establishment and maintenance of fundamental geographic databases, etc.

In addition to these services, Metria also carries out a wide range of services on a repayment basis to other customers, such as municipalities, industrial and forestry companies, and utilities. Examples of these services are the production of large-scale maps and plans, derived maps and database products based on the national map series/fundamental geographic databases, geodetic measurements, and support to GIS users.

The research and development department

The R&D department holds the competence for new developments concerning geodesy, photogrammetry, cartography, and information technology. The work is mainly carried out in project form, often with other departments as customers and with project members drawn from other parts of the organization. This department also has the responsibility for the preparation of strategic plans and decisions for the entire organization, concerning, for example, information technology.

The service department

The service department gives support to the whole NLS in regard to finances, personnel, accommodation, administration, computer operations, graphic production, and other services.

The staff unit

The staff unit gives support to the Director General on strategic questions and other questions of common interest for the whole organization.

The re-organization department

This temporary department was formed to support about 120 people who became superfluous as a consequence of the re-organization on 1 January 1996. It works actively together with the Job Security Foundation, county employment boards, and other bodies to offer training, contributions to trial employment, support to those wishing to start their own companies, and so on.

ESTABLISHING THE NEW ORGANIZATION

From 1 July 1995, a new Director General was appointed with responsibility both for CFD and NLS. This was an important prerequisite for a successful integration of the two organizations. The process of building up the new integrated organization began with decisions on the new organizational structure. The heads of the new divisions were appointed and a number of working groups prepared different policies and procedures, such as the handling of personnel, financial models and systems, management organization, the information technology strategy, the accommodation needs, and the handling of archives. One group worked with the integration process itself; they described the existing and desired cultures within the organizations involved and prepared plans to foster good internal communications, education, and 'getting together'.

The new organization has already led to:

- a single-minded focus on the main objectives of the organization;
- a reduction of organizational levels. The number of managers has decreased from some 250 to fewer than 100 and the administrative costs have been reduced;
- introduction of a clearly defined customer–supplier concept;
- more tightly implemented project organization, especially concerning development.

The new organization has been established and a great number of changes have been carried out. It is, however, important to stress that the organization just formed is a vehicle for making necessary alterations, to change and develop the handling of quality, the implementation of new methods, enhance co-operation with other agencies, etc. An immense amount of work has, therefore, been organized through a number internal changes. Further change is inevitable and the future will also depend on decisions by the government and the Parliament. Two questions are of particular interest at the moment to those involved – Metria's future and the financing of the operations.

The government has given the NLS directions to investigate and make proposals concerning Metria's future. Questions to be addressed include whether Metria or parts of the department should be organized as a limited company, remain as a part of the state agency, or be organized in another form. And what steps would need to be taken to prepare for any such organizational change? The NLS will present their findings in a report to government at the end of 1996.

Funding NLS's activities

The NLS has also been ordered to investigate and make proposals to government concerning the long-term financing of their production functions. Today the NLS has an annual turnover of about 1400 million Swedish Crowns (MSEK) – i.e. about £120 million or US$200 million. Of this total, 500 MSEK derives from parliamentary votes, another 500 MSEK from fees levied for official activities, and the remaining 400 MSEK from charges made for repayment services. Table 18.1 below shows how the figures break down by area of activity.

Table 18.1 National Land Survey income by sector of activity

Activity sector	Vote (MSEK)	Fees (monopoly) (MSEK)	Fees (competition) (MSEK)	Activity total
Cadastral services	175	350	75	600
Land & Geographic Information Service	325	150	–	475
Metria	–	–	325	325
TOTAL	500	500	400	1400

The organizational change of 1 January 1996 was paralleled by a reduction of parliamentary funds of 30 MSEK (as compared with the combined funds of CFD and NLS in 1995). There will be a further reduction of 17 MSEK in 1997 and a preliminary decision has been made by government to cut these funds by another 78 MSEK in 1998. A five-year finance plan is being drawn up with the objective of progressively reducing the call on parliamentary funding. This was to be presented to government in spring 1997.

Refocusing NLS

The programme of changes going on within NLS is designed to improve the utility of the organization to the community, focus on the needs of customers, enhance quality of products and services, improve internal and external co-operation, and produce greater efficiencies. To achieve all these aims, it is essential to have an understanding of the value of what NLS does, to ensure that what is available is well known amongst the populace and to know what is really needed and how this is changing over time. Efforts have been increased to disseminate details of the NLS products and services. A pilot study has been made of the costs and benefits of NLS's activities, and a full study was begun in late 1996. A comprehensive independent study has been commissioned into user views of NLS and this will be repeated periodically. The first study suggested that the NLS is seen as providing a well-qualified and well-priced service, but that there are areas in which it can improve.

Adapting to the need to meet customers' requirements involves a change of NLS culture, the development of better advisory functions (including representatives of user bodies, not just government officials) and support of applications rather than a 'one-off' supply of data or services. It necessitates further efforts to shorten the time scales needed to handle jobs and enquiries and to reduce fees. New goals have been set for quality of products and services and a Quality Manager has been appointed to co-ordinate and stimulate this work. Much greater focus has been placed on extracting value from information technology (IT). At operational level, IT is a matter for the different departments but an IT strategist is charged with creating the ground rules for acquisition and use of such facilities and taking an active role in NLS's strategic and operational planning generally. Vulnerability and security are now also major issues in an IT-based organization and these are addressed at the strategic level by the deputy head of security. In general, NLS now operates internally on a customer/contractor principle in most respects, i.e. one party orders goods or services from another and that other party is responsible for providing the 'deliverables' to agreed costs, quality, and timetable. So far as external matters are concerned, NLS is seeking new forms of collaboration at both strategic and operational level with other organizations.

Improved efficiency is a primary driving force for the change programme. It is being sought through clearer specification of what is needed and delivered and through better management processes and work flows. In particular, great emphasis is laid through policy and practice on effective and standardized forms of project management. Exposing certain activities to external competition and benchmarking activities against those in other organizations are two other methods of improving efficiency.

Change can only succeed through suitably skilled and committed staff. Staff development is being achieved through continuous development of personal competences in an organizational atmosphere of learning. Creation of good working conditions which stimulate creativity and facilitate recruitment, allied to an active equal opportunities policy, are management priorities. For these reasons, we have drawn up a number of personnel policies and strategies, including ones on management and on salaries.

A major potential for efficiency has arisen from the merger of property formation and property registration in the new NLS. This potential has been boosted further by the operational completion of the property data system, the progress in creating a digital map system, and the development of IT generally. In 'normal' cases of property surveys (i.e. about 80 percent of the total at present), each one takes about six months to process. Our goal is to reduce this to six weeks and halve their costs. Studies suggest that there are possibilities to save about 170 MSEK on an annual turnover of 500 MSEK by the year 2000. This would reduce the property formation staff involved from 1000 to about 500 or 600.

Many other activities are now ongoing in the NLS, including enhanced information dissemination both within and outside the organization. In general, however, almost everything is being questioned, and improvements are being sought in all parts of NLS.

CONCLUSIONS

Proposals to change a government organization normally take much time and effort to agree, refine, and implement. This is particularly true when politically sensitive matters are involved. However, when political imperatives exist, change can be rapid: NLS had eight months to form the new organization, to staff it, and to make all other preparations such as setting up financial models and systems, establishing a new management, forming and implementing an IT strategy, and adjusting to new accommodation needs (for instance, some 600 people at head office changed offices as a consequence of the changes).

The times when organizational change could be planned in detail, implemented slowly, and when the new organization could endure for lengthy periods is over. We are all now subject to ongoing change. In Sweden, we must decide how best to operate Metria; we have to find a good solution to the long-term financing of production functions; we expect to reduce staff greatly over the coming years; and land registration is being reviewed again (government has decided to investigate how it can be moved from the general lower courts to the NLS).

The success of the new organization will be assessed in different ways. Government has decided to carry out an overall review in 1998 (or later). Until then, NLS will report annually on progress. The Chief Executive has responsibility to achieve the targets and goals set. In addition, these external assessments will be complemented by internal evaluations, such as those of progress in improving quality systems and of customer satisfaction. Like many other public bodies in many countries, the National Land Survey of Sweden is expected to be accountable, effective, and efficient – and to be seen to be so.

CHAPTER 19

The reform of national mapping organizations: the New Zealand experience

William A Robertson and Carolina Gartner

SUMMARY

The New Zealand (NZ) experience of change in the survey and mapping industry has been unique in the world. These changes began with the major reforms of the public sector from 1986 onwards, requiring the Department of Survey and Land Information (DOSLI) to adopt a cost-recovery regime. They have been ongoing and the latest restructuring in 1996 separated out the regulatory from the commercial functions through the creation of two new organizations.

Over this time, DOSLI was a world-wide trend-setter in the management of major change, the mix of commercial and regulatory functions, the definition of its core business, and alignment with government's needs from a survey and mapping organization. This culminated in government's re-affirming its ongoing needs for an organization such as DOSLI. This chapter describes the rationale for the reform process and how it was managed.

A SUMMARY OF THE CHANGES

The process of change in the NZ survey industry was begun when DOSLI was established in April 1987. This was effected under the Survey Act 1986 as a result of a split-up of the pre-existing Department of Lands and Survey. The new department was the principal government civil and military survey, mapping, and land information agency in New Zealand. As a department of state, it received public funds in order to produce various land information and land administration related products and services for the government, other state agencies, the commercial sector, and individuals. Products and services for the last three of these groups were provided on a cost-recovery basis which offset the government appropriation. The department was headed by a Director General/Surveyor General as its Chief Executive.

The period 1987–88 marked a new era for the department. DOSLI had inherited a reputation for excellence in surveying and mapping going back over 100 years. Of its approximately 1000 staff, 80 percent were technical experts in their field. Marketing and an awareness of clients' needs were new concepts to them: until 1987, the staff thought they knew better than the client what the latter needed. Government funding mechanisms and culture ensured that it was also important to spend the allocated budget each year – or risk having it reduced in the following year. For example, huge quantities of maps were produced and printed because it was cheaper to print larger quantities than smaller ones, not because there was a market for them. Staff were quite content to wait for clients to come to them rather than actively seek business. Customers could have any product or service as long as it was in the form that it was already produced, since no variations or exceptions were allowed.

In these circumstances, the biggest challenge was to educate people who were clearly very competent in the technical area of the business but who knew little or nothing about the market for which they were producing. Clearly, we had to organize ourselves to become client- and market-orientated. All elements of the marketing function needed to be addressed by talking to our clients to find out whether the products we were then offering met their needs, reviewing the price of our existing products and services, planning how to promote and distribute these, how to recognize the competition and deal with it, review the products themselves, and make the necessary improvements.

An initial cost recovery target of 30 percent was achieved in 1987–88 and annual increments in this took the level to 70 percent by 1994–95. This was done via a combination of factors. The true cost of some of our products and services was identified and recovery factors set accordingly. A price review increased the fees and charges to a level which more accurately reflected what the product or service was worth to the user (a value-based rather than just a cost-based pricing structure). The sensitivity of the market to the subsequent increase in fees and charges became very clear, with frequent complaints that our products and services were becoming too expensive; to a market used to obtaining our products for what was really only a nominal fee, this new 'user pays' concept was a shock. We became sensitive to accusations of abuse of monopoly power and that we were making the taxpayers pay twice for what they felt they were entitled to free of charge in the first place.

FORCES FOSTERING REFORM

To change from a culture and tradition of a stable and highly regulated environment requires a major shift in values and strategic thinking. In New Zealand, this shift was precipitated by the complete change of government direction initiated in 1984 and continued by successive governments ever since.

In detail, the forces for reform that shaped DOSLI in New Zealand are no doubt peculiar to our country. However – as other chapters in this book demonstrate – some general pressures for reforms in survey and mapping organizations can be identified around the world. The rapid and continuous development of technology is hugely reducing unit costs of traditional activities in survey and mapping and enables a complete re-engineering of our processes and systems. These characteristics encourage new entrants to the industry and force traditional professionals to innovate and transform their established ways of operating. The pervasiveness of the new technology provides a new facility to integrate databases and to distribute spatial information on a scale previously thought impracticable.

Government funding is being significantly reduced in some jurisdictions either because the quantum of activity is lowered or because priorities change. In the latter case, survey and mapping cannot always rely on retaining priority in the face of more direct benefits desired in social, civil, or defence sectors. In addition, in some countries at least, the government services' share of GDP is being reduced as a matter of policy. Even where the absolute level of government funding is not under direct pressure, the challenge to demonstrate benefits or value for money from existing funding levels is still a force for reform. Where the combination of reduced government funding and a higher expectation of its benefits exists, this dramatically enforces a need for increased performance from surveying and mapping. The typical consequence is to initiate changes in work management and human resource development systems and practice. A prerequisite for effective total quality performance is the development of much higher levels of staff ownership and motivation in relation to their work and performance. In addition to these intra-organization changes, the challenges to traditional survey and mapping activities in New Zealand required a much greater public perception of the role and benefits of the national services DOSLI provided. It became vital to obtain both public and political support.

COST RECOVERY AS A DRIVER OF CHANGE

In 1988–89, the 'goal posts were moved' – our target cost recovery was increased in a huge leap to 56 percent of Crown funding. More formal marketing strategies had to be developed and introduced. Through market research, DOSLI determined that:

- we needed to get closer to our clients. We had made too many assumptions about what they wanted rather than understanding their business and how we could provide solutions to their needs;
- we had a good reputation in the market but needed to capitalize on it. Only our traditional, long-term clients knew about us and our capabilities. We were one of the best-kept secrets in the country;

- we were perceived as servicing the 'top end' of the market – seen as providing 'Rolls-Royce' products when many clients were looking for a 'bicycle'. We needed to develop flexibility.

As a result, we reviewed our fees and charges yearly and made adjustments to them to reflect costs better and also what we perceived was the value of our products to users. But using price increases alone to increase revenue was recognized as a short-term and dangerous strategy. What was needed was an expansion in the size of the market itself and then for DOSLI to capture it.

We established a client servicing structure which went some way towards improving communication with the market. We also introduced a promotions plan to let people know who we were and what we had to offer. The main remaining problem was that marketing planning was not linked to business and corporate planning, with the result that our marketing strategies were operating somewhat independently of the rest of the organization's thrust.

In 1989–90, our cost recovery target was raised yet again – this time to 70 percent. We started to look ever more actively for new markets, opportunities for joint ventures and overseas projects and began to develop new products and ways to increase our revenue. 'Tailor-made' products were produced by a special unit within our Cartographic Group dedicated to responding to clients' specific requirements for maps and related products. Product-testing and research involving users was introduced. A users' education strategy was implemented and we attended more conferences, exhibitions, and displays to explain our products to existing and potential clients. An education programme for Ministers and key officials from control agencies (Audit Department, Treasury, State Services Commission) was also introduced to help them understand our business and what happened to the funding which the Crown provided.

The period from 1990 to 1994 saw the department move forward in leaps and bounds. Business and corporate planning became a recognized annual function, with market research one of the essential elements. The staff's awareness of clients markedly increased, the traditional ways of the public servant began making way for enterprise, intuition, and innovation.

In 1993, the department embarked on a major internal re-organization and cultural change programme. This involved focusing our attention on clients rather than on production, setting up specific business streams to increase efficiency and effectiveness in customer servicing, providing career development for the staff, and involving them directly in the day-to-day operations. We pushed management down the line, introducing empowerment and the team concept. While all of these changes were accepted by the staff, it became clear that their complete integration into the culture of the department was still some time away. Staff feedback, however, clearly indicated that it was not a case of 'when' but rather 'how soon' these changes would take root.

A particular difficulty was the external culture in which we operated – a difficult and still immature market where potential users of our products or services often attempted to 'do-it-yourself' or to do without rather than investing in spatial products already developed by DOSLI. In our experience, users often do not see the false economies and inefficiencies of these other options. Part of our strategy was to show them that it was more economical to purchase data already available from our data banks than create them themselves.

As a result of all these changes DOSLI was in a position by the early 1990s to identify what everything cost to produce or service. This became ever more crucial as we moved to an environment of greater accountability and more accurate reporting. Cross-subsidization between outputs was not allowed in any case. But we could not have achieved the transparency and accountability required by Treasury had it not been for a very sophisticated financial management information system that recorded all costs, an accounting system based on accrual accounting, and a detailed performance recording and measurement system.

KEY FACTORS IN ACHIEVING THE CHANGES

DOSLI met a 70 percent cost recovery target four years in succession. The following were key factors in achieving this target:

- *the willingness of staff to make the changes asked of them by their leaders.* Not everyone was able to adapt to the new cost-recovery, 'user-pays' environment. However, the great majority of staff did so and, without this change, the result would not have been so positive;
- *staff training in marketing.* In hindsight, more, earlier, and more frequent training of this kind would have been better. Also, it was not always effective to use existing staff; specially trained sales people would have been a better option in some cases;
- *creation of a customer-facing structure.* This was developed over time and the restructuring of DOSLI was aimed at achieving a refocus on customers and regrouping into business units (rather than the previous, production-based structure);
- *a regular review of fees and charges.* As new products were developed and the market matured, users valued and became more dependent on our products. Value-based pricing was therefore important;
- *identification of costs and increased internal efficiencies.* With the aid of relevant performance measures and accurate, detailed time/cost recording systems, more was achieved with less. A total quality management approach also helped to achieve efficiency gains;
- *education of Ministers, politicians, control agencies, and key stakeholders.* This was made difficult by the frequent change in the individuals with whom

we dealt; the education process had often to begin all over again. However, to ensure continuing funding, we identified as a key strategy that it was crucial to our existence for these people to understand what we did and how it benefited the country as a whole;

- *market research and our response to this.* A regular, yearly programme of research into the users' needs provided us with the 'ammunition' to develop strategies and move forward;
- *market-sensitive pricing.* We introduced a choice of digital data licences which offered the client a short-term or long-term option. We also did research on price perception and acceptance and adjusted (downwards) some data charges that were discouraging use;
- *increased awareness and education of the market.* We promoted the range and application of spatial products, coupled with a raised public profile, to show why DOSLI was needed;
- *a more flexible approach was adopted to product development.* We offered tailor-made products and slowly broke away from always providing premium, luxury spatial products when in fact the client wanted something less 'up-market' but still of quality;
- *widening of the spatial data market.* This was a key strategy to secure our future, especially in such a small market as New Zealand;
- *identification of new markets and opportunities with the private sector.* This was a fairly new area and one which proved to be a real challenge. However, we saw this as an area for growth of the market and an opportunity for DOSLI to act as a core servicing agency in supporting New Zealand's infrastructure.

OBSTACLES TO ACHIEVING THE TARGET

The requirement by government that DOSLI become more commercial in its activities was challenging and we were certainly not prepared for the difficulties facing us. Having developed some of the other marketing elements, we worked on developing the relationship with the private sector. However, we found that there were a number of obstacles to us entering into such partnerships with it. For example in 1993 we sought a legal opinion from the Crown Law Office regarding a joint venture proposal. It was their opinion that the Survey Act 1986 under which DOSLI was established did not allow us to enter into joint ventures: they argued that the terms of the Act are not wide enough to include the power to enter into such arrangements where the profits are shared after deduction of costs. The implications of this discussion were:

- we could not put the Crown at any risk and therefore a relationship based on the legal definition of 'partnership' (equal liability carried by both parties) was out of the question. Even 'joint venture' could not be used so we used the term 'joint working relationship';

- we could not have exclusive relationships with any one 'partner': as a government body, we had to be seen as being available to everyone equally – even if they were our competitors or competitors with each other. Some potential 'partners' objected to this lack of exclusivity and to our dealing with their competitors. We also had to be very careful in these instances that we did not divulge confidential information provided by one potential 'partner' to another;
- if not handled scrupulously, any joint working relationship could be the subject of questions in Parliament. Whether generated by genuine interest or by malicious intent, the result was still the same – publicity and ministerial questions which detracted from the benefits;
- setting the price of any new product was difficult as our prices were set by legislation and had to be approved by Parliament via the Survey (Departmental Fees and Charges) Regulations and this process took place usually only once a year. Every increase above the rate of inflation had to be publicly justified. Even once the price increase was gazetted, anyone had the right to object within 28 days and make representations to government that our prices were too high or that we were subsidized and therefore had an unfair advantage.
- we were not profit-driven. We were limited to cost recovery only, so the question of who kept the profit made from any joint relationships had to be resolved and spelt out quite explicitly. We sometimes agreed to a share of revenue based on cost contribution only and in other cases settled on a net revenue-sharing ratio;
- the results of our market research, which was often the source of some competitive advantage, were generally available to anyone (including competitors) under the Official Information Act 1982. This made a traditional marketing approach very difficult.

No other government department in New Zealand, and no mapping and surveying agency in the world other than Ordnance Survey, achieved a cost-recovery factor as high as ours. At the same time, there were no guidelines available to help us with what was or was not allowed in the pursuit of cost recovery and revenue generation. We constantly broke new ground and developed our own rules, testing and checking them with control agencies such as Audit Department, State Services Commission, Treasury, and the Crown Law Office as we went along. Fortunately, they generally took a 'management by exception' view where they let us know when they did not like what we did.

Paradoxically in view of all these difficulties, it is the New Zealand government's policy and direction to the public sector that it should work with the private sector, support them, and look for opportunities to benefit both. In addition, the Chief Executive of DOSLI was responsible to the Minister of Survey and Land Information under the State Sector Act 1988 for the financial management and financial performance of the department (S.33) and for its efficient, effective, and economical management (S.32). All of this pointed to DOSLI's taking a more commercial approach to its business, including joint working relationships with the private sector. However, the necessary system and processes were not in place to facilitate this approach.

MANAGING JOINT WORKING RELATIONSHIPS WITH THE PRIVATE SECTOR

In dealing with the private sector, we took the following approach:

- in most cases, we acted as a sub-contractor to the private firm. We charged only costs and left the profit-making to them;
- joint working relationships were limited to activities other than policy or regulatory/statutory ones;
- the power to enter into these relationships rested with the Director General, rather than with the Minister. This enabled the decision to be made at a level closer to the client and hence facilitated negotiation;
- we used Memoranda of Understanding rather than formal contracts. As a result, there was no joint responsibility and the debts were separated so that each organization had no responsibility for the other's liabilities.

However, because we were dissatisfied with the inherent restraints still in place (see above), we continued to pursue the matter. In a decision given to us in January 1995, the Crown Law Office decided that there is nothing in the Survey Act 1986 or State Sector Act 1988 which precluded the Chief Executive of a government organization from entering into contracts which enabled his or her duties to be performed. Indeed, they referred to S.32 of the State Sector Act as evidence that a somewhat wider view may be taken of functions and responsibilities, including giving the Chief Executive the power to carry out the policies of the government.

Some projects undertaken with the private sector

DOSLI supported the private sector in New Zealand. It transferred knowledge, expertise, skills, and technology to component parts of the sector. Indeed, we saw technology transfer as one of the roles of a core department in helping the government to achieve its goals. If DOSLI had been wholly commercial, we would no doubt have jealously guarded our technological advantage. Instead, we viewed the introduction of new technology as something for the good of the industry and country as a whole. New Zealand, with a population of only 3.5 million people, is a very small market: in the business we are in, we depend on one another for survival. Hence, we enjoyed a cordial relationship with allies as well as competitors, and the Surveyor General played a major role in keeping the survey profession informed of the direction DOSLI was taking. We also had a policy of contracting out survey work that we ourselves could not service.

Some examples of DOSLI's work with the private sector include:

- assisting a large surveying, planning, and engineering consultancy to develop a major ARC/INFO database in Brunei. DOSLI provided help by digitizing 28 of their maps, tested equipment for compatibility of hardware and software, trained their staff in Brunei, allowed them to hire one of our staff and developed methodologies and specifications for them;
- DOSLI's Global Positioning System (GPS) unit assisted and trained staff from a large NZ survey and planning consultancy firm to undertake a road project in Tanzania;
- R&D staff provided technical advice and software to a consultancy doing a project in New Zealand developing a marine investigation package to predict positions utilizing a combination of a range of fixing systems;
- DOSLI signed a Memorandum of Understanding with a consultant who developed a digital data graphical landbase map product combining topographical features, photography, and cadastral data. The department shared the cost of production and received a market-based rate of return for this work plus a share of revenue from every sale made. The price set was based on an estimation of what the market would bear;
- a national atlas of New Zealand was produced in conjunction with a large publishing company. The arrangement was based on DOSLI's providing the production work and a full set of 1:250 000 topographic maps and the publisher's carrying the cost of publication and distribution. DOSLI received a royalty from each book sold;
- the hire of DOSLI equipment and expertise, provision of training, consultancy, and transferring knowledge to local authorities, consultants, overseas agencies, and educational institutions.

Government agencies have substantial expertise, often built up over many decades, and can offer a wide range of skills. There is thus a great deal to be gained by the private sector in having a relationship with us. In turn, we benefit from being exposed to the disciplines of a competitive, commercial market. It allows us to test ourselves away from the procedures, rules, and regulations that are part of our usual government environment.

Guidelines for assessing our involvement with a private sector project

We developed some guidelines to help us assess whether we should enter into a joint relationship with a private sector firm. The project or client did not have to satisfy all criteria and a fair degree of common sense was applied. Three types of guidelines were devised and are summarized below:

Strategic guidelines

- Was there a legislative mandate for us to undertake the work, e.g. under the Survey Act 1986, State Sector Act 1988, or other legislation?
- Did it support DOSLI's mission statement?
- Did it support our status as government's authority on spatial data?
- Was it tied to government's key strategic policies and objectives?
- Did it help DOSLI develop new skills and expertise?

Marketing guidelines

- Could DOSLI add value to the product or service proposed by the private sector, i.e. through data or skills?
- Did DOSLI have a competitive advantage that it could contribute?
- What was the financial benefit to DOSLI?
- Were there other intangible benefits to DOSLI such as kudos, good public relations, behaving as a good employer, or the exposure of staff to new environments?
- Was there a long-term lifetime or value in having a relationship with this firm?
- Would the relationship bring in additional work or work for another business group?
- Did the product and its marketing comply with trade practices legislation?
- Did the 'partner' have adequate financial resources to carry its share of the costs?
- Did the 'other party' have a 'clean bill of health' from a business ethics and reputation point of view?
- Did the overall benefit outweigh the cost?

Operational guidelines

- Did the department have the resources, after taking into account other priorities, and time to undertake the work?
- Would there be a requirement for DOSLI to have an ongoing role in maintaining the product (and therefore what was the long-term cost of this)?

RESPONDING TO MAJOR CHANGE

The challenge we have faced as a traditional public spatial information provider is how we can continue to contribute to national objectives in an ever-changing and increasingly demanding political and economic environment. The survival of organizations in this environment of continuous change depends both on coping with immediate requirements and targets and on having a long-term appreciation of that organization's role or business. Without the long-term view, the short-term remedial activity can position an organization away from its core business – inviting its disestablishment or privatization. Alternatively, acceding to the short-term pressure of cost recovery targets can divert attention and resources from long-term investments in core business, leaving an organization unable to plan and develop pathways to its long-term core business future.

At a time of major turbulence, the identification of a vision and strategic paths towards that vision is most essential. Although urgent circumstances may require long-term activities to be put on hold in the short-term, planning and preparing for the future can only be deferred with extreme risk. Moreover, with only limited resources available, any misdirection or inefficiency of effort can lead to missing a critical opportunity to build a key component of the future.

The early emphasis in New Zealand was on achieving cost-recovery targets whilst investing in systemic conversion of traditional manual systems to digital automated systems. In 1993 we re-organized to reform other areas that needed change and development. Our aim was to expedite a full transformation of the business. This involved a complete disbanding of traditional structures, including identifying core business systems, over-arching single department business planning and reporting, client orientation, re-engineering of systems to take advantage of efficiencies derived from new technology, plus a re-orientation of human resource management. The flattened organizational structure emphasized the role of management as 'enablers', team builders, and performance coaches. A serious attempt was made to facilitate vastly increased self-management and individual motivation and ownership by all staff.

An effective vision is, by its very nature, necessarily a long-term goal. In New Zealand – despite the prescriptive character of the change and the imposed cost-recovery regime – the department managed to have a long-term strategy for planning and automation activities. The timing of economic change coincided with the application of new technology and the potential to transform manual survey and mapping activity into an electronic environment.

Managing the change

The signs of impending change can often be perceived well beforehand. However, the sheer inertia of the existing systems and environment can dampen the ability and willingness to read or anticipate early signals. Other than the need for a clear vision of the future business (see above), lessons learned from the New Zealand experience include:

- in adjusting to change, the earlier that the reality and direction of change can be identified the more options and the less risk organizations face in adapting to it. Unsuspected or unanticipated major change tends to force 'big bang' reactions, with concomitant major risks and a lack of capability to manage the suddenly imposed new range of attendant requirements;

- our tradition of bureaucracy, rules, and conformity needs to be transformed to responsiveness, innovation, self-management, and teamwork. This tradition meant that many of our staff were uncomfortable with change and a complete change of culture was imperative;

- the management of a large order of change involves a series of significant steps, each followed by process improvements. Without significant step changes, process improvement on its own remains a fine tuning of processes. Even if desirable, these become increasingly less appropriate and effective;

- a necessary facility is a realistic survey of the jurisdictional environment and a perceptive analysis of the forces of change pending or discernible. Each jurisdiction's environment will be different but much international commonality does exist because of the global impact of international trade and the market economy. An understanding of the role of survey and mapping in one's own country, together with its past achievements, current circumstances, and possible future contributions, is also a prerequisite for development of a strategy;

- generic management thinking and techniques, including strategic planning and change management, can with benefit be applied to the particular conditions that apply in our industry. Concepts and practices such as advances in human resource management, staff motivation and ownership, training and learning, team dynamics, total quality management and process improvement, culture change, and client orientation are all readily transferred from other organizations.

Perhaps the most important of all these lessons was that today's competitive environment demands that we enlist the full capabilities of *all* staff. DOSLI therefore planned to create an organizational climate with a change focus and a culture in which staff were empowered to meet client needs. The departmental vision was to have *every* staff member responsible for their own work through self-management and teamwork. To achieve this, we embarked on the largest training exercise in our history.

Different jurisdictions will be responding to a widely different range of change factors and technical and financial environments. Given the global situation, however, any jurisdiction can leap-frog from a manual stage to leading-edge practice in cost reduction, new technology applications, or new human resource management systems without the need to pass through every evolutionary stage progressively. To that degree, late entrants into the spatial information field can in a few short years catch up with and even surpass those which have long been at the forefront.

DEFINING THE CORE BUSINESS

In the management of change it is critically important to identify the role and nature of the core business. In New Zealand, the infrastructure nature of our traditional surveying and mapping core business has always been evident. However, identifying the infrastructural role in a digitally based future required much more imagination and vision. This new infrastructure role involves an increasing emphasis on national systems procedures and consistency. It is important to note that the development of infrastructure is not about growth for its own sake. Infrastructure effectiveness in New Zealand is gauged not simply by the output of the single core organization concerned but is judged by the health and growth in service of the industry, the sector, and the whole country.

In identifying our core business activity, it was vital to ask ourselves what is important about what we do. We were able to identify the millions of records we maintain that underpin the land and property assets in the community. These records and the associated cadastral survey function enable the operation of an efficient market in land and property and national development and administration. The spatial infrastructure we provide enables others in this industry or related ones to deliver goods and services efficiently and reliably.

In articulating and identifying our core business, it is also useful to examine what would happen if it is not undertaken at all or if it is seriously inadequate. In the case of the national spatial data infrastructure, we have concluded that:

- occasionally (perhaps rarely) lives are threatened or lost;
- there would be uncertainty in and occasional loss of property and asset rights;
- there would be markedly increased rates in interest and insurances and, over time, delays on assets transferred in the land market; and
- environment and land resource planning would be more difficult and expensive and carry much greater risk through the lack of basic information.

In imagining and articulating a vision for our department, we have found the concept of a national spatial data infrastructure (NSDI) as identified in North America and currently being developed in the USA, highly relevant. It is a good representation of the role and service which can be designed and facilitated by our department for the future. Our major customer is government and, in providing a NSDI, we need to facilitate more user control of national data, easier and faster access, more accurate and congruent data, and lower costs. Many of these electronic components are very much embryonic at this stage, but nevertheless a huge potential for ready access to spatial information for all citizens is opening up.

The new survey and mapping core business serves as an investment for New Zealand's future growth. It provides a framework for linking and matching spatial and associated data; doing the necessary work essential to ensure authoritative, accurate, and recent records; and for pioneering new methods for industry to apply as a whole. Those forging the spatial infrastructure need to maintain and develop the confidence of all citizens in the accuracy and utility of land information. History is a particularly important data component: data trails from current to historic data should be continually maintained and made accessible to the nation. Finally, as well as facilitating national growth and development, our core business is concerned with avoiding or limiting liabilities which the national government would otherwise incur.

The value of the core business activities to the state were demonstrated in the disposal and privatization programme. DOSLI's skills and records were basic to the identification, description, and processing of government land and property assets and liabilities to enable corporatization or full privatization to take place. Our spatial infrastructure, through its survey control, reference systems, databases, standards, and institutional arrangements, proved essential to the asset transfer process.

The out-turn of this rethinking and practical demonstration was that, during the review of the future of DOSLI in 1995, the NZ government accepted the importance of the department's core business. As a consequence, it agreed to the core outcomes and general requirements for land and property rights and land information as shown in Table 19.1.

THE NEXT STAGE

Based on the recommendations of a 1995 scoping report and a working party of officials, the NZ government agreed to a fundamental restructuring of the Department of Survey and Land Information. In making its decision, government endorsed again the fundamental importance of the core function. It declared that:

- the spatial data system is of great importance to the NZ economy;
- the existence of a DOSLI or equivalent organization is of relevance to the NZ economy;
- a fundamental restructuring of DOSLI was needed to ensure effective and efficient delivery of both public good and commercial services;
- a new department should be established amalgamating public good databases held within DOSLI and the Land Titles Office (LTO), and be responsible for the maintenance of the seabed cadastre. This would be responsible for ensuring the delivery of the government's core requirements;
- all contestable activities (that is non-core activities) be placed in a stand-alone Crown company. This would compete for contracts for delivery of the government's core contestable survey and land-related outputs and develop, on a commercial basis, other land information products and services.

Table 19.1 Core outcomes and general requirements for land and property rights and land information

Core outcomes required by the NZ government	General NZ government requirements from the department
Outcome One: The ongoing delivery of an efficient regulatory framework that establishes: (i) parameters for definition and dealing in land property rights; and (ii) standards and specifications for provisions of land data	● Framework for land (includes land, seabed and air) property rights including provision of legislative (including regulation) and operational policy advice ● Monitoring of regulatory compliance, efficiency and outcomes ● Regulation of core spatial framework and standards
Outcome Two: The establishment of clearly defined, marketable and secure land property rights, and maintenance of the resulting records, to underpin economic activity in New Zealand	● Certainty of title, by registration and sound survey definition ● Maintenance of access to the Land Titles Register ● Legal framework, including definitions of rights and provision of the state guarantee ● Maintenance of survey system and cadastral records ● Quality assurance processes ● Alignment of land tenure systems
Outcome Three: The efficient management of Crown land related liabilities and responsibilities through either: (i) efficient management and disposal of surplus Crown land assets and land-related liabilities; or (ii) efficient oversight and/or management of Crown land purchase and disposal regulatory instruments	● Crown land register and documents ● Public property management, disposal and acquisition services ● Crown liability and contaminated sites management ● Management of legal claims against the Crown ● Statutory and regulatory land investigations
Outcome Four: The ongoing maintenance of publicly available core Geographic Information that supports the constitutional framework, national security and emergency services responses	● Constitutional framework requirements ● Electoral and administrative boundaries ● Authoritative record of geographic place names ● Topographical mapping with: – national coverage and consistent standards – degree of quality and quantity defined by: Defence Force, Police, Fire Service, Ambulance, Search and Rescue, Agricultural, Horticultural and Forestry Ministries (biological disaster) – provision of geographic place names and electoral and administrative boundaries ● Provide protocols for access to core information by other users

For over nine years, DOSLI had worked to develop its commercial functions, achieving an unprecedented cost-recovery level of over 70 percent in the 1994/95 year. As cost-recovery was progressed in DOSLI, however, it was clear that the mixture of a cost-recovery approach and regulatory functions suffered major restraints. There was perceived conflict between delivering to the market and to government clients, and to government as owner and client; and there was inadequate flexibility in the NZ model. As indicated earlier, DOSLI had to face a number of obstacles on its road to commercialization – including limitations on the types of relationships that we could forge with the private sector, close scrutiny from control agencies, disclosure of commercially sensitive information, inflexibility of pricing structures, no profit-making, and the restructure of human resources policies. Despite considerable ingenuity on DOSLI's part, it was perhaps inevitable that the uncomfortable mix of regulatory and commercial functions should ultimately be seen as inappropriate

In response to this uncomfortable mix, a new department, Land Information New Zealand (LINZ) and a new state-owned enterprise, Terralink, were established on 1 July 1996. This action clearly separated regulatory from commercial activities. In designing the new structure of LINZ, particular attention was paid to separating the functional activities of policy, regulation, and service delivery in order to achieve transparency of functional responsibilities. LINZ's focus will therefore be to:

- provide a secure environment for buying, selling, and subdividing property through:
  - guaranteed title for property dealings,
  - an accurate system of land boundary definition;
- administer the Crown's interests in land through:
  - acquisition of Crown land,
  - disposal of Crown land,
  - administration of Crown land,
  - management of Crown land liabilities;
- assist government and its agencies address Treaty of Waitangi-led issues through the provision of excellent information on land history and status;
- ensure that New Zealand has high-quality databases for its survey, mapping, hydrographic, and property activities.

One major change is that LINZ will operate through use of a system of warranting the private sector for such things as plan examination and approvals, Crown land dealings, and title approvals. This approach will involve a significant legislative change programme and a breakdown of the traditional regulatory monopoly that the department has had in the past. LINZ is also now responsible for the full integration of survey and title information into an integrated, automated, and decentralized system.

Terralink is the new state-owned enterprise which acquired the commercial functions of DOSLI. It is now New Zealand's largest surveying and mapping organization with offices in 15 locations. It has four business units: mapping; survey services; systems solutions; and property services. Its commercial activities include delivering major contracts on behalf of LINZ, such as the production of topographic maps, maintenance of the topographic database and the Crown's geodetic survey control network. Other commercial activities include geographic information systems (GIS) solutions, off-shore projects, joint ventures with other agencies, consultancy services, and value-added solutions. While Terralink has first choice of most of LINZ's work put out on contract, this is only for two years. After this time they will have to compete with the rest of the private sector.

CONCLUSIONS

As other chapters in this book make clear, a world-wide wave of change is affecting surveying and mapping organizations, albeit to varying degrees. The only constant is continuing change. The core survey and mapping function and service is still as necessary as it was in earlier times of settlement and expansion. However, we must be able to articulate what is now our core function and what benefits it yields to the national entity and local communities. From this understanding, we need to identify a vision and mission for the long-term future in our particular jurisdictions. Through establishing such a vision and consequential directions, we in New Zealand have positioned ourselves to respond to the over-arching principles of economic restructuring required by our government. Despite our traditional environment, competitive performance is now a requirement of our organization for survival. As a result, the search for high-quality performance in our business is demanding an intelligent application of a range of modern management thinking and techniques.

In New Zealand, cost-recovery targets provided a transitional phase for building a capacity for change. After successfully developing a major cost-recovery basis, the opportunity was taken by government to separate out those activities which can be more efficiently undertaken on a commercial basis, as well as the contracting out of routine operational functions. The latest restructuring is aimed at making regulatory and administrative functions fully independent and at getting the best value for money for all surveying and mapping and land information services which government needs to purchase to meet its particular requirement.

We are all in an environment where we face major pressures forcing change, such as government minimizing its costs, new national priorities, the development of technology, more demanding customers, etc. We can thrive in such an environment if we align our core business with government direction, have a clear, compelling vision and mission, develop our people, and continually improve our management and operation skills.

CHAPTER 20

Pursuing sustainability through fundamental change: the Danish experience

Peter Jakobsen

SUMMARY

The national responsibility for topographic mapping, nautical charting, cadastre and basic geodetic research in Denmark has since the end of the 1980s been placed in one governmental organization: Kort & Matrikelstyrelsen (National Survey and Cadastre – Denmark.). This is still somewhat unusual compared to many other countries where these activities are undertaken by several different official organizations. The creation of Kort & Matrikelstyrelsen (KMS) as a market-orientated organization and preparing it for a life under conditions similar to those in the private industry has been – and still is – a major challenge.

The reason for the creation of KMS in this form has been the fundamentally changed role of government. So far as the production of maps and charts are concerned, for centuries this has been considered a national responsibility. The changes in philosophy ensure that this will not necessarily be so in the future. It is even less certain that a national responsibility should necessarily be solved through a governmental institution. It follows from this that, if the national mapping agencies of the world want to survive and continue to carry out their activities in the next century, they must change or somebody else will take over their work.

I have had the pleasure to be responsible for great organizational and technical changes in the Danish mapping, charting, and geodata sector since the beginning of the 1980s. In this chapter, I focus on these experiences in order to ensure others benefit from the mistakes I made and the lessons I learned. The main things to be learned are that:

- all organizational processes take longer than you expect;
- if you want to change something in an organization, you must make it clear to yourself and to the organization what you want it to do;
- the customers/users are your long-term guarantee for survival; and
- you must be prepared to change to survive.

KMS – THE ENTERPRISE

KMS employs about 550 staff. It is responsible for the Danish topographical mapping and nautical charting. It is a national research institute in geodesy and seismology, and is responsible for the Danish cadastre. The geographical extent of its activities comprises Denmark, the Faeroe Islands, and Greenland. It is a state enterprise, and at the same time, a state authority under the Ministry of Housing and Building. KMS total expenditure in 1996 will be around Dkr 300 million or about 40 million ECU (or US$). One-third of this revenue is obtained as income from the market and the rest is provided by government.

The KMS mission

The National Survey and Cadastre shall collect, manipulate, store, and distribute Geographical Information about Denmark, the Faeroe Islands, and Greenland and co-ordinate the activities of others in this field.

The history of KMS

The National Survey and Cadastre was officially established on 1 January 1989 by law no. L 749 1988, as the result of a merger between:

- Geodætisk Institut (the Geodetic Institute, established in 1928)
- Søkortarkivet (the Nautical Archives, established in 1784)
- Matrikeldirektoratet (the Danish Cadastre, established in 1919).

Even though two of the founding institutions appear to date from the earlier part of this century, in practice all the components had a long administrative history of several centuries before reaching the form they had at the time of the merger. Attempts to merge the three national geodata institutions into one had been made several times before during the last century, without success. This was due partly to opposition from within the institutions. Another contributory factor, however, was that their activities in topographical mapping, cadastre, nautical charting, and research were not overlapping and the potential benefit to be gained from a merger was considered to be small.

As part of a general administrative reform in the Danish state administration, the government decided after a short study of the matter in 1985/86 that the three institutions should be moved from their traditional ministries – i.e. in the ministries of Agriculture (Cadastre), and Defence (Geodetic Institute and Nautical Archives) – to the ministry of Housing and Building with effect from 10 September 1987. It was clear that there was an intention to enforce a merger as soon as possible thereafter.

The intention behind the decision was administrative reform. The purpose was to save money for the state and local authorities in the process of introducing digital products and production methods in the field of geo-graphical and cadastral information. Now, a decade later, the merger is almost complete in the sense that the identities of the old founding institu-tions have almost gone and a new one is established, but great changes had to take place during the process. These changes have included:

- a reduction of staff by about one-third, a great part of which was effected through involuntary retirement;
- several changes of the organizational structure;
- moving from eight different locations in the Copenhagen area into one common location. This was only possible after a debate lasting almost two years which even involved the Parliament, the most contentious issue being whether or not the KMS should move from Copenhagen to a provincial town;
- a change of government pricing policy concerning maps and other geo-data from no or relatively small fees for official use, to an increased level of user finance; and
- greatly increased use of sub-contractors in the production of maps and geodata.

KMS's operating environment

KMS is established under a financial and managerial regime that is still somewhat unusual in a Danish context. It is a state enterprise and, at the same time, a government authority. A state enterprise is controlled by Parliament and the Ministry of Housing and Building via a net budget, i.e. the difference between income and government appropriations on the one hand and expenditure on the other. A surplus or a deficit can be carried over from one year to the next within certain limits (up to 20 percent sur-plus and as much as a 10 percent deficit). KMS may employ as many staff as it can finance within its budget and it can use sub-contractors as it believes appropriate, subject to having the necessary funding.

In addition to its status as a state enterprise, KMS´s financial conditions are based on a four-year agreement with government and Parliament. This specifies the goals to be reached within the said period. These goals can be of both an economic and a non-economic nature. On the other hand, a state enterprise cannot change individual salaries for KMS staff or management except within very limited ranges. Nor can it borrow money on the market. Finally, it cannot buy real estate or partnerships in other enterprises without the consent of the government.

The KMS management and staff greatly value these conditions because of the degree of freedom they give to adapt to changing circumstances. The conditions are, however, still fairly new and we are not absolutely certain that government and Parliament will continue to grant this kind of freedom to state enterprises in the long run.

THE CHALLENGE OF CREATING THE NEW KMS

When KMS was established as an administrative and organizational entity, one of its first tasks as a new organization was to formulate a new draft bill on its future role and working conditions and to present it to Parliament for adoption. This bill was finally agreed by Parliament as from 1 January 1989.

The major part of creating the new organization was entrusted to the existing staff of the component organizations. A new Director General was appointed and made responsible for the whole process. Between them, this management had little experience in merging organizations and in running a rather large organization of around 800 staff. The staff were highly motivated people with great professional expertise, who took great pride in their work. They were, however, not all motivated to generate change nor were they all happy about the planned merger. Yet the creation of the new organization ensured that we all had to make changes in almost everything, and that many changes took place simultaneously. This inevitably created a very high degree of insecurity amongst staff. Such insecurity is, however, a necessity when you want to change something. But to make it a success, you must not forget to give everybody a new sense of purpose as soon as possible: failure to do this will breed demotivation.

The main areas of change were:

- creating the new organization through the merger;
- technological change;
- enhanced market orientation and increased user payments;
- the use of sub-contractors and contracting out;
- creating the tools to run a business;
- the need to learn about management, as opposed to administration.

Creating the new organization through the merger

The first task for the new organization was to create a sense of belonging to a new, common organization. This had to exist among both management and staff. Everyone had to be made to see their own efforts as being part of a common effort. It has taken a long time to achieve this, but it is now almost accomplished. It is difficult to over-stress the importance of the cultural aspects of a merger: if different parts of an organization are competing against – rather than supporting – one another, it drains the organization of its strength. In this context, it is most important that management stand united. Three factors proved helpful in this process. The first was a move to a new common location, even though this generated much additional work. The second factor was a change of 'ownership' through the move to a different ministry. The final factor was the ability – taken immediately – of collectively asserting the rights, role, and ambitions of the new organization in discussions with customers and users.

On the other hand, one major factor complicated the creation of the new organization. This was the long-established and quite separate cultures of the original organizations. Each of these was positive and excellent in its own way but all were very different, making joint action quite difficult. The Geodetic Institute, for example, was in many ways still characterized by a combination of a military culture and an academic approach. The Cadastre was very close to agriculture and to a legalistic way of thinking. The nautical culture was again a quite different one. All these cultures were deeply embedded and could (and should) only be replaced by something better. Experience of culture change in other organizations, however, indicates that such change often takes many years.

Another confusing issue was whether KMS should be regarded mostly as a government authority or whether we were better off being 'a state enterprise'. This created something of an identity crisis. The advocates for one or the other line of thinking each looked for a new security in promoting their views. We found that the best thing to do in this situation was to establish new common goals and objectives for the whole organization as soon as possible. This was done by making the whole organization – not just the senior management – participate in the process of creating the goals.

Technological change

One of the reasons for creating the KMS was the need to introduce technological change and to convert from analogue (paper-based) to digital (computer-based) products and production methods. This part of the process was not so difficult. Fortunately, we were in a position where the financing of this change (largely by government) was not the main problem; by and large, the whole organization benefited quickly from the technological experiences in its different parts.

Even here, however, there were lessons to be learned. One part of the organization had long experience in making everything itself and had not relied on standard solutions to problems; they also had no great experience of or inclination to co-operate with sub-contractors. Other parts of the organization held quite opposite views. The result of the process across all of KMS was ultimately a more open mind in co-operating with others while still maintaining basic expertise inside the organization. A related problem area was in learning to live with the fact that the best possible technical solution is not necessarily the optimal one. The idea that customers and even the owners (i.e. the government) can properly interfere with the decision on technical solutions was widely regarded as a slur on (highly valued) professional competence. This had to be handled by bringing together both producer and the consumer to establish the nature of the real needs and, through this process, make the producer understand that he/she plays a real role in problem-solving.

Whatever the benefits, there is certainly a downside about changing from old to new technology. It typically involves both de-skilling and some danger of loss of collective knowledge about how things used to be done. This is important, especially where databases are derived from pre-existing maps and information.

Enhanced market orientation and increased user payments

When KMS was created, it was the intention of the government that the organization should co-ordinate the activities of other official producers and users of maps and geodata. The rationale for this was to save money for the taxpayer and at the same time finance more of KMS's own activities with income from the market. This concept has proved difficult, but not impossible, to operate in practice. For KMS it involved:

- the need to make other public authorities pay for maps and other geo-data instead of getting them almost free of charge as before;
- a considerable effort to become familiar with the actual needs of the customer, accepting that his/her needs are your reason for existing and adapting products in such a way that they fulfil the demand of the customer as far as possible;
- accepting the fact that KMS is in a competitive situation.

Competition is now a fact of life. It can indeed be argued that KMS's predecessor bodies were used to competition. Many government institutions fight for better conditions and more finance from Parliament or government or they fight among themselves for 'territory' and importance. That is the old situation. The new situation is the fight for the final customer. Here you fight with other potential suppliers of the same service or with the customer themselves, if he/she is in a position to do the job in-house instead of paying you to do it. Moreover, a government enterprise, even competing in a market where there are only 'potential' private competitors, is very vulnerable to accusations of unfair competition and must behave more scrupulously than a private company.

The use of sub-contractors and contracting out

The KMS has always used sub-contractors but, as mentioned earlier, not with the same enthusiasm throughout whole organization. Furthermore, there had generally been very little economic consideration behind the decision of whether a job should be performed within the organization or by sub-contractors. The primary factor had been availability of sufficient resources and skills in-house.

As part of a general reform of government in Denmark in the last few years, government organizations are now obliged from time to time to evaluate whether they should still carry out work in-house or subject it partly or wholly to public tender. The objective is to ascertain who can do the job 'best and most cheaply'. Since 1995, the KMS has sub-contracted much more work than ever before. We have chosen to do this in areas where we would not ourselves compete for the job. This means mostly service jobs (e.g. cleaning) and converting analogue data to digital form but we have also increased our use of consultants, external computer programmers, and systems developers. This development has given us new knowledge. When you carry out a job in-house, you very seldom specify it correctly or define in any detail why you need it done and how much it may cost. In contrast, when you want to buy the same service from somebody else, you must learn to define a task so that others can understand it, give it a price, and decide how to assess and control what you get. You must also learn to accept the fact that, by educating an external supplier to do a certain job, you may thereby have turned him into a potential competitor (though you have also created new possibilities for yourself by using your resources more effectively).

Creating the tools to run a business

As indicated earlier, the KMS is both a state enterprise and a government authority. When KMS was created, many of the administrative tools for running such an organization were not available in an efficient form. The shortfall included tools for planning, accounting, pricing, etc. An important matter is that management tools for business and management tools for handling the political environment are not identical. The political system is often more interested in looking after probity and propriety (i.e. legality of action) and less about profitability. In practice, the political environment is also often inclined to look for aspects of an enterprise that can be quantified while other subjects that cannot be measured go unnoticed (a trait which is not restricted to the public sector!). It is also our experience that you will often find yourself in a dilemma when you try to manage a governmental 'business' controlled by politicians. Your best plans and assessments for the future development of the organization will be subsumed in some else's published statements. At a later stage, you will have to explain why another route of action was followed and why slightly different goals were reached than the ones foreseen in the plan.

When you are planning for the future in a world of continuous and imperfectly predictable change, it is important to realize that all planning has constantly to adapt to changing circumstances. Planning is thus a continuous process rather than an episodic one. You must therefore try to make both your colleagues and your 'owners' understand that to deviate from planned goals and routes of action may also be regarded as a success. These considerations make simultaneous planning and managing of business and politics rather difficult. Despite this difficulty, it is essential to establish some kind of system that permits you to monitor what you do, to realize if you have reached the goals you have set for yourself, and to establish the costs of different, alternative routes of action.

The need to learn about management

Management in a traditional government authority has often been understood to mean guaranteeing the legality of the actions of others and/or overseeing the quality of a process. It seldom involved setting goals, controlling efficiency, competing with others, running economic risks, or other normal aspects of management in the private sector. In a scientific and technically-driven environment typical of many national mapping organizations (NMOs) until recent years, management was also often considered as something inferior to the 'real' activities of an organization – i.e. production or research. In such organizations, management is often pejoratively termed 'administration': everybody knows that 'administration' means unwanted interference that adds no value and should be avoided. It is therefore necessary to upgrade the art of management in a professional world such as that of NMOs and make it respectable. It has to be recognized as a natural and important part of the process of getting results. And it has to be respected as a valid discipline by itself, demanding skills of its own – and not as a status or level which other professionals can get through promotion as reward for scientific or technical services rendered. Once obtained, management positions should not be considered as positions to be held for life, but rather as positions which constantly need to be earned: managers have great power and influence and can exercise them by doing good or doing harm – but also by doing nothing. The Danish experience therefore suggests that the managers in the top two or three levels of an organization should not be hired for life. Rather they should have contracts for shorter spans of time, say five-year periods, to be extended a maximum of two or three times if all goes well.

METHODS FOR RE-ENGINEERING AN ORGANIZATION

To create a new organization out of an old one and to change people's attitudes and skills, requires that:

- something must happen;
- there is action by management; and
- initiative is displayed.

Therefore: do something! Do (almost) anything! And keep the process alive.

The process is seldom a rational one

You will very seldom be in a position where you can copy past experience. You will have to improvise. A good starting point is to learn about management, at least to the degree where you take it seriously. Not only the top executives, but also your fellow managers, should have benefited from such an education. If this is not the case, the director will be isolated when trying to plan and implement policy.

It is essential to make a broad, long-term plan or a *vision* of what you want to achieve within the organization. Dare to want to do something. Discuss your goals with everyone in your organization. Try to convince them about your ideas and make them believe in them too. But listen carefully to all suggestions you get and see if you can improve your vision by using them.

It is vital that the leader and his/her staff learn to take calculated risks. Most management take decisions on the basis of insufficient evidence. The leader should stay in charge of an organization only as long as he/she enjoys it and feels able and willing to take such risks.

In most cases, the staff are the organization's greatest asset, but they can be the biggest liability if they are mishandled. Considering them as a prime resource to reach the stated goals necessitates treating them properly. Leaders should:

- listen to what staff say and try to follow their advice (trust them!);
- be open in all communications with them;
- do not lie to them and never promise them more than can be delivered;
- see to it that they are well-educated, trained, and equipped to do the things demanded from them;
- praise them when there is the opportunity to do so;
- create a positive attitude towards change and make people seek security in it and not in stability based on the old ways;
- celebrate their victories and mourn your defeats together with their personnel.

WHAT DID WE LEARN?

The creation of KMS was a Danish national experience. But it is possible to draw conclusions of a more general nature from a country-specific experience. Many of these conclusions have been set out earlier; many of them echo the contents of the management literature. The lessons we have learned have already been experienced in many other industries.

It is possible to change almost everything in an organization but it takes time and effort. Everything takes longer than you expect, and there is no short cut when major cultural change is required. The timing of a process is also often very important: there are times where an organization is more inclined to change than another. Finally, you will have to be very stubborn when you want to change an organization or those involved will fall back on old habits and live their own life irrespective of your vision; persistence is essential.

To be successful, leaders need to develop a good concept of success and failure and share it with their organization. Whether you are a success or a failure is very much a psychological question. Thus it is wise not to fall into the trap where goals are set just that much higher than is possible: people will lose motivation in trying to reach them. But setting them so low that they do not present a real challenge is just as serious in that it breeds complacency and diminishes the capacity to compete. Needless to say, once the organization is in a position of success you will have to work even harder to stay there!

A modern mapping institution – like any other organization – is based on a need, felt by others, for that organization. If nobody needs you, you will disappear. Moreover, if a traditional public service (like map-making) can be supplied by private industry in the future, the government will tend to consider it as less a public service than hitherto. It is therefore important to find and rely on the people (users and customers) who really need your services and to deliver to them the services they want. You must therefore be much closer to the market than before. You must also be able to deliver quality improvements in order to provide fulfilment of ever greater consumer expectations.

Customers are frustrating: they usually want something today that you can only supply tomorrow. When you explain something is impossible they often disappear again and a good opportunity is lost: opportunities should be grasped when they appear!

Two fundamental lessons for NMOs have been learned from the last ten years of management experience in the public sector. The first is that competition in the market is permanent and NMOs must face it constantly to survive. The second is that we can no longer assume a right to exist forever. NMOs must prove their usefulness and fight for their existence. Most other organizations are in the same position.

CHAPTER 21

Facing the challenges: redesigning and rebuilding Ordnance Survey

David Rhind

SUMMARY

This chapter describes how Ordnance Survey – a government department – has faced the challenges of the UK government's commitment to competition and privatization, the threats and opportunities posed by new technology, the growth of globalization in our business, and the rapidly changing needs of our customers. It describes the situation in which OS existed in 1991 and the reasons why radical change was essential. It sets out how OS has reformed itself, both structurally and in performance terms, in the last five years: our databases and hence the national geographical framework are more up-to-date than ever before and are all in computer form. The cost of operating OS to the taxpayer is significantly less and our products and services are more widely used.

For OS, change is now an unending process. Key issues in making such change beneficial include organizational culture, the need for continuing investment, and the assessment of future customer needs; these too are discussed in this chapter. It is concluded that the model described herein may have some relevance elsewhere in the world, especially as state budgets become more constrained. The local developments in Britain, however, do not address the global framework issues raised elsewhere in this book. To do so is a matter for government policy rather than for national mapping organizations (NMOs) as organizations. Finally, the globalization of 'the framework industry' is proceeding rapidly, with competition, collaboration, and learning from others becoming commonplace. This has many implications for the way in which NMOs face the future.

INTRODUCTION

Previous chapters in this book have dealt with the key issues facing NMOs, such as the impact of new technology. Some chapters have stressed the new demands facing NMOs for improved, more consistent, and lower-cost framework data; others have described the painful and substantial organizational re-engineering necessary to meet challenging targets for effectiveness and efficiency and work within the New Public Management paradigm. This chapter considers how one organization – Ordnance Survey (OS) – has faced many of the challenges identified in the other chapters and how its staff have set out to anticipate and influence the future. In focusing on OS, no suggestion is made that the British model will work everywhere or that the OS management has uniquely found omnipotence: with hindsight, we could have done some things better. This, then, is an honest description of an attempt to build a new NMO in conditions of extreme uncertainty – but founded on a belief that satisfying customers and stakeholders is the only way to ensure long-term sustainability.

THE BRITISH GOVERNMENT CONTEXT

The UK government in power from 1979 to 1997 regarded the improvement of public services and reduction of their cost as major elements of its policy. Immediately after the general election of 1997, it seems   likely that these will also be policies of the new government. As Foster and Plowden (1996) point out, these objectives have been adopted by a number of national governments almost synchronously though the out-turns of the New Public Management vary from one country to another. In particular, this approach has similarities to that advocated by Osborne and Gaebler (1992) but has been implemented much more widely across the national and local governments than is the situation in the USA. To put the pre-1997 government's aims into effect, citizens and government departments alike are regarded as the customers of service providers. These customers have a right to good service. To foster the reduction of costs and improve quality, government that enforced the testing of services provided by the Civil Service against the best that the private sector can offer. Failure to succeed in such competition generally led to the service being contracted out to the private sector. The policy applied across almost all of the state's remit. Though the UK government has not spelled out in detail what are the services that only the state can provide – unlike the situation in the USA – the presumption was that very few activities must *necessarily* be carried out directly by the state. In addition, the user rather than the taxpayer should pay for the services wherever possible. As a consequence of this and the need to help to fund higher budgets elsewhere in the government sector, state funding of OS via funds voted to it by Parliament – the parliamentary vote – has been cut back: Figure 21.1 shows how this has decreased substantially since 1979.

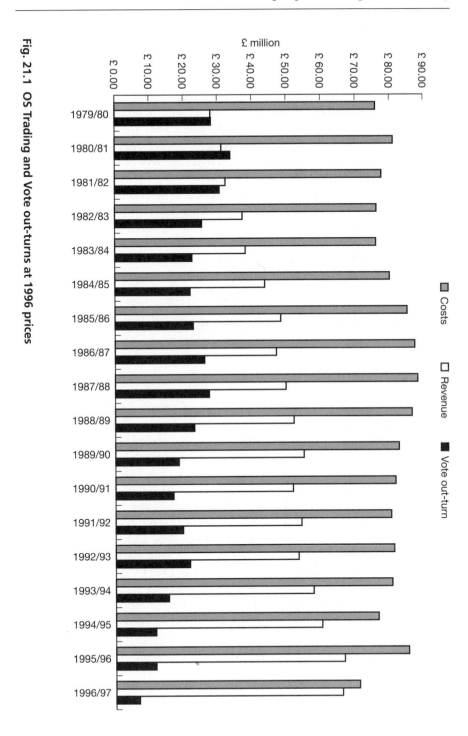

Fig. 21.1   OS Trading and Vote out-turns at 1996 prices

To achieve better management of services in the UK still provided by the state itself and get greater value for taxpayers' money, some 75 percent of all civil servants formerly working in government departments have been transferred to over 140 executive agencies in the period since 1989. Each agency has to create a corporate plan and meet annual targets set by ministers covering financial measures, operational efficiency, and quality of service. The targets and results are widely publicized and performance pay (and even jobs) depend upon their achievement. League tables ranking agency performance are being discussed. Recruitment of non-civil servants as chief executives has occurred in nearly half of these agencies; open recruitment through advertising is the norm. To help it achieve its targets, each agency has somewhat greater freedoms than hitherto in the public sector, though these do not include raising loan capital or competing aggressively with the private sector. Finally, each agency is reviewed every five years to see whether its function still needs to be met and, if so, whether this can be better met by the private sector. It will be obvious that such operating circumstances have significant effects upon the actions of the executive agencies. Certainly these have affected the way OS – an agency as well as a government department in its own right – has operated since 1990.

REMIT VERSUS RESOURCES

The remit under which OS has operated since 1979 arose from the Report of the Ordnance Survey Review Committee (HMSO 1979). This committee was set up by a Labour government in 1978 to examine and redefine the role of the OS after completion of the re-mapping of Britain begun in 1946. The report was a thorough and wide-ranging document which re-affirmed the national need for country-wide map coverage at scales of 1:1250 (in urban areas), 1:2500 (in rural areas), and 1:10,000 scale (in mountain and moorland areas). It accepted the need for continuous revision of the maps rather than cyclic revision and urged OS to proceed as rapidly as possible with its programme of converting its paper maps to computer form. Whilst generally supportive of the then management's plans, it was critical of an inward-looking culture and the lack of adequate investment in Research and Development (R&D). Most crucially, it argued that there were benefits in OS obtaining as much revenue as it could from the sale of its maps: this would foster market-focus and minimize the burden on the taxpayer. Since cost recovery in 1979 was about 40 percent (see Figure 21.2), however, the committee was clear that the Exchequer should continue to fund the difference between costs and revenue. The report's recommendations were largely accepted by the Conservative government in 1984; the long delay in its acceptance reflected the incoming government's distaste with the terms of reference and the largely public sector composition of the committee. In practice, the recommendations had mostly been adopted by OS before formal acceptance.

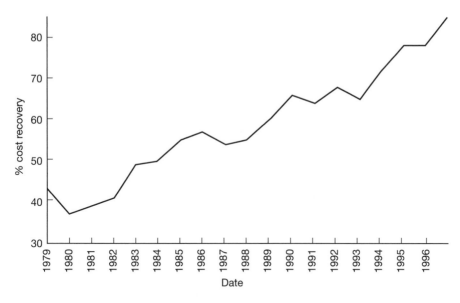

Fig. 21.2 Rising levels of annual cost recovery achieved by Ordnance Survey (the 1997 figure is subject to audit)

The consequence of the funding mechanism came to pose a progressively greater problem for OS over the next 18 years. Each year, ministers and Treasury officials looked for efficiency gains (i.e. cost-cutting) and improvements in revenues through improved marketing. The consequent effect of this was a progressive reduction in the vote from Parliament: Figure 21.1 shows how this has dwindled in 1997 to about one-quarter of what it was in real terms in 1979. Although effective in minimizing taxpayer funding, this has had several severe disadvantages. In the first instance, it perpetuated a misleading view that OS needed to be subsidized because of its (diminishing) ineptness. Even more seriously, it disguised the tension between a remit to map the whole country yet find funds for that work from only the modest proportion of Britain which seems to be commercially viable (90 percent of the population of Britain lives in about 10 percent of the land area and many sales of mapping are population-related). This cross-subsidy is inequitable to customers and facilitates the entry of competitors who do not have to cover such a geographical overhead. Finally, the funding mechanism did not provide transparency and accountability: the taxpayer had no real idea what she/he was getting for the parliamentary funding provided.

Further influences on the OS remit and priorities came in the form of the Report of the House of Lords Select Committee on Science and Technology in 1985 (Rhind 1986) and the Report of the Government's Committee of Inquiry into the Handling of Geographical Information (often called the Chorley Report after the Committee's Chairman) in 1987 (HMSO 1987; Rhind and Mounsey 1989). Amongst many other recommendation, both of these urged OS to speed the rate of conversion of its 230,000 paper maps to computer form. The cumulative effect of these and other influences was increasing pressure on resources and a greater expectation of results from OS as the 1980s drew to a close. Some part of this tension is implicitly present in the first Ordnance Survey Framework Document (OS 1990), published as OS became an agency in May 1990. These documents effectively define the role and responsibilities – but not the resources – of an agency.

In addition to this growing tension between resources and remit, OS has operated within an inappropriate financial environment. Despite having to operate on a trading basis with accounting carried out very largely on the basis of standard commercial practices, it had very limited freedoms: under Treasury rules it is unable to carry over surpluses except for some limited capital funds. Failure to break even after allowing for the vote or be in surplus at the end of the financial year was liable to lead to significant penalties and opprobrium; any surpluses had to be remitted to the Treasury. Since much of the OS funding now arises from sales of goods and services, since such revenue is volatile – especially at the end of the financial year – the cumulative effect of this has normally led to loss (to OS) of investment and demoralization of staff, notably in marketing areas which struggled hard to obtain revenues and then saw part of them 'lost' to Her Majesty's Treasury.

THE CHALLENGES OF TECHNOLOGY

OS was essentially a factory producing paper and microfilm maps until the late 1980s (McMaster 1991; Rhind 1991). Staff were largely artisans, recruited from school and retained until retirement: in 1979, only 23 of the 3,500 staff were graduates or had equivalent professional qualifications (HMSO 1979). Planning was long-term: the programme to re-map Britain as a consequence of under-investment in the 1920s and 1930s ran from 1946 until about 1980. Within this long-term plan, annual planning was highly detailed and the methods by which work was carried out varied relatively slowly. Until 1974, the head of the Survey was a Major General in the British Army and military officers filled a number of key posts until 1984. Their task was to clone operations across the whole country and maintain the currency of 230,000 different maps at a wide variety of scales (see Plates 2 (a) to 2 (f)).

Ordnance Survey first began to use computers around 1966. Like other organizations, it initially saw these as calculators and later as financial system tools. An apocryphal but probably true story is that the first digital maps were drawn inside OS in 1970 using a graph plotter procured for drawing histograms by the finance section. For many years thereafter, quite separate computer systems were used for technical and management purposes. R&D and cartographic editing was carried out on mini-computers and workstations but production 'databanking' and data supply plus all management information systems was mainframe-based.

A key factor in determining OS use of computers was the lack of any external pressure for computer data: even though Ordnance Survey set up what was probably the world's first production line for digitizing in 1973, there was little or no customer demand (other than from some academics) for such data until the late 1980s and even later. Digital mapping was therefore necessarily legitimated on the need to improve production rates and cost reduction for the paper mapping for which OS had a remit. In parallel with this was the consequence of little relevant software being available from the commercial sector until the mid- or late 1980s: as a consequence, many of the tools used until the 1990s were home-grown and tailored towards automating previous processes. The resulting data were organized in a way which facilitated making high-quality paper maps, rather than describing the physical and cultural nature of the world – there was, for instance, no concept whatsoever of an area (e.g. a field) in OS data until the late 1980s.

Another indicator of the nature of the pre-1990s organization was the way in which R&D was financed and managed. It was recognized by the management in the 1970s and 1980s that R&D had a major role to play but there was no obvious metric for judging how much was needed and how its value was to be assessed. In practice, a budget figure of between 2.0 and 2.5 percent of total expenditure was allocated for R&D but (as in many other organizations) no very successful way of measuring the benefit of this or alternative levels of investment was found. Some research eventually found its way into operational practices: for instance, OS field surveyors began in 1995 to use pen-based computers for recording change data in the field, rather than recording the change on maps on wooden mapping boards, then later transferring the detail to a computer; use of field-based computers had been pioneered by OS R&D some years before but many other pieces of research were not utilized at all or published. R&D is now more focused on potential products and applications and on strategic developments, with tracking of more basic research.

THE CHANGING NEEDS OF CUSTOMERS

Prior to 1991, Ordnance Survey's last substantial new product had been the 1:50,000 scale map (Landranger) in 1973, replacing the previous One Inch (1:63,360 scale) map. Having begun the conversion of its 230,000 large-scale maps into computer form in 1973, OS still had some 50 percent of these to convert by 1991. Only four years earlier it had predicted that this process would not be complete for urban areas until 2005 and for other areas of the country where justified until 2015 (HMSO 1987). Other than the modest number of large-scale maps sold in computer form, all of its products were remarkably similar to those of half a century before.

Until at least the end of the 1980s, many of OS's customers were much less knowledgeable about databases, survey, and mapping than was

Ordnance Survey itself. A culture of deference still pertained to a substantial extent, fostered by dealings with a 200-year-old organization (and the calibre of its staff). Internally, there remained a strong production ethos (see below) which itself supported this situation. Thus OS set its map revision programme in relation largely to what it saw as an acceptable compromise of user needs, an economic method of survey, and the government resources available. The re-mapping of any one area would typically have to wait for a sufficient volume of change to accumulate until it was economic to send out a surveyor. In the worst cases, some rural areas were only re-visited every 40 years or so. The advent of computer systems (see below) which could reproduce instantly the most recent mapping – and customer reactions to speedy drawing of out-of-date mapping – gave a powerful impetus to the need to revise the mapping more frequently.

From about the start of the 1990s, however, there was a rapid growth of expertise in the outside world and a progressive shift in the perception by customers of what they required. The latter at least had long been anticipated: in 1974/75, a major Ordnance Survey study was carried out to devise ways of restructuring the cartographic data into 'real world objects', but the lack of external demand and the complications and expense of the processes ensured this was never adopted. Partly because of the culture of higher expectations and legitimacy of complaint fostered by the government, the OS of the early 1990s realized that quite different approaches had to be taken if it was to continue to be successful.

THE ORDNANCE SURVEY CULTURE

At the time of its bicentenary in 1991, Ordnance Survey's Mission Statement was 'to maintain the map on which Britain's development depends'. Whilst OS was unusual in even having such an explicit focus at that time, this statement reflected a common staff view of their continuing importance to the operation of a centrally co-ordinated state: what had worked for 200 years must be a sound basis for the future. The organizational structure consisted of three directorates – Survey and Production; Marketing, Planning and Development; and Establishments (Personnel, Estates, Internal Audit and Training) and Finance (E&F). With the exception of the merger of cartography and survey directorates and the steady growth of marketing since 1970, this structure was near-identical to that of 1947. Traditional Civil Service procedures were the basis on which the organization operated. It was normally more important to make decisions properly by due process rather than quickly, and time-to-market was usually long. Staff were recruited with particular aspirations and expectations of a long career of public service. Circulation of papers on files, to be signed off by a senior officer, was the norm. Deference to senior staff, especially the Director General, was highly developed. Perfectionism was much respected, at least so far as it was manifested in the cartographic quality and geometric accuracy of detailed, country-wide mapping. The concept of a business-like 'can do' culture was absent in many parts of the organization. Funds from government were controlled by the Finance staff and E&F Director who had greater influence on what was tackled than did the senior marketing staff for the great bulk of the period from 1970 to 1990.

This situation should not be judged out of context or exaggerated. In many respects, OS was more emancipated and forward-thinking than most government bodies at the time. It had had a long involvement in commercial matters: for instance, it first defended its copyright case in the early nineteenth century but began to generate significant sums in revenue from the sale of goods or services and licensing from 1966 onwards. By virtue of all this, it was rather more aware of 'outside world' developments than were other government departments. Strong management action had been taken in various respects: much of the digitizing of the maps had been contracted out to the private sector from 1987 onwards and the one-time network of nearly 200 field offices was slimmed down to around 80. In addition, it was blessed – partly by serendipity – with a particular group of staff who were to play a key role in its transformation in the 1990s. In 1984, the Directorate of Overseas Survey (DOS) was merged with Ordnance Survey as aid finance for its activities was run down (Macdonald 1996). Its elite surveyors were drawn from graduates who were then trained on an advanced course and sent on overseas postings in their early twenties in any one of the 78 countries in which DOS operated. Each had early responsibility for the management, safety, and success of a party of up to 100 staff. This experience had strongly beneficial effects. In 1984 – at the peak of its size in OS – former DOS staff made up only 5 percent of the total workforce; yet, since 1991, eight of the eleven individuals who have served as Directors of OS came from the DOS cadre and – with their colleagues at lower levels in OS – they have provided strong leadership, made dramatic changes to the organization, and adapted quickly to new circumstances.

THE CHALLENGES AND THE LEGACY

By 1991, OS:

- was a traditional – but excellent by any contemporary standards – NMO which saw its primary role as one of map maintenance rather than of defining the framework and exploiting its databases;
- was facing a government intent on making radical change to the public sector, committed to privatization and contracting out of services, and unwilling to finance investment from public funds voted by Parliament;
- was facing a growing demand from customers who wanted better

products for less money and had a much greater awareness than previously of what was possible and of the characteristics of OS goods and services;

- was increasingly dependent on volatile revenues from customers rather than predictable vote funding from government yet continued to operate in a constraining and possibly wasteful environment of financial rules;
- was faced with a sharp down-turn in the national economy after the boom years of 1988–89, resulting in lower revenues;
- had licensing arrangements with a number of commercial map-makers for use of paper OS mapping but had no such arrangements in relation to its computerised databases (such as they were at that time);
- was recognizing that it had not kept up to date technologically in certain respects;
- had an ageing portfolio of standard products, all produced on multiple different flowlines;
- was only 50 percent of the way through conversion of its maps into computer form and was predicting completion of the task well after the turn of the century;
- had a workforce larger than it would need even in the short term and with an inappropriate skills mix for the future;
- was facing growing competition from other organizations, some of which were quite prepared to steal, disguise, and reproduce OS mapping.

Given this situation, it was obvious that some major changes were necessary if OS was to be sustainable and even prosper in the future. The next section of this chapter describes how OS management set out to define what needed to change, how the organization and its products were modified, and the level of success achieved.

RE-BUILDING ORDNANCE SURVEY

Following an internal review carried out by various teams in the first five months of 1992, a new vision for OS was put to its minister in May of that year. A version of this, comprising many of its key points, was given at the Association for Geographic Information conference six months later and widely published (Rhind 1992).

Over the next few years, priority was given to the following points:

- re-shaping the organization to meet current customer needs and anticipate future needs;
- stabilizing and increasing revenues;
- generating new products;
- changing the culture and skills base of the OS staff;
- migrating to a database, rather than a digital map, basis of operations;

- greater involvement with the private sector;
- redefining the role of OS with government and other 'stakeholders' and the financial environment in which we operate;
- demonstrating the effectiveness and efficiency of OS and the national need for its goods and services.

The actions taken to achieve several of these are now described.

Re-shaping the organization

The aims of the Change Programme instituted in 1993 were to improve OS's performance. It was also to be a tangible demonstration of the management's commitment to radical change of OS towards a customer-focused, rather than a production-driven, organization. We sought less centralism in decision-making, greater customer focus, and faster-to-market capabilities through a move to business units. The creation of an internal market was designed to identify and drive down costs. Central to the philosophy adopted was that there was no real possibility of getting everything completely 'right': rather the aim was to get it '80 percent right' and re-evaluate and tune thereafter. It was anticipated that future change would in any case be ongoing. All of this was counter-cultural and caused some staff dismay (see below).

The new mission and corporate aims

Fundamental change is likely to fail unless it is driven by a clear vision of the future organization and its role. This must be readily communicable to staff and others and be meaningful, internally consistent, and achievable. For this reason, a new mission statement and new corporate aims were debated, refined, promulgated, and nurtured throughout OS. The aims are amplified in OS's Strategic Plan for 1996-2001 (OS 1996). Comparison of these with earlier descriptions makes clear the intended shift in organizational focus involved. The Mission Statement is: 'to be customers' first choice for mapping today and tomorrow'. It recognizes the existence of customers, rather than users, the need to delight those customers, and our determination to be a sustainable and successful 'business'. We intend to achieve this through our corporate aims, which are:

- to be leaders in the field of geospatial and topographic data, linking mapping, information, and technology;
- to anticipate and meet the needs of our customers with services and goods that are fit-for-purpose;
- to build long-term, mutually beneficial relationships with our customers, suppliers, and business partners;

- to maintain, constantly improve, and safeguard the National Topographic Database;
- to make continuous improvements in quality and efficiency;
- to excel through confident and committed staff;
- to operate within and contribute to government policies.

The restructuring of OS

The Change Programme was partly achieved through the implementation of a wholly new structure comprising six business units 'trading' in an internal market through the operation of Service Level Agreements and other charging mechanisms (Figure 21.3). A small Corporate Office of five people plus the Internal Audit function completed the design. This was all implemented in January 1994. The market was a pseudo one in that there were restrictions on the level of purchasing of services from outside OS, but it was predicated upon the view that everyone had a customer for their goods and services and that the customer – whether internal or external – had to be satisfied with the level of service obtained and had recourse to some sanctions in the case of failure. In this way, greater clarity was secured in the real costs of activities hitherto funded in general 'buckets' and an incentive was established to drive down costs through the budgeting process.

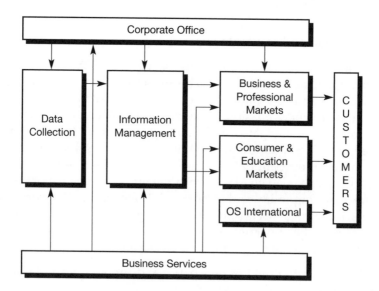

Fig. 21.3 The Business Unit structure as implemented in 1994 (the 3 'outward-facing Units – Business and Professional Markets, Consumer and Education Markets, and OS International – were restructured into a Marketing Business Unit and a Sales Business Unit in April 1997)

In addition, all jobs in the organization were effectively scrapped: by starting from a 'zero base' some 600 new jobs were designed, though some of these were generic (e.g. the surveyors' and cartographers' jobs did not change a great deal at that stage). All were formally defined and evaluated and many job descriptions were tuned subsequently. Suitable candidates were then posted to these new jobs, leaving a pool of additional staff (mostly managers) who were assigned project work; many of these individuals subsequently took early retirement. Some 90 middle management posts were excised from the previous 450 and the pyramid compressed – the design aim of having no more than five levels of posts underneath the Chief Executive was largely achieved. Over the three-year period from implementation of the business unit structure in January 1994, some 648 staff left OS whilst 218 with different skills were recruited.

At a later stage, when permitted by new government reforms, the existing Civil Service pay scheme and the terms and conditions of the staff were also replaced by local equivalents designed to suit OS's needs rather than those of the Civil Service as a whole. As part of this, all staff were transferred to a performance pay-based system. This was operated through a process of setting departmental objectives, including published targets, then cascading responsibility for these down through individual objectives, with progress against these objectives being formally assessed every four months.

At any one time, the Management Board of Ordnance Survey includes three Non-Executive Directors as well as the OS Executive Directors. The various individuals in the former capacity, all successful in the private sector, were extremely influential in this turbulent period through their experience of such changes and managing uncertainty.

All of the above relates to a particular change though much has evolved since 1994, notably in the re-structuring of 'outward facing' business units (see Figure 21.3). In addition to the mechanical stages of implementing the Change Programme, however, a major attempt has been made to change the culture which permeates OS. Some of the ways in which this continuing operation is being carried out are described later, but one specific item is relevant here: the change of the planning process. Prior to the early 1990s, OS planning was long-term, centralized, and highly detailed, leading to the comment that the Chief Executive must know exactly what any particular member of staff would be doing up to a year ahead! This was replaced by a Strategic Planning process illustrated in Figure 21.4 and a shift of responsibility for many activities, including much planning, to the business units – but all within the framework of the corporate aims and objectives and the OS budgeting and planning process.

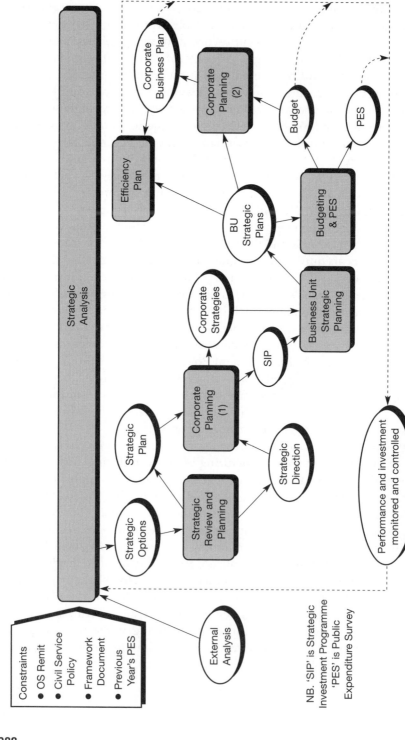

Constraints
● OS Remit
● Civil Service Policy
● Framework Document
● Previous Year's PES

NB. 'SIP' is Strategic Investment Programme
'PES' is Public Expenditure Survey

Fig. 21.4 OS Strategic Planning process

The staff

It will be obvious that changes on the scale indicated were initially surprising and unwelcome to many staff. For many, the threats to OS's success were not obvious and were initially treated as management dementia or a charade. The changes already described to pay, terms and conditions of employment, and the nature of jobs were paralleled by the abolition of the familiar grading system, the throwing open of all posts to applications from any staff member, the opening of Director-level posts to public competition, and the advocacy of much greater empowerment. Of all these, the understanding and take-up of empowerment was perhaps the least successful initially: some (but not all) staff were disorientated by a move from a familiar, rules-based, and extensively checked approach to one where they were expected to find the best way to do something and use initiative within broad guidelines and the quality system (see below).

As a consequence of all the change, staff morale – except for those centrally involved – sank quickly. The nadir of this, including strong suspicion of management's motives (at a time when privatization of other government bodies was ongoing), plus a significant subsequent recovery of morale and trust, are recorded in the two OS staff opinion surveys carried out in 1993 and 1995. Figure 21.5 illustrates how responses to one question changed over that period. The full results of these questionnaire surveys, of Post Implementation Reviews of the Change Programme, and analyses of performance marks across the organization, were made available to all staff: the view taken was that commitment would only come from confidence in the management and a belief in their honesty and openness. The value of such commitment is an intangible one in most cases but seems certain to be more crucial where staff innovation and their intellect and enterprise become more important than craft skills, as was the case in OS. Whilst much has improved since the period of the first restructuring of OS, a number of human resource problems remain. Two continuing ones are higher levels of stress than hitherto, in part created through excessive working by some key staff and perceived inconsistencies between business units in application of corporate policies on performance assessment, personal development, etc.

In times of such rapid change, it is essential to develop existing staff to meet their new roles. Some of course had already developed themselves: for example, nine staff had taken Master of Business Administration (MBA) degrees. Table 21.1 shows the comparison in higher educational attainment levels in 1979 and 1997. All those with management roles and aspirations to them took some key in-house courses: such courses were run for about 200 staff on financial awareness and on leadership. Many more went on specific courses. Just as important, ways were devised of assessing the competencies needed by the whole organization and for specific jobs;

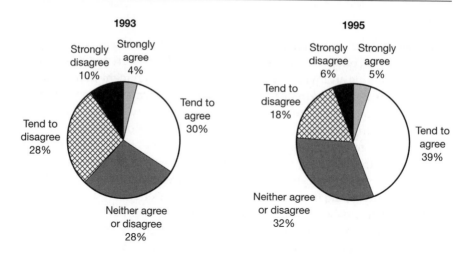

Fig. 21.5 Responses to one of the 73 questions in the 1995 Employee Opinion Survey: 'I believe Senior Management are honest about Ordnance Survey's Future'

these then formed the basis of job advertisements and candidate interviews. On this basis, a scheme was devised and implemented to assess personal development needs. All of these elements contributed to a corporate human resources strategy, the many components of which are shown in Figure 21.6.

Table 21.1 Changes in levels of higher educational attainment as percentage of the staff, 1979 and 1997

Year	Percent with Bachelor's degree or equivalent professional qualification	Percent with Master's degree	Percent with PhD
1979	0.7	not known: probably under 1	nil
1997	13	5	0.3

Perhaps the single most significant element of the staff/management interaction, however, came through the formulation of Behaviours We Value, a publication forged by about 120 volunteers who defined what OS should expect from them and what in turn they would expect from the OS. It defines what this large group of individuals from across all parts and levels of OS, operating through focus groups without management guidance, believed were the necessary attitudes and actions of all staff if the OS   mission and aims were to be achieved. The conclusions dealt with the behaviour of individuals, of team members, and of leaders. It demanded in return a corporate

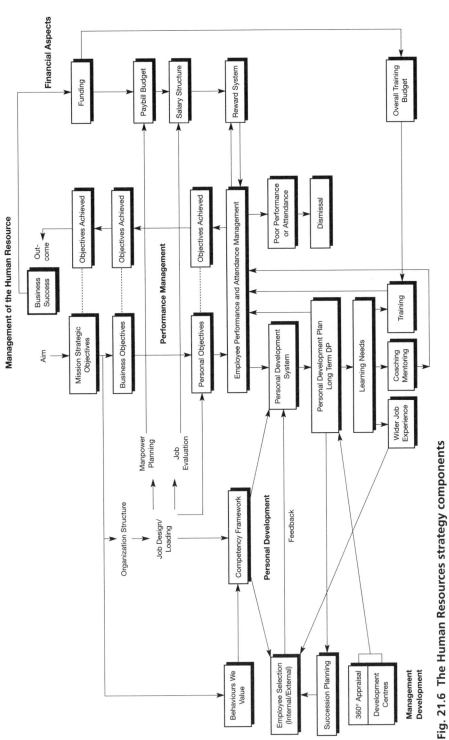

Fig. 21.6 The Human Resources strategy components

environment with particular characteristics such as good vertical and lateral communications, personal development policies, and access to good business information and systems needed. Behaviours We Value was (and remains) a very substantial contributory factor to making staff feel that they were part of the change process and guiding attitudes and actions.

Using external assessment to improve performance

Three devices which have been used to improve OS performance are registration to the ISO 9000 quality standard, competition for a Charter Mark, and registration for Investors in People status. These are the main components of our drive towards 'business excellence'.

The first of these has a long pre-history in OS. Traditionally, OS had a regime of checking of work, especially in the production areas, at least twice and sometimes on three occasions. This was expensive and far from fool-proof. In order to raise awareness of quality issues amongst staff, a 'Quality Each Day' (QED) campaign was run during 1989. This more than paid for itself in terms of improvements implemented. At the same time it demonstrated that the staff were prepared to raise suggestions and ideas and that all members of staff were concerned about the quality of product they produced. OS then launched a total quality management (TQM) campaign in 1991. This was intended to encourage staff to look critically, and in a structured manner, at the various processes within OS. Staff were trained in tools such as brainstorming, problem analysis, and identification of customer/supplier chains. The unfortunate offshoot of the way this was organized led to staff believing it was a one-off initiative, rather than forming the building blocks on which later developments such as ISO 9000 could build. One benefit of the TQM campaign, however, was that it convincingly demonstrated that nonconformance, leading to waste, was surprisingly commonplace throughout OS.

In November 1992, directors agreed to go ahead with the implementation of a programme for OS to be accredited to the ISO 9000 quality standard. This was done on a rolling basis, beginning with the 'production areas' – Reprographics, Data Collection, and Information Management. The benefits of ISO 9000 registration were initially anticipated as providing a structured framework within which future change could be accommodated without huge disruption. The purely fiscal benefit of reducing non-conformance, whilst of major concern, was not the sole criterion. At the time of writing (early 1997), some 53 percent of the organization is registered to ISO 9000 standards with the rest being scheduled to be included by early 1998. Adherence to the standard and the processes inside OS – now all carefully re-defined – is re-examined by independent inspectors every six months. In principle, ISO 9000 creates a self-improving system since suggestions for improvements are encouraged and must be evaluated and implemented if found valuable and feasible: during 1996, for example, Information Management Business Unit staff submitted over 1200 ideas for improving IM processes. Whilst many of these were of a minor nature and deal with detail, some are far more fundamental. The management in the Data Collection Business Unit claim savings in non-conformance amounting to some 40 percent of the 1994 value (at that time, non-conformance costs incurred through re-work, etc. were identified as equivalent to approximately 5.4 percent of total available staff time).

Charter Mark is a British government initiative to foster better standards of public service. In principle, over 20,000 public bodies are eligible for the award which is held for three years. An application for a Charter Mark demands evidence of published standards of performance and adherence to them, of consultation with customers and courtesy in dealing with them, redress for any errors or shortcomings, a register of all complaints, and use of this information in improvements of services, demonstrable value for money in the services provided, improvements in performance over the previous two years and examples of innovation of new services at no cost to the taxpayer. OS first won a Charter Mark (of 93 awarded) for excellence in the delivery of public services in 1993 and re-won one (of 323 awarded) in 1996.

Investors in People (IIP) is the British national standard for effective investment in the training and development of people in order to achieve organizational goals. Based on practical experience of the UK's most successful companies, it is widely regarded as a benchmark of best practice. Achieving the standard involves a planned approach to setting and communicating organizational goals, developing the staff to meet those goals, and measuring the impact of that development. IIP is consistent with earlier human resources strategies in OS, including the communications strategy, the staff development strategy, the performance appraisal system, the personal development system based on competencies, and the job advertising and selection policy. The relationships between these strategies is shown in Figure 21.6. Investors in People fits closely with the OS aim to achieve continuous improvement of the organization through continuing development of staff; as a consequence, we have committed ourselves to gain accreditation by 1998.

Generating stable and higher revenues

The volatility of OS revenues has already been described. This and the need to increase them substantially from a base of diminishing revenues after the 1988–89 UK economic boom led to determined action. Several different strategies were followed; four of these are described briefly below.

Improving the frequency of update

It was clear (see earlier) that the old revision regime, whereby OS decided when to re-map selected areas and published statistics only in the form of the total number of units of change surveyed, was unsustainable in the light of customers' needs and expectations. The customers are much more interested in how up-to-date is the database. For this reason, a new revision regime was designed, discussed with Consultative Committees and other parties and implemented. It was radically different from the previous regime in guaranteeing that all change of a certain 'major' (and defined) type would be in the database within six months of its creation and all of the country would be swept for all other changes every five years or ten years (mountain or moorland). Given preceding levels of service and the cost of improved revision, this was a bold and ambitious approach. To make it work has required the development of new techniques of survey and photogrammetry, the gathering of intelligence on change to focus work allocation, and significant contracting out of survey work. Progress is evident from comparison of revision costs today with those for 1990. The cost in real terms of periodic revision for rural and moorland areas, now with much shorter gaps between each revision, has dropped by approximately 50 percent. For urban areas under continuous revision, much-improved currency has been achieved without any increase in real terms in the annual average cost per square kilometre.

Setting up Service Level Agreements

After discussions lasting as much as two years, a number of Service Level Agreements (SLA) were signed with representatives of key user segments. The first to be signed was a collective agreement with all 515 Local Authorities (LAs) in Britain. Negotiated through the Local Government Management Board, this provided a large basket of OS goods for participating governments. In return for what was a single bulk deal, some volume discount was negotiated for the cost of data supply, use under copyright terms, and an update facility. In addition, the governments could obtain detailed OS mapping in either digital or paper form for the same cost. The consequence of the initial three-year SLA (since renewed) is that the use of digital data has soared from around 20 percent of all LAs to around 90 percent. This in turn has stimulated the software and added value services industry. Other SLAs have been signed with HM Land Registry, the Scottish Office (covering central government bodies in Scotland), the utility companies, and various other bodies. Such an arrangement not only increases revenue by bringing in more customers, it also provides some predictability of revenue.

Creating and selling new products and services

The long-standing lack of new products was reversed after 1991 (see Table 21.2), in large measure due to the rapid completion of digitizing of

Table 21.2 Selected new products introduced by OS since 1991

Product	Source scale	Number of maps/ records	When complete	Comments
Superplan	1:1250, 1:2500, 1:10,000	230,000	1995	First ever 'Plot on Demand' production mapping system
Landplan			1998	First ever derived scale 'Plot on Demand' production mapping
OSCAR – road centre lines plus road names	1:1250 to 1:10,000	0.5 million km of road	1994	Covers every driveable road in Britain. Updated every 6 months. Available in 3 different levels of generalization
ADDRESS-POINT	n/a	25 million records	1995	National Address database with 0.1 m resolution co-ordinates on each address. Updated every 6 months
1:50,000 scale colour raster	1:50,000	812 'tiles'	1994	Created in partnership with private sector
1:10,000 scale black and white raster	1:10,000	10,556 maps	1994	Created in partnership with private sector
Meridian		805	1995	'Medium-scale' database compiled from a variety of sources, created on the basis of market research and featuring roads as the main element
ED-LINE	1:10,000	109,670 EDs	1992	Boundaries of all Population Census areas in England and Wales. Produced in partnership with private sector
Boundary-Line	1:10,000	320+	1991	Annually updated records of administrative and electoral boundaries and names
Land-Form PROFILE	1:10,000	10,556 maps	1996 (contours)	The National Height Model as 5 and 10 m contours and a Digital Terrain Model of height values on a 10 m grid.
Explorer map series	1:25,000		2001 subject to market success	Replacement for 1300 Pathfinder maps in 350 sheets, much more frequently updated.
CD-ROMs	various	many	1996	Several CD-ROMs have been produced such as the OS Interactive Atlas of Great Britain, Discover London and Street Atlases.
Data transformations			1996	Two transformations have been created for conversion of OS National Grid co-ordinates to WGS84 (i.e. GPS) ones. The 2 m accuracy one is in the public domain; the 20 cm accuracy one is embedded in a transformation service operated by OS.

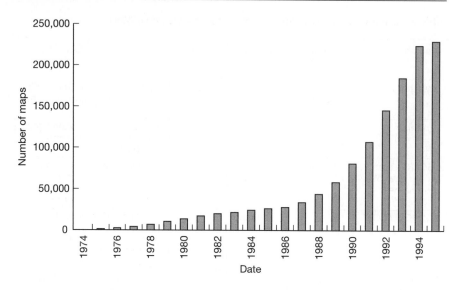

Fig. 21.7 Growth in the number of OS maps in digital form

all 230,000 large-scale maps. Figure 21.7 shows how the rate of digitizing had in fact been ramped up greatly after publication of the Chorley Report (HMSO 1987). As a result, the 1987 predictions of completion of digitizing well into the next century were realized by the end of 1995.

The new products include Superplan, the world's first 'Print on Demand' mapping system which now operates from 35 agents' shops in major towns in Britain. It permits maps to be plotted at scales from 1:100 to about 1:4000, centred on the user-specified position and showing only chosen features which may be highlighted in different ways. Landplan is the first-ever production generalized mapping, derived from its Superplan parent and capable of being plotted from about 1:4000 to about 1:14,000 scale (see Plate 2 (b)). Perhaps more unusual is the ADDRESS-POINT product, consisting of 1 metre accuracy grid reference for each of the 25 million mail delivery points in Britain, together with a full postal address and other codes. More products are now in continuous development, most being spun off from the National Topographic Database or less-detailed cartographic databases. This has speeded up the development and hence shortened the time-to-market for products considerably: ADDRESS-POINT was initially created in three years and Meridian in nine months. The growth in data supply has paralleled the growth of new products: in 1996, about 777 gigabytes of data were supplied to customers; i.e. an average of 13,900 bytes for every person in Britain. New developments include scanning by OS and a partner of about 200,000 historical maps dating from the middle of the nineteenth century onwards: we anticipate these playing a key role in monitoring for possible sites of environmental contamination and in legal disputes as well as forming a convenient archive for historical research and other purposes.

Central to all this is the anticipation and exploitation of new technology, with systems specified, developed, and functioning within much shorter time scales than was commonplace only a few years ago. OS operates a formal Technology Tracking system which now provides timely information to decision-makers about what can be expected to be available in the coming months and years. Our R&D is focused very much on matters germane to our strategic objectives. Nevertheless, there are always more calls for resources than exist so prioritization of IT-based investments, along with others (such as spending on staff development), are considered within a corporate Strategic Investment Programme (see Figure 21.4).

Working with the private sector

Two long-standing relationships had been in existence between OS and the private sector prior to 1991. These were with travel guide and atlas publishers, who used OS paper mapping under licence, and with the commercial digitizing sector which converted many OS large-scale maps into computer form: at the end of the digitizing programme, some 90 percent of all such conversions were carried out by that sector.

In 1991, however, OS sold all its digital data from its headquarters in Southampton; it was seen as a specialist operation requiring skilled technicians and one involving a risk of loss of control by OS of its key asset. The position has again changed radically: data are now sold through a series of licensed agents, through a data-brokering organization, and are incorporated in many products produced by other organizations such as Microsoft. In all, OS had over 50 value-added resellers at the end of 1996 and around 200 licensed developers of software. This had led to a healthy increase in revenues plus a much better relationship between OS and the various vendors. Each side now knows something of the other's plans under confidentiality agreements and consultation has reduced the incidence of mistakes and misunderstandings.

Defending OS's intellectual property rights

It is impossible to generate significant revenue in the information field unless certain conditions are met, such as that the information is highly transient or there are strong legal protection mechanisms in place (Rhind 1996). All of OS's products are covered by Crown Copyright and hence protected by strong legislation compared to that in many other countries. Nevertheless this is in no sense a licence to act in any draconian fashion: other legal mechanisms such as fair trading legislation and government rules such as the Fees and Charging Guide strongly influence behaviour and the freedom of manoeuvre. To facilitate information trading, OS has published its terms and conditions of trade (and has won national awards for the clarity of the documents) and its business code of practice.

Sadly, we have come across an increasing number of cases in the last five years where (often small) organizations have copied and disguised OS mapping using desktop publishing tools and sold the results, normally to unsuspecting customers. The Management Board has determined to take a hard line with all those whom we discover to be acting fraudulently, not least because this places law-abiding licensees of OS mapping (of whom there are many commercial firms) at a competitive disadvantage. A number of hard-fought court cases have all resulted thus far in victory for OS.

The results

The results in terms of rising revenues are shown in Figure 21.1: in the five years since 1991, OS revenues have risen 48 percent (29 percent in 1996 constant prices). In the same period, revenue per staff member has risen by 81 percent from just over £18,000 (in 1996 prices it has risen by 51 percent).

Re-engineering the relationship with government

In 1994, OS went through a Prior Options Review. This review is applied to all agencies and is a fundamental examination of how well it has performed recently and whether there is still a need for the organization's outputs. If it has performed poorly, new management may well be introduced. If the outputs are still found to be needed, the preference is for them to be provided by the private sector through privatization or by mass contracting out. The final alternative is for the organization to remain an agency within government if none of the other alternatives prove possible – until the next review.

This review was an exceptionally important one for OS. The review of past performance went well, with two independent review groups testifying to the re-invigoration and greater focus of the organization; ministers indicated in Parliament in October 1994 that they accepted the consultants' conclusions. Thereafter, corporate finance consultants were employed to examine the options for OS's future status. Their conclusions were also that OS had operated very successfully as an agency and could be expected to continue to do so in future. The consultants argued against converting the organization to act simply as a 'data warehouse' which produced mapping and data for others to exploit. This, they said, would remove the incentives for OS to be steered by user needs as mediated through the market place. They therefore urged that OS should continue to be involved in marketing products and services, often in conjunction with the private sector. The consultants believed that introducing mass contractorization to OS (e.g. by bringing in private sector management to reduce costs) was the worst of all options. But they believed that privatization had potential benefits for government even though these benefits or costs could not be quantified at present. Moreover, several legal, financial, regulatory, and other issues precluded such a step in the immediate future and the consultants stressed that such a step was only appropriate if OS was likely to prove a sustainable business in the longer term: 'asset stripping' was unacceptable on any grounds. Government ministers accepted these recommendations in early 1995 and OS will stay an agency at least until another review, probably in 1999. In the meantime, OS has a programme of work to clarify the obstacles which complicate privatization. From this review came Ordnance Survey's current Framework Document which specifies our current role, responsibilities, and accountability. It is much more focused on geographical information than maps *per se* and it gives greater flexibility to OS in various ways (OS 1995).

Two other ways in which the relationship between government and OS has evolved relate to the financial environment in which it operates (described earlier). Particular problems addressed were the *de facto* cross-subsidy in operation through (for example) supporting the cost of rural updating of the database from sales of urban mapping, and the end-of-financial year and related constraints.

The proposed National Interest in Mapping Service Agreement and OS Trading Fund

In 1995, OS began a major project known as the National Interest in Mapping Service Agreement (NIMSA). It was widely – but not universally – acknowledged that some national mapping-related activities are wholly uncommercial yet are essential in the national interest. In particular, funding the maintenance and enhancement of large parts of the National Topographic Database clearly falls in this category though supply of products derived from it were deemed not to be part of NIMSA. In principle, this agreement would be between a surrogate customer (the Department of the Environment – DoE), acting on behalf of the national interest, and OS. Because this would in effect be a contract for specific services, NIMSA moneys could be treated as revenues rather than a government vote or 'subsidy'.

A Working Group of officials drawn from DoE, HM Treasury, and OS, acting under ministerial guidance, was charged with defining the national interest and the activities subsumed within it. To that end, a major consultation exercise was carried out in late 1995 involving almost 200 bodies. These were drawn from central and local government, business, learned societies and academia, other user organizations like the Ramblers Association, and various other entities.

The results of this consultation were published and widely distributed (OS and DoE 1996). The agreed definition of the national interest in mapping is set out below:

- the public interest arising from the mapping of areas which would not otherwise be mapped if the judgement was made solely in terms of revenue generated by sales of that mapping alone. This is particularly crucial in regard to contingencies where there is typically no time to create new mapping: the information must be available 'off the shelf', as in the case of oil spillages;

- the benefits of having national consistency of content, currency, style, and manner of mapping which is dictated by needs other than those of the local market. Two different categories of this exist: these are where the information is needed for defence purposes and where sizeable external economic benefits occur (such as from everyone using the same topographic framework and hence all other data collected 'fitting together' correctly);
- the inescapable requirement for the creation or maintenance of the underpinning infrastructure of the mapping (notably the geodetic framework), which is widely used by other bodies and by the public and where charging for use is either inappropriate or impossible (such as for use of the National Grid).

The Working Group subsequently analysed OS's proposed set of activities falling under this definition. Aided by an independent consultant who scrutinized each activity, the group agreed a set of activities as being a valid and defensible statement of the national interest though these did not meet *all* the proposals made in the consultation exercise. Despite this agreement, the final funding of NIMSA for the year starting in April 1997 proved impossible to agree due to the late stage at which the cost of the national interest became clear and the pressure on public resources (the 'bill' was significantly larger than the parliamentary vote funding already planned). Another problem arises from the fact that the Public Expenditure Survey process does not function well where the expenditure is for a task which permeates the policies of many departments, sometimes in relatively intangible ways (as pointed out in Coopers and Lybrand 1996). In any event, the problem needs to be addressed again for 1998. Considerable support, moral and in principle, for NIMSA was obtained from other government departments but the disappointing out-turn has evoked a highly critical reaction from Barr (1997) and others.

The final way in which OS has sought to change the environment in which it operates is through moving to a Trading Fund. This essentially ensures more control over resources and obviates some of the end-of-year financial constraints and permits carry-over of funds and the taking out of loans to fund investment. As such, it moves the organization towards a more commercial financial environment though it also brings some disadvantages with it. To operate successfully under such a regime, however, demands that OS is able to trade successfully on the basis solely of revenues so far as can be ascertained in the foreseeable future; the demise of NIMSA rendered this impossible in the short term. The issue will be revisited as soon as a suitable NIMSA is agreed.

Demonstrating performance improvements

The consequences of the changes described above have been profound for OS and for its stakeholders. There has been a dramatic reduction in the number of staff directly employed, as shown in Figure 21.8. On the other hand, the extent of contracting out of work and the economic benefits of the market stimulus OS has delivered through SLAs and other innovations has probably amounted to well over 200 posts in other organizations.

In terms of published, ministerially set targets, OS has met 16 of the 17 in the last three years. The only failure in this period was due to the accounting treatment of an in-year change of plan to provide additional funding for voluntary early retirement. Cost recovery at the end of the 1996/97 financial year is over 22 percent higher than four years earlier and revenues in cash terms are up by no less than 39 percent. In addition to these achievements, large numbers of internally set targets related to our corporate aims have been achieved. These have included much better revision timetables and reduced costs of survey and mapping: our costs for map revision for our popular 1:25,000 scale paper mapping, for instance, have been cut by over 20 percent. Many of our products are cheaper in real terms than they were a few years ago, some by over 25 percent. We have set ourselves demanding challenges for the next few years as well as any others which ministers will wish to see achieved, and we have defined a future both desirable and achievable – involving doing more in the 'solutions business', in addition to data supply, and in overseas markets. At the same time, we have not forgone our public sector commitment to public good: OS has, for instance, played a major role in setting up the National Geospatial Data Framework – somewhat similar to the NSDI in the USA (see Tosta's chapter

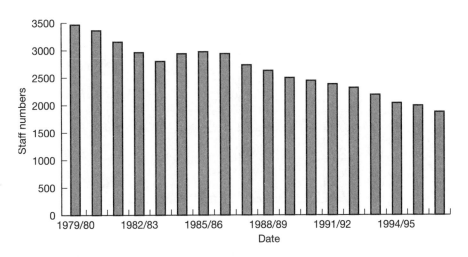

Fig. 21.8 Staff numbers in Ordnance Survey

in this book) – to facilitate collaboration between data providers, foster the use of standards, and enhance awareness of data availability and the value of Geographical Information.

However, these achievements, and those described earlier, are less important than some others. In the last few years, OS has been reviewed by a variety of organizations and has done well on all occasions. We take pride in having won two Charter Marks and multiple private sector prizes for innovation (in competition with the best of private and public sector organizations). The innovation prizes and numerous new systems in place suggest we are making broadly effective use of new technology. Most important of all, we take comfort – but no complacency – from the results of the independent surveys of customer satisfaction. Figure 21.9 shows the overall result: whilst we must seek to eradicate *all* poor performance, it is heartening that the proportion of those claiming to receive good or better service has risen to high levels in recent years.

So far as the theme of this book is concerned – the geographical framework – the British sub-set of it is probably in better form than it has ever been: it is more up-to-date, is entirely in computer form, is available still in a consistent form across the whole country, can be transformed to be consistent with the results from the Global Positioning System, and is made available through many different products. Moreover, through the Service Level Agreements now in place, the detailed framework of Britain – whose maintenance is the largest single cost to OS – is used by more people and for the benefit of more people than ever before.

On a wider front, OS has no remit to be involved with creating a geographical framework for Europe or beyond unless this can be done on a commercial basis. For this reason, we have moved cautiously with our European equivalents towards a pan-European framework database. This is

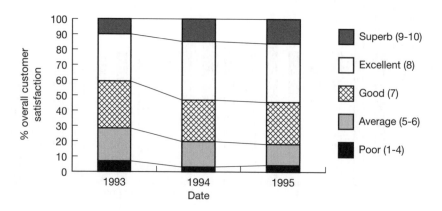

Fig. 21.9 Overall levels of customer satisfaction with OS products and services, measured as 'marks out of 10'

an area where further developments can be expected, but the type of support for global work advocated by Htun and Collins and Rhind elsewhere in this book can only be achieved through formal government commitment and resourcing.

CONCLUSIONS

Almost all of what has been written above is apparently specific to Britain: it shows that, under a particular set of political, legal, and market circumstances, it is possible to reform a NMO and to take it to a position where it can pay for itself (assuming the problem of mapping hugely uncommercial areas is recognized through a NIMSA deal). At least for the period covered by this review, it has proved possible to work within government policies and financial controls on investment, etc. *and* produce a more effective organization – even though some of the financial environment militates against good business practice. As shown in other chapters of the book, it is clearly possible to exploit technology to good advantage, obtaining new products and services faster and more cheaply than before. Not everything has worked perfectly: obtaining the right balance between local (business unit) autonomy and enterprise and adherence to OS-wide policies has proved difficult and some staff have felt under great pressure (especially as compared to their prior experience).

But the findings in this chapter have wider ramifications. Some of the approaches outlined here and elsewhere in the book may be applicable to other countries. Some of the findings – in terms of the ability to maintain high-quality, up-to-date data through financial support by users – gives practical confirmation to economic theory. But just as important is one other aspect of our experience: the globalization of our business. OS's international operations currently form a small part of the whole organization. Yet in three years it has co-operated with public and private sector partners from no fewer than 12 countries in working or bidding for work in areas as dispersed as Albania, Hong Kong, Kyrgyz, Lebanon, Palestine, and Zimbabwe. Nor is this a one-way process: one of OS's four contractors for rural area update is a Danish firm (and the Danish NMO's database is being built in part by a British firm). Digitizing of maps into computer form is now routinely done in low labour cost of areas in the developing world and Eastern Europe. In summary, then, we are all becoming part of a truly global business.

On a broader front, OS staff recognize that there is no monopoly in good ideas and practice: for that reason, we will benchmark ourselves against other NMOs and seek improvements from wherever they may arise in the world. In addition to the formal geographical framework provided by the topographic mapping around the world, there is increasingly a framework of international collaboration, competition, and learning to which NMOs like OS must subscribe if they are to play their role effectively and be sustainable and defensible organizations.

REFERENCES

Barr R 1997 Not in the national interest. *Mapping Awareness*. February: 17–19

Coopers and Lybrand 1996 *Economic aspects of the collection, dissemination and integration of government's geospatial information*. Southampton, Ordnance Survey

Foster C, Plowden F 1996 *The state under stress*. Buckingham, Open University Press

HMSO 1979 *Report of the Ordnance Survey Review Committee*. London, Her Majesty's Stationery Office

HMSO 1987 *Report of the Government's Committee of Inquiry into the handling of Geographic Information*. London, Her Majesty's Stationery Office

Macdonald A 1996 *Mapping the world*. London, Her Majesty's Stationery Office

McMaster P 1991 The Ordnance Survey: 200 years of mapping and on. *Journal of the Royal Society of Arts* CXXXIX (5421): 581–93

OS 1990 *Ordnance Survey Framework Document*, May. Southampton, Ordnance Survey

OS 1995 *Ordnance Survey Framework Document*, April. Southampton, Ordnance Survey

OS 1996 *Mapping the way to the next millennium: Ordnance Survey Strategic Plan 1996–2001*. Southampton, Ordnance Survey

OS and DoE 1996 *Results of the consultation exercise on the 'National Interest in Mapping'*. Southampton, Ordnance Survey and Department of the Environment

Osborne D, Gaebler T 1992 *Reinventing government*. Reading, Mass., Addison-Wesley

Rhind DW 1986 Remote sensing, digital mapping and Geographical Information Systems: the creation of government policy in the UK. *Environment and Planning C; Government and Policy* 4: 91–102

Rhind DW 1991 The role of the Ordnance Survey of Great Britain. *Cartographic Journal* 28: 188–99

Rhind DW 1992 Policy on the supply and availability of Ordnance Survey information over the next five years. *Proceedings AGI 92 Conference, 1992* (also published later in *Mapping Awareness* 7 (1): 37–41, and 7 (2))

Rhind DW 1996 Economic, legal, and public policy issues influencing the creation, accessibility and use of GIS databases. *Transactions in GIS* 1 (1): 3–12

Rhind DW, Mounsey HM 1989 The Chorley Committee and 'Handling Geographic Information'. *Environment and Planning A* 21: 571–85

Where next for the framework and the national mapping organizations?

If it has been successful, this book should have convinced the assiduous reader that the original objectives have been achieved. These were to demonstrate conclusively that national mapping organizations (NMOs) currently play a key role in the operation of the nation states, that they increasingly support business effectively, that a growing number of them are important players in the 'information market', and that they face continuing technological and other challenges in the years ahead. Most important of all, however, the authors set out to demonstrate that, because of the investments of governments to date, there is an imperfect but improving geographical framework to support human life on this planet.

The rationale for publishing the book was predicated upon a view that great forces are currently affecting the nature of the geographical framework for the world and the organizations which have thus far created and maintained it. These forces were previously described as:

- the impact of new technologies on NMOs, changing what they do, how they do it, and the consequences for their customers;
- rapid change in the expectations of users of the framework. Few are now content to be told what they can have and, as a result of this and financial changes, the power of the customer or user is now much greater. Fewer and fewer NMOs are now production-led;
- changes in society values, such as the greater concern for privacy and a diminution of trust in government;
- the effects of reform in government, such as massive reductions in staffing, new management approaches, new approaches to financing the framework, and public exposure of successes and failure. Some are manifested in new roles for NMOs, as seems to be arising from the 1994 Executive Order of the President of the USA;
- the effects of regionalization and globalization of business and even government. In Europe, Directives made centrally within the Union force change in national laws on intellectual property, trading practices, and much else. At the global scale, the work of the World Trade Organization may well impact on information trading. The advent of commercial organizations selling satellite imagery on a global basis in 1997 may well be

very significant for NMOs and their customers. All this should be contrasted with the need for global data for scientific purposes where little funding is usually available to pay for the data.

Change and uncertainty are now facts of life for all employees and citizens. The traditional world of government roles and employment – on which national sub-sets of the geographical framework for the world have been created – are fast changing in many countries, breeding fear and even stress for many people. Few of the changes described in this book have been less than painful for some groups of individuals; some of the changes have resulted in false steps and a need for further change. Yet looked at from a distance and in aggregate, the situation is better than it used to be: the framework is better than it was a decade ago, notably in being increasingly in computer form, and will continue to improve. Taxpayers and customers are getting more for their money and the data users have more influence over what they get than in the past. Recognizing the social and financial costs of transition is important, but there can be considerable optimism that both the framework and its creators will become ever more valued for the changes of recent years.

ABOUT THE AUTHORS

Carl Calvert Chief Geodesist and Survey Consultant, Ordnance Survey,
Romsey Road, Southampton SO16 4GU, UK
Telephone: +44 1703 792663 Fax: +44 1703 792250
E-mail: ccalvert@ordsvy.gov.uk
Ordnance Survey's Geodetic Adviser. After studying at the London Nautical School he joined the Ordnance Survey in 1967 and then studied surveying, geodesy, and mathematics at the universities of Oxford, Southampton, and East London. In the 30 years of his career in OS he has alternated between geodesy and information technology – holding management positions as well as professional qualifications in both disciplines. Early in his career he held a commission in the Royal Engineers (Volunteers) and has recently been external examiner for the Military Survey MSc course. He was the Education Co-ordinator for the Land and Hydrographic Division of the Royal Institution of Chartered Surveyors for seven years and is a member of various technical and educational committees, including the Editorial Board of Survey Review and AGI/RICS GPS Standards.

Derek G Clarke Director of Mapping, Chief Directorate of Surveys and Land
Information, Department of Land Affairs,
Mowbray, Cape Town, Republic of South Africa
Telephone: +27 21 6854070 Fax: +27 21 6891351
E-mail: dclarke@sli.wcape.gov.za
Director of Mapping with the South African NMO, an organization with which he has served for the past 18 years, involved in all aspects of national mapping and Geographical Information Systems. A registered professional land surveyor, he has a BSc (Survey), Diploma in Datametrics, and Master in Public Administration (*cum laude*) degrees. He has recently initiated the Mapping Awareness/Map Literacy Project, designed to increase map use among all the people of the country and effective utilization of spatial information for the development of South Africa.

Mark Collins Chief Executive, World Conservation Monitoring Centre,
219 Huntingdon Road, Cambridge CB3 0DL, UK
Telephone: +44 1223 277314 Fax: +44 1223 277136
E-mail: mark.collins@wcmc.org.uk
A zoologist with a BA from Oxford and a PhD in tropical ecology from Imperial College, University of London, he also holds a Professional Diploma in management from the Open University. Worked as a tropical ecologist with a particular interest in decomposition processes and nutrient cycling, 1972–82, a period of research which took him to Nigeria, Kenya, Sarawak, and many other tropical locations. In 1982, joined the World Conservation Monitoring Centre as a specialist in invertebrate conservation, eventually leading the Centre's move towards a more integrated approach to data management by developing its GIS. Became Chief Executive of WCMC in 1994, establishing its current strategic direction in biodiversity data management, information services, and capacity building. Serves as Trustee of Fauna and Flora International and Wildscreen World, and is Honorary Vice-President of the Cambridge University Explorers' and Travellers' Club as well as Chairman of the Steering Group of the Sustainable City initiative in Cambridge. With over 100 scientific papers to his name he has also edited and authored nine books.

Carolina Gartner Land Information New Zealand,
Level 3, Mayfair House, 44–52 The Terrace, PO Box 5104, Wellington, New Zealand
Telephone: +64 4 474 3518 Fax: +64 4 494 9404
E-mail: Carolina@wn.linz.govt.nz

Is currently General Manager Regional Services for Land Information New Zealand, a new government department resulting from the restructure of the Department of Survey and Land Information (DOSLI) in July 1996. She is responsible for all of the service delivery functions in Land Information New Zealand via its five regions. Has spent almost 20 years in the surveying, mapping, and land information business in a marketing and management role, and nearly 10 years in Australia with the New South Wales Department of Lands' Central Mapping Authority, building their map sales and service delivery area. In 1987 she moved to New Zealand to DOSLI as their Director of Marketing to develop and implement marketing strategies to support cost-recovery policies. This was followed by two years as Regional Manager in the Christchurch region managing the delivery of all products and services until the restructure in 1996. She has a BA in Regional Science, a Graduate Diploma in Marketing, and a Master of Letters in Geography.

Professor Donald M Grant Surveyor General of New South Wales, Land
Information Centre,
Bathurst, NSW 2795, Australia
Telephone: +61 63 328201 Fax: +61 63 322320
E-mail: grantd@lic.gov.au

Has been Surveyor General of New South Wales, Director of the Land Information Centre, and President of the Board of Surveyors since 1986. In 1993 he was made a Professional Associate in the Faculty of Science and Agriculture at Charles Stuart University. In the 1994 Queen's Honours List he was appointed a Member of the Order of Australia and was recently made a Doctor of Applied Science, honoris causa at Charles Stuart University and Doctor of Science, honoris causa at the University of New South Wales. He is a Fellow of the Institution of Surveyors, Australia, a Fellow of the Royal Institution of Chartered Surveyors, UK, a Fellow of the Institution of Engineers, Australia, and a Fellow of the Australian Institute of Company Directors. He is also the Australian representative of Commission VII of the International Federation of Surveyors.

He has worked in most Australian states, in the public and private sectors and in the defence forces. He has consulted or advised in the Sultanate of Brunei, the Maritime Provinces of Canada, Sri Lanka, Hong Kong, Indonesia, Thailand, Malaysia, Zimbabwe, and the People's Republic of China. As an Electoral Boundaries Commissioner, he has been involved in both state and federal re-distributions. As Chairman of the Public Sector Mapping Agencies, he has joined with all other jurisdictions in Australia to meet the national census mapping needs and forge the precursor to the National Spatial Data Infrastructure. As Foundation Chairman of the Australian Institute of Spatial Information Sciences and Technology (AISIST), he has directed training and consultancy services to a range of countries including Lao People's Democratic Republic, Indonesia, Sri Lanka, the People's Republic of China, Malaysia, and the Maldives. He is a Registered Surveyor and holds a Master of Environmental Studies degree.

Jean-Philippe Grelot Commercial Director, Institut Géographique National,
136 bis rue de Grenelle, 75700 Paris 07 SP, France
Telephone: +33 1 43 98 82 95 Fax: +33 1 43 98 84 00
He received engineer's degrees from the Ecole Polytechnique, Paris, in 1977 and from the French National School for Geographical Sciences in 1979, since when he has been working at the Institut Géographique National, France, as a researcher and head of the thematic cartography division, then as head of the printing division; in 1988 he was appointed Sales and Marketing Director. He has taught mathematics and cartography, and has lectured in digital cartography and theoretical cartography in a number of countries including Germany, Morocco, China, Indonesia, Algeria, and the Netherlands. He has been Secretary General and Treasurer of the International Cartographic Association since 1991. He has published over 80 papers and lectures.

Nay Htun Assistant Secretary General of the United Nations and Assistant Administrator and Regional Director, Regional Bureau for Asia and the Pacific, United Nations Development Programme,
1 United Nations Plaza, New York, NY 10017, USA
Telephone: +1 212 906 5800 Fax: +1 212 906 5898
Before 1994, when he assumed his present post and responsibility for an annual US$1.2 billion of grant development co-operation assistance in 24 countries, he was Deputy Executive Director of the UN Environment Programme. He was seconded to the UN Conference on Environment and Development (UNCED) Secretariat in Geneva where (1990–92) he helped to organize the Earth Summit; his responsibilities included liaison with businesses and industry. He has been closely involved with environment and development work at the policy, strategy, and technical levels for 30 years. Before working at the United Nations he worked at a senior management level for Exxon Thailand and as a Professor in the postgraduate level Asian Institute of Technology. Graduating with a PhD in Chemical Engineering from Imperial College of Science, Technology and Medicine, University of London, he has since held visiting professorships at major universities around the world. A board member of many non-profit organizations, he also advises many commercial organizations on their environmental policies.

Peter Jakobsen Director General of Kort & Matrikelstyrelsen,
Rentemestervej 8, DK 2400, Copenhagen NV, Denmark
Telephone: +45 35 87 5050 Fax: +45 35 87 5059
E-mail: pj@kms.min.dk
He graduated in 1968 from the University of Copenhagen with a degree in Economics (Cand Polit). After a career in the Danish Ministry of Agriculture where he was mostly occupied with international agricultural policies, especially regarding the EU's market arrangements and latterly its structural policies regarding agriculture, he was appointed Director of the Danish Cadastre in 1980. In 1987, on the Cadastre's merger with the Geodetical Institute and the Nautical Archives to form a new institution, Kort & Matrikelstyrelsen, he was appointed its first Director. He has taken an active interest in furthering international co-operation in the area of GIS for land and sea.

Carlos M Jarque Director, Instituto Nacional de Estadística, Geografía e Informática (INEGI),
Aguascalientes, Mexico
Telephone: +91 49 18 11 05 Fax: +91 49 18 30 83

Gained the degree of Actuarial Science in the Anahuac University in Mexico City, and then a Master's degree in Statistics from the London School of Economics and Political Science. He carried out postgraduate studies in Urban and Regional Planning and Economic Policy at the University of Oslo, Norway, and later obtained a Doctorate in Economics at the Australian National University and a postdoctorate qualification in Econometrics at Harvard University, in all instances graduating with Honours.

In his 25 years of professional experience, he has held such posts as Manager of Economic Studies of Teléfonos de México; General Director of Statistics of the Ministry of Budget and Planning; President of the Interministerial Committee of Public Finance; Adviser for the Banco del Centro; and Director of the International Statistics Institute (ISI) in The Hague. At present, he is in charge of the Presidency of the National Institute of Statistics, Geography and Informatics (INEGI) of Mexico, a Cabinet position in the Mexican government. His academic posts have included a professorship at the Faculty of Economics in the National University of Australia and a visiting professorship at the Department of Economics at Harvard University.

He has received the Banamex National Award of Science and Technology and the First National Award of Actuarial Science. He is author of over 90 publications on the subjects of geography, econometrics, statistics, economics, and planning. Currently, he is President of the Statistical Commission of the United Nations.

Roberta E Lenczowski Associate Deputy Director for Operations, National Imagery and Mapping Agency,
8613 Lee Highway, Fairfax, Virginia, USA
Telephone: +1 703 275 8537 Fax: +1 703 275 8645
E-mail: lenczowr@nima.mil

Before becoming Associate Deputy Director for Operations at the National Imagery and Mapping Agency in the United States, she was the Director for Acquisition and Technology at the Defense Mapping Agency. Before that she had served nearly three years as the senior scientist for GIS when she developed the concept of operations for an initiative called Global Geospatial Information and Systems intended to move the agency from the production of standard map products into an era of digital information extraction, management, and distribution. She gained her undergraduate BA degree in Philosophy and also completed a MA in that field. She also earned an MSc in Geodetic Science.

Dató Abdul Majid Mohamed Director General of Survey and Mapping,
Department of Survey and Mapping Malaysia,
Jalan Semarak, 50578 Kuala Lumpur, Malaysia
Telephone: +603 2925932 Fax: +603 2917457
E-mail: kpup@po.jaring.my

Dató Majid, as he is called locally, is Director General of Survey and Mapping, Malaysia, as well as the Chairman of the Land Surveyors Board of Peninsular Malaysia. He is also an Honorary Colonel in the Regiment of Engineers and the Director of Military Surveys, Malaysia. He graduated with a Bachelor of Surveying degree from the University of New South Wales in 1971, and holds a Postgraduate Diploma in Photogrammetric Engineering from the ITC, the Netherlands in

1973, and an MSc in Geodesy from Oxford University in 1978. He joined the Department of Survey and Mapping in 1971, and held several key posts before his present appointment.

As one of the longer-serving Directors General, he has introduced long-term plans aimed at modernizing his office, and in so doing, the survey and mapping profession in Malaysia. Over some 12 years he has successfully implemented several projects utilizing digital technology not only in the government sector, but also, as Chairman of the Land Surveyors Board, has spearheaded the widespread use of computerized systems by private sector land surveyors.

He has held several posts in the Institution of Surveyors Malaysia, and was its President for its 1987/88 session. He continues to represent Malaysia in various capacities.

Desmond J Mooney General Manager, Land Information Centre,
Bathurst NSW 2795, Australia
Telephone: +61 63 328100 Fax: +61 63 322320
E-mail: mooneyd@lic.gov.au
Has held senior positions in both the private and public sectors. He was a senior partner of Punch, Mooney and Associates from 1980 to 1983 as well as being a Director of Land Design Pty Ltd and owner/manager of the All Purpose Map Centre. In 1984 he joined the Department of Lands and has held the positions of Regional Manager, Manager of Management Improvement, and Manager of the Crown Lands Information Project. In 1988 he joined the Department of Administrative Services as Manager of Management and Information. Rejoining the Department of Lands in 1989 as General Manager of the Land Information Centre (a position he currently holds), he was instrumental in transforming the Centre from a traditional public sector organization to an innovative, commercially competitive business unit. He has acted as Surveyor General of New South Wales on many occasions during this time. He is a Registered Surveyor, Registered Valuer, and Justice of the Peace. He has an honours degree in Surveying, a Master of Business Administration (Sydney), and a Company Directors' Diploma. He is a Fellow of the Australian Institute of Management and a Fellow of the Australian Institute of Company Directors.

Joel L Morrison Chief of Geography Division, US Bureau of the Census,
Washington, DC 20233
Telephone: +1 301 457 1132
E-mail: jmorrison@geo.census.gov
As Chief, Geography Division, US Bureau of the Census, he manages the general geographic support activities of the Bureau with the assistance of approximately 225 cartographers, geographers, and computer scientists. Before 1995, he was Assistant Division Chief for Research in the National Mapping Division of the US Geological Survey and served as the Senior Scientific Advisor for Geography to the Chief of the National Mapping Division (1983–86). Before joining USGS in 1983, Morrison was a Professor of Geography at the University of Wisconsin in Madison (1967–83), where he also served as Chairman of the Department of Geography (1977–80). He has a BA in Mathematics from Miami University and an MSc and PhD from the University of Wisconsin.

He served as President of the International Cartographic Association (ICA) (1984–87). He was President (1981) of the American Congress on Surveying and

Mapping, Secretary on the AM/FM International Board of Directors (1989–91), and Chairman of the Board of Directors of the National Center for Geographic Information and Analysis (1990–94). In 1995 he co-edited *Elements of spatial data quality*, published for the ICA by Pergamon. Morrison is co-author of *Elements of cartography*, 6th edn (John Wiley & Sons, Inc., 1995) and senior consultant to *Goodes world atlas*, 19th edn (Rand McNally, 1995).

Keith Murray Head of Geospatial Programmes, Ordnance Survey Research Unit, Romsey Road, Southampton SO16 4GU, UK
Telephone: +44 1703 792729 Fax: +44 1703 792078
E-mail: kmurray@ordsvy.gov.uk

Has been the Ordnance Survey Research Unit Manager since 1995 and Geospatial Data Programme (GDP) Manager since 1996. Research has included development of portable digital field survey systems, database development, business process re-engineering, and major initiatives in geospatial data development. The GDP involves major re-structuring and extension of the existing OS National Topographic Database and preparation of it to support the National Geospatial Data Framework. Earlier he managed the development of digital photogrammetric systems, devised tools for up-dating existing mapping, was involved in the early use of SPOT imagery in mapping Yemen in 1988, and worked in the development of high-resolution Digital Elevation Models and 2.5D visualization. He received an MSc in Photogrammetry from University College, London, in 1986, supplementing a land survey and cartographic education. He is an associate member of the Royal Institution of Chartered Surveyors, and a member of the photogrammetry and remote sensing societies in Britain and the United States.

Kunio Nonomura Director General, Geographical Survey Institute, Ministry of Construction, Japan,
Tsukuba, Ibaraki, 305 Japan
Telephone: +81 298 64 1111 Fax: +81 298 64 8087
E-mail: nonomura@gsi-mc.go.jp)

He took an MSc in Geography at the University of Tokyo in 1967. After employment in the Geographical Survey Institute (GSI), he became Chief of the Planning Division of the Environment Agency in 1971. He returned to GSI in 1978 and held a succession of posts, including being head of three separate functions between 1980 and 1988. In the next five years, he held the posts of Director of the Topographic Department, Director of the Geodetic Department, and Director of the Planning Department. For three years he was Deputy Director General, and became Director General in 1996.

J Hugh O'Donnell Managing Director of Geomatics, SHL
VISION*SOLUTIONS,
50 O'Connor Street, Suite 501, Ottawa, Ontario K1P 6L2, Canada
Telephone: +1 613 236 9734 Fax: +1 613 567 5433
E-mail: hodonnell@gis.shl.com

He has 28 years of professional experience with government and industry in the fields of surveying, mapping, remote sensing, and GIS. While in the private sector, he managed a large division of a multi-disciplinary engineering firm, as the head of world-wide operations in surveying and mapping. In the Ontario government as Surveyor General of Ontario he was instrumental in securing major funding to assist the province's private sector in upgrading its technology for digital mapping and GIS. For eight years, he was Assistant Deputy Minister of Geomatics Canada, a sector of Natural Resources Canada. In this capacity, he was responsible for Canada's national surveying, mapping, and remote sensing programmes, when he provided leadership to such programmes as RADARSAT, the National Digital Topographic database activity, contracting out to industry, and the implementation of strong international relationships with foreign governments. More recently, he was Executive Secretary of the International Union of Surveying and Mapping. He holds professional licences in land surveying in the provinces of Ontario and Quebec.

Cyril R Penton Senior Advisor, Strategy and Priorities, Earth Sciences Sector, Natural Resources Canada,
615 Booth Street, Ottawa, Ontario K1A 0E9, Canada
Telephone: +1 613 995 4282 Fax: +1 613 947 3602
E-mail: Cyril.Penton@geocan.nrcan.gc.ca

He has 28 years of professional experience in geomatics with the government of Canada, focusing primarily on geodesy. Starting his career as a Survey Technologist with the Geodetic Survey of Canada in 1969, he continued there until 1987, with a four-year interruption in 1970 to obtain a BSc in Surveying Engineering and a one-year absence in 1981 to study towards a master's degree in geodesy, both at the University of New Brunswick. In 1987 became a senior adviser to the Assistant Deputy Minister of Geomatics Canada and was actively involved in the strategic planning for Canada's national agency for the delivery of surveying, mapping, and remote sensing programmes. After a six-month term as Acting Director, he assumed his duties as Senior Advisor in March 1997.

David Rhind Director General of Ordnance Survey,
Romsey Road, Southampton SO16 4GU, UK
Telephone: +44 1703 792 559 Fax: +44 1703 792 660
E-mail: drhind@ordsvy.gov.uk

He took up his post at Ordnance Survey in 1992. His role involves not only full responsibility for the strategy, operations, and finances of OS but also other involvement at senior levels in British government – for instance, he is the UK government's adviser on GIS, survey, and mapping, which has been used to good effect in founding the National Geospatial Data Framework. Before working in OS, he was Professor of Geography in Birkbeck College, University of London, where he was head of a group of five departments. His research since the late 1960s has largely been in GIS and mapping. He has been Honorary Secretary of the Royal Geographical Society, Vice-President of the International Cartography Association, a member of the UK government's (Chorley) Committee of Inquiry into the Handling of Geographical Information, and adviser to the House of Lords Select Committee on Science and Technology. He has a BSc in Geography and Geology, a PhD in Geomorphology, a DSc in Geographical Information Systems, and two honorary doctorates in Science from Bristol and Loughborough universities.

Jonathan Rhind World Conservation Monitoring Centre,
219 Huntingdon Road, Cambridge CB3 0DL, UK
Telephone: +44 1223 277314 Fax: +44 1223 277136
E-mail: jonathan.rhind@wcmc.org.uk

He is the GIS Technical Officer in the World Conservation Monitoring Centre (WCMC). Joining WCMC in 1991, he has been involved in developing various in-house systems and working with colleagues in Indonesia, Thailand, Russia, and other countries. He gained a BSc in Biology at Royal Holloway and Bedford College, University of London, and an MSc in Geographical Information Systems from the University of Edinburgh. His attempts to avoid working on topics which overlap with his father's concerns have not been wholly successful. Fortunately, their views differ somewhat on a number of these topics.

William A Robertson PO Box 50 736, Porirua, New Zealand
Telephone: +64 4 233 1768 Fax: +64 4 233 1762
E-mail: billrobertson@xtra.co.nz

He completed nine years as the Director General/Surveyor General of the New Zealand Government, Department of Survey and Land Information (DOSLI) in 1996. As Chief Executive Officer of DOSLI, he was responsible for the leadership and strategic direction of the department as it implemented full cost-recovery policies, the wide-spread application of new digital surveying and mapping technology, and modern approaches to human resource management and learning. He had an important transitional role in building a sustainable capacity from its predecessor department – a highly traditional government survey and mapping organization – to a modern form, while still providing the key spatial infrastructure services essential to NZ economic restructuring. He has qualifications in surveying, planning, and public policy, and has recently been elected President of the Commonwealth Association of Planners. He is currently working as an independent consultant on public sector management, environmental information management, and surveying and mapping issues.

François Salgé Ingénieur en Chef Géographe, Institut Géographique National,
136 bis rue de Grenelle, 75700 Paris 07 SP, France
Telephone: +33 1 43 98 82 70 Fax: +33 1 43 98 84 00
E-mail: francois.salge@ign.fr

As adviser to the Director General of the Institut Géographique National (IGN), the French NMO, on European and spatial affairs, he is the permanent corresponding member of CERCO (the 32-nation group of European NMOs) and Management Board member of MEGRIN and Spot Image. He is a graduate of the French Ecole Polytechnique, the major engineering school in France, and of the Ecole Nationale des Sciences Géographiques, where he was educated in all the scientific disciplines in Geographic Information. He joined the IGN in 1979 as member of a CNES-IGN team in charge of defining the ground station of the SPOT satellite system. In 1983 he returned to IGN in St Mandé in Paris, successively in charge of the definition of the French BDCarto and as the Deputy Technical Director. From 1991 to end-1996, he was the executive Director of MEGRIN, the commercially orientated initiative of 19 European NMAs.

Since 1991 he has been Chairman of the European CEN/TC287 standardization team for Geographic Information. He is also the Co-director of the ESF-GISDATA programme, and played a leading role in the definition and creation of EUROGI, the European 'umbrella body' for Geographic Information.

Ulf Sandgren Director of Planning, National Land Survey,
S-801 82 GfVLE, Sweden
Telephone: +46 26 633092 Fax: +46 26 613277
E-mail: ulf.sandgren@lm.se

Since graduating from the Royal Institute of Technology in Stockholm in 1971, he has been working mainly within the National Land Survey of Sweden at local, regional, and central level. He has, for example, been a manager with responsibility for market analyses, design of database structures, and production planning. He has also been Commission Secretary at the Ministry of Industry and at the Ministry of Housing and Building. In addition, he has been Administrative Director of the Swedish Research and Development Council for Land Information Technology.

Neil Smith Chief Science Adviser, Ordnance Survey,
Romsey Road, Southampton SO16 4GU, UK
Telephone: +44 1703 792052 Fax: +44 1703 792078
E-mail: nssmith@ordsvy.gov.uk

With a degree in Geology and Geography, he then trained as a land surveyor at the School of Military Survey in 1972. He worked in Africa and the Middle East with the Directorate of Overseas Surveys before joining Ordnance Survey in 1979. In 1980 he obtained an MSc in Spatial Data Analysis at the University of Durham and then worked for 12 years in OS's R&D department on large- and small-scale digital mapping systems, GIS, databases, and computer systems. In 1991–92 he represented OS on a small team investigating the feasibility of combining European National Mapping Agency data sets; this is now being realized as MEGRIN. Since 1992 he has been acting in an advisory and consultancy role within OS, dealing with long-term research isssues such as the development of national geospatial databases. He has also been leader of a team commissioned to develop a European standard for defining quality of Geographic Information.

Nancy Tosta Director of Forecasting and Growth Strategy, Puget Sound Regional Council,
1011 Western Avenue, Suite 500, Seattle, WA 98104-1035, USA
Telephone: +1 206 587 5665 Fax: +1 206 587 4825
E-mail: tosta@psrc.wa.com

She has been Director of Forecasting and Growth Strategy for the Puget Sound Regional Council, Seattle, Washington State since July 1996. From 1992 to 1996 she was Staff Director for the Federal Geographic Data Committee and Special Assistant for Geographic Data Co-ordination to the Secretary of the Interior. In that capacity she was employed by the National Mapping Division of the US Geological Survey but was expected to operate on behalf of the whole community of geospatial data users in the USA. She is widely credited with playing a key role in gaining public, government, and political acceptance of the National Spatial Data Infrastructure concept and helping to turn it into a reality. Before working in federal government she held positions with the State of California Teale Data Center including Deputy Director in charge of strategic planning and technology innovation (1988–92). She also held positions with the California Department of Forestry and Fire Protection from 1976 to 1988. She holds BS and MS degrees from the University of California Berkeley in Natural Resources.

Yoshio Warita Ex-Director General, Geographical Survey Institute, Ministry of Construction, Japan,
Tsukuba, Ibaraki, 305 Japan
Telephone: +81 298 64 1111 Fax: +81 298 64 8087
E-mail: intex@gsi-mc.go.jp)

With a Master's degree in Civil Engineering from Kyoto University, he then worked for the Japanese Ministry of Construction. In 1975 he was appointed Head of the Planning Division of Chubu Regional Construction Bureau and became Director of that Planning Department in 1989 after a series of other jobs, notably in relation to flood control and river planning. In 1992 he became Director of the River Planning Division and, a year later, Assistant Vice-Minister for Engineering Affairs in the Minister's Secretariat. In 1994 he was appointed Director General of Kanto Regional Construction Bureau and in, 1995, Director General of the Geographical Survey Institute. He retired in 1996 but remains Director of the Foundation of River and Basin Integrated Communications.

Nikolai Zhdanov President, Federal Service of Geodesy and Cartography of Russia,
2, korpus,14, Krzhizhanovskogo St., 117801 Moscow, Russia
Telephone: +95 124 35 35 Fax: +95 124 35 35

After graduation from the Military Engineering Academy in 1967, Nikolai Zhdanov served in the USSR Military Forces. From 1971 to 1991 he worked for the General Staff of the Ministry of Defence and became its Deputy Chief of the Military Topographic Department. He was then appointed Chief of Main Administration for Cartography (Russia's NMO) as a consequence of a decree by the Russian Council of Ministries. A year later, a Presidential decree appointed him as President of the Federal Service of Geodesy and Cartography of Russia. He is an Academician of the Academy of Technology Sciences, specializing in the conceptualization, design, and implementation of digital mapping. His work includes automated detection of map features and hardware design. In 1985 he was honoured with a Government Award in recognition of his achievements in scientific and technical fields.

AUTHOR INDEX

SUBJECT INDEX